Annual Perspectives in Mathematics Education

Reflective and Collaborative Processes to Improve Mathematics Teaching

2017

Lucy West
Volume Editor
Metamorphosis Teaching Learning Communities
New York, New York

Melissa Boston
Series Editor
Duquesne University
Pittsburgh, Pennsylvania

Lucy West
Volume Editor
Metamorphosis Teaching Learning Communities
New York, New York

Melissa Boston
Series Editor
Duquesne University
Pittsburgh, Pennsylvania

NATIONAL COUNCIL OF
TEACHERS OF MATHEMATICS

more**4u**
www.nctm.org/more4u
Access code: REF15450

The National Council of Teachers of Mathematics is the public voice of mathematics education, supporting teachers to ensure equitable mathematics learning of the highest quality for each and every student through vision, leadership, professional development, and research.

CONTENTS

Preface

In the 2017 volume of the National Council of Teachers of Mathematics' (NCTM) *Annual Perspectives in Mathematics Education* (*APME*) series, we showcase mathematics teachers' efforts to ensure effective and high-quality mathematics teaching and learning. The twenty-four chapters included here provide illustrations of initiatives based in classrooms, schools, districts, professional development projects, and teacher education programs that promote mathematics teachers' professional growth and self-assessment, grounded in research and practice. Examples of collaborative initiatives featured in this volume include professional learning communities (PLCs), teacher-teams, peer collaborations, and lesson study groups. Some chapters highlight professional development done not *to* teachers but *with* teachers; for example, professional development that supports collaboration and fosters reflection, sustainability, and teachers' self-direction and/or self-assessment. Other chapters illustrate ways of increasing teachers' voice and participation in the evaluation of mathematics instruction, including positioning mathematics teachers as reflective practitioners, using products of teaching observations or student assessments to improve practice, and implementing instructional practices to enhance students' learning of specific mathematical topics.

The "teachers" featured across the volume include in-service teachers in secondary, middle school, and elementary mathematics classrooms; preservice mathematics teachers; and university mathematicians and mathematics teacher educators. The chapters often provide vignettes, students' work, or other classroom-based examples and artifacts that feature specific mathematical topics (e.g. number sense in elementary mathematics, mathematical proof in high school geometry), mathematical processes (e.g., the Common Core Standards for Mathematical Practice), technology (e.g., screencasts of students' work), students' mathematical identity (e.g., perceptions of mathematical strengths), and STEM explorations (e.g., exponential growth and disease control). Many of the chapters have additional resources available online through NCTM's More4U website. (See the title page for the web address and access code required to view this book's More4U materials.)

We intend for this volume to provide counter-narratives that challenge the underlying assumptions in public conversations and mandated policies that teachers need to be monitored, pressured, and held accountable by external agencies in order for them to provide high-quality instruction and/or engage in improving their practice. These chapters portray teachers who are proactively engaged in promoting and ensuring high-quality mathematics instruction and learning. Together with peers, instructional coaches, or university partners, these teachers have formed meaningful collaborations, where they have a voice in the design of their own professional learning and the direction of their own professional growth. The initiatives described in this volume promote sustainability, equipping teachers with the tools to continue to reflect on and improve practice and empowering teachers to take action to ensure high-quality teaching.

In the call for manuscripts for *APME* 2017, we asked authors to submit chapters highlighting reflective and collaborative processes for improving mathematics instruction. While we cast a broad net that included teachers' self-directed efforts toward professional growth, initiatives coordinated by instructional coaches or district-based leaders, professional development, or mathematics teacher education, the critical component was that the initiatives fosters reflection, sustainability, and/or teachers' self-direction and self-assessment. We received sixty-two manuscripts, all of which were blind-reviewed by two editorial panel members. Selected manuscripts were then reviewed by either the volume editor or series editor and sent to authors for revisions. Revised manuscripts were blind-reviewed again by one of the two original editorial panel reviewers. This process resulted in the set of twenty-four manuscripts featured in this volume.

The volume is subdivided into five sections. The first section, **Enhancing Mathematics Teaching from the Teacher's Voice**, opens the volume with examples of mathematics teachers serving as primary agents of instructional change, engaging in the design and delivery of professional development for themselves and their peers and guiding the direction and focus of their professional learning. The second section, **Enhancing Mathematics Teaching within Schools and Districts**, features efforts for improving mathematics instruction that occur within schools, led by instructional coaches and/ or professional development providers. Chapters in the third section, **Models and Frameworks for Enhancing Mathematics Teaching**, provide tools for mathematics teachers' reflection and growth, often by supporting teachers to attend to students' thinking, evidence of students' learning, and the instructional practices that appear to positively affect students' learning. In the fourth section, **Enhancing Mathematics Teaching across Multiple Stakeholders**, authors describe collaborations that support mathematics teaching, students' learning, and teacher development in partnerships between schools and universities and between university mathematicians and mathematics teacher educators. The last section, **Enhancing Preservice Mathematics Teachers' Development,** showcases efforts to promote self-assessment, reflection, and collaboration in preservice mathematics teachers.

We acknowledge that the sections are not mutually exclusive; however, we have grouped sets of chapters together based on the main purpose of the chapter and its contribution to the volume. For example, chapters throughout the book may contain examples of collaboration across multiple stakeholders, but for chapters in that specific section, the nature of the collaboration and involvement of different stakeholders is central to the work, makes a unique contribution to the volume, and is foregrounded in the authors' writing. For chapters in other sections, involvement of multiple stakeholders may occur, but not as the primary purpose and focus of the chapter.

Acknowledgements

Along with Lucy West, the 2017 *APME* volume editor, I would like to express our thanks to the many individuals who contributed to the development and success of this volume. First, we extend our respect and admiration to the chapter authors for the work they do to promote professional learning, reflection, and collaboration in mathematics teaching and teacher education. We are very grateful for their decision to share their work with NCTM's membership. We extend deep appreciation to the Editorial Panel, who generously read and reviewed multiple manuscripts multiple times: Thomasenia Adams, Ellen Knudson, Charlene Marchese, Lynn McGarvey, Hal Melnik, Robyn Silbey, and Michael Steele. We also thank all of the NCTM staff who contributed to the APME, especially Joanne Hodges and Larry Shea for their direction and guidance with the production of *APME* and Kathleen Richardson for her support in arranging the editorial panel meeting. Finally, we would like to thank NCTM's 2015 Educational Materials Committee, chaired by Margaret Kinzel, for their insight and ideas in crafting the theme for this *APME* volume.

Melissa Boston
Series Editor, APME 2017–2019
Associate Professor, School of Education
Duquesne University

PART I

Enhancing Mathematics Teaching from the Teacher's Voice

Introduction

Ellen Knudson, *Bismarck Public Schools, North Dakota*
Lynn McGarvey, *University of Alberta, Edmonton*

Teaching is an intellectual endeavor. Informally and formally, teachers engage in continuous inquiry into their own practice by collecting information about student learning, reflecting on decision making, analyzing resources, and broadening content knowledge. These reflective practices enhance personal professional growth. Unfortunately, such inquiry into teaching, learning, and mathematics often stays within the confines of a teacher's classroom, even though the teacher down the hall or in the next district is wrestling with similar issues.

In the past few decades, teachers have been stepping out of the isolation of their classrooms by participating in teacher study groups, professional learning communities, and action research projects. As teachers work alongside colleagues, they have opportunities to engage in critical dialogue and inquiry into the practice of teaching. Such activities have significant impact not only on personal pedagogy but also on local communities of practice.

Yet, teacher insights, knowledge, and experiences need not be contained at the local level. In fact, teachers' collaborative inquiry and reflection have the potential to contribute to the collective knowledge of teaching, influence research practice, increase teacher professionalism, provide a forum for feedback, and initiate grassroots pedagogical change. For broader dissemination to occur, there is a need in the research literature for the voices of teachers. In this section, we present four such chapters in which spaces have been purposefully created for teachers or initiated by teachers so that their voices can be heard. The spaces and structures are different in each chapter.

The four chapters in this section demonstrate the value of teachers as co-producers of both professional and scientific knowledge rather than as passive recipients or local contributors (Kieran, Krainer, and Shaughnessy 2014). In chapters 1 and 4, teachers play the lead role in initiating inquiry and writing about their insights into teaching and learning. Lesson study provided the professional learning structure for chapter 1. The authors, both classroom teachers at the time of the project, discuss the power of public teaching. Chapter 4 is written by three teachers, a school director, and two mathematics educators (who were also community members and parents) and arises from the collaborative activity within their school and the need to consider how research might inform day-to-day practice. The collaborative space of lesson study enabled the teachers to experiment with and implement research ideas in the classroom. They describe themselves as co-creators of knowledge within their classrooms; and through the act of writing, their knowledge can be shared with other educators.

In chapters 2 and 3, researchers play an important role in providing both the support and space for teachers to participate and share in collaborative inquiry. In chapter 2, a university researcher worked with teachers through professional development sessions over several years. Teachers share in the authorship of the chapter, describing how the partnership between teachers and researcher affected practice. In chapter 3, five teachers engaged in independent classroom-inquiry projects based on a shared concern and common tool developed by and with two mathematics teacher educators through their professional learning community.

The following paragraphs summarize each chapter in this section, highlighting how the chapter represents teachers' voices in reflective and collaborative processes to enhance teaching.

In chapter 1, **The NYC Math Lab: Lessons from a Turn toward *Teaching* Evaluation,** Van Duzer and Cipparone demonstrate how the shift from *teacher* evaluation to *teaching* evaluation can offer growth for both teachers and students. They note that the current evaluative system sees "teachers marching in place when it comes to their development" (Jacob and McGovern 2015, p. 13). Teachers are offered feedback but little follow-up to improve instruction. Instead, the authors illustrate how, when teachers move from objects of evaluation to becoming their own agents in the evaluative process, improvements occur in learning and instruction. As a result of the authors' previous work with lesson study, they partnered with a nonprofit organization to create a summer math lab involving twenty fifth-grade students from low-income families. Teachers worked together to plan, observe, teach, and analyze their practice and student artifacts. The authors offer "public teaching" as an example of the type of professional development and evaluative process in which teachers play an active part in the improvement of math instruction.

In **Decomposing Mathematical Proof with Secondary Teachers,** Cirillo, a university researcher, and McCall, Murtha, and Walters, three high school teachers, tackle the challenging task of making geometric proof meaningful for students. In this collaborative research project, the teachers examined the van Hiele levels for geometric thinking to understand students' developmental progression toward proof. Through data analysis and reflection on the van Hiele levels, Cirillo began to note the range of competencies needed to be successful and subsequently developed the Geometry Proof Scaffold (GPS). The teachers in the study tested and refined the subgoals and engaged in teaching experiments in their classrooms. The classroom-based projects, along with the opportunity to share and refine the GPS together, increased the teachers' awareness of what was needed for student success and increased their confidence in teaching. The collaborative research provided a means for teachers to critically reflect on their own practice and use a research-based approach for instructional improvements.

Educators Learning from Middle School Students' Views of Mathematical Strengths discusses the implementation of and implications for four teachers' inquiry projects developed as part of a professional learning community. The writing team includes two mathematics teacher educators (White and Gomez), along with five participating teachers (Patel, Hussain, Simpson, Rushing, and Pratt). Through this collaborative effort, teachers developed inquiry projects to support students to identify mathematical strengths and how those strengths are demonstrated in the mathematics classrooms. The framework for the inquiry projects was based on the researchers' Taxonomy of Students' Mathematical Strengths (TMS), which includes strengths in mathematical knowledge, motivation, problem solving, communication, and as a doer of mathematics. By using the process of action research, each teacher took responsibility for implementing an inquiry-based project in a way that reflected his or her own teaching, the class context, and student needs. The chapter demonstrates the importance of teacher research and reflection paired with sharing learning and difficulties in a supportive community of colleagues.

In the last chapter of this section, **Teachers' Voices: How Collaboration Helps Us Put Research into Practice,** Martin, Meerts, Oehmke, Tyler, Matsuura, and Sword reveal how a sustained professional learning community, centered on research-based practices, led to an "upward spiral" of mathematical understanding for teachers and students. "Working through an intentional process of self-driven professional development," three teachers of grades 4 and 5, along with two parents (also math educators) and the school director used lesson study as a way to collaborate on teacher and student understanding of content and pedagogy. The teachers decided to pool their students, engage in team teaching, and use flexible groupings to meet the range of students' needs and the way those needs change in relation to different mathematical content. The authors provide an example from the context of number sense. The process of lesson study enabled the teachers to determine the source of students' errors and devise problems and tools to enhance understanding of numbers and relationship in the base-ten system. The teachers found their collaborative network afforded the space and support to ask questions, examine their practice and seek the information necessary to enhance students' mathematical understanding.

The four chapters demonstrate the power of teachers' voices in research and reflection. As you read the chapters in this section and others in this volume, consider the following questions:

- What collaborative structures and spaces can be created for teachers or initiated by teachers to continue to bridge research and practice?

- What forms of inquiry and documentation of inquiry can encourage teachers to contribute to the collective knowledge of the profession?

- What are the questions of practice and student learning that are of value for teachers to pursue and share in public forums?

- What supports are needed so that teachers' voices can continue to have an influence on the direction of research?

References

Jacob, Andy, and Kate McGovern. "The Mirage: Confronting the Hard Truth about Our Quest for Teacher Development." *TNTP* (2015).

Kieran, Carolyn, Konrad Krainer, and J. Michael Shaughnessy. "Linking Research to Practice: Teachers as Key Stakeholders in Mathematics Education Research." In *Third International Handbook of Research in Mathematics Education,* edited by K. Clements, A. Bishop, C. Keitel, J. Kilpatrick, and F. Leung, pp. 361–92. New York: Springer, 2013.

CHAPTER 1

The NYC Math Lab:
Lessons from a Turn toward *Teaching* Evaluation

Kim Van Duzer, *Public School 29, Brooklyn, New York*
Peter Cipparone, *University of Michigan, Ann Arbor*

A teacher's day is packed with responsibilities. There are children to console and counsel, field trip forms to collect, and up to five lessons per day to prepare and teach. As a result, teachers rarely have time to collaborate, let alone see each other in action. Yet research suggests that having time to discuss and analyze teaching may be an effective lever for improving teaching and learning (Gallimore et al. 2009; Ronfeldt et al. 2015). Indeed, teachers in countries whose students perform better than the United States on Programme for International Student Assessment (PISA) examinations (such as Japan) often have more time for collaboration than do teachers in the United States. (LeTendre et al. 2001; Kane 1994). Having the opportunity to study live teaching may also be beneficial, as it offers teachers images of new teaching methods and fosters a professional community in which teaching is regularly analyzed and improved.

Instead of focusing on creating opportunities for greater collaboration and collective study of teaching practice, however, the recent conversation in the public sphere about improving teaching and learning has centered on teacher evaluation (Baker, Oluwole, and Green 2013). Over the past decade, most states have developed new teacher evaluation systems (Doherty and Jacobs 2015). These evaluation systems often mandate more observations and new rubrics for assessing teaching, but systematic plans for illustrating the types of teaching skills outlined in these rubrics remain nonexistent. The need to provide images of effective teaching is particularly acute in mathematics education, where procedural instruction persists despite decades of research (Hiebert 2013) and widespread consensus on effective practice (National Council of Teachers of Mathematics [NCTM] 2014).

This chapter describes the NYC Math Lab, a weeklong professional development institute created by three teachers, in which participants observed, analyzed, and engaged in the teaching of twenty rising fifth-grade students attending a summer program at a local nonprofit organization. Teachers unanimously reported that Math Lab had a big impact on their mathematics teaching practice. In this chapter, we describe the rationale for developing the NYC Math Lab, the process through which it was created, and our initial conclusions about the ways in which public teaching might facilitate teacher learning. In providing a detailed portrait of our work, we hope to provoke interest in developing math labs as a form of teaching evaluation, and we offer ideas on the ways one might begin.

■ Teacher Evaluation vs. Teaching Evaluation

Teacher evaluation has played a pivotal role in conversations about improving public education for the first part of the twenty-first century. Significant attention, from both researchers and policy-makers, has been directed toward developing new teacher evaluation formulas and linking teacher evaluation to student achievement data (Baker, Oluwole, and Green 2013). Yet evaluations based on administrator observations and student test scores may not catalyze improvement. According to The New Teacher Project's (TNTP) 2015 report on teacher development, although teachers are being regularly evaluated, "Most teachers in the districts we studied seem to be marching in place when it comes to their development" (Jacob and McGovern 2015, p. 13). Teachers feel the disconnect between evaluative feedback and professional growth, too; when asked to report on the "activity that has helped me learn how to improve the most," only 3 percent of teachers in TNTP's study named observations and feedback (Jacob and McGovern 2015, p. 21).

One problem with using teacher evaluation as a lever for change is that it positions teachers as the passive subjects of review, rather than agents of their own growth. Teachers receive feedback from supervisors a few times a year, with little follow-up to see if that feedback has improved their teaching. This is problematic, as follow-up is consistently proven to be one of the features of successful professional development (Fishman, Davis, and Chan 2014). Without this follow-up, teacher evaluation becomes translated as a teacher rating system rather than a teacher improvement system. When teachers receive the same rating year after year, it reinforces the belief that some teachers will always be successful while others will not, leaving little impetus for growth. In *Building a Better Teacher*, Elizabeth Green exposes the "Myth of the Natural-Born Teacher" (Green 2014, p. 6) and reveals the ways in which this myth has been widely detrimental to the development of the profession.

For elementary school teachers of mathematics, teacher evaluation rarely provides support in the critical area of content knowledge. According to Stipek et al. (2001), "Most American teachers have a conception of mathematics as a static body of knowledge, involving a set of rules and procedures that are applied to yield one right answer" (p. 214). Elementary school teachers may not have robust content knowledge in mathematics, and they often operate from a conception of mathematics teaching that is procedural rather than one focused on developing mathematical understanding (Ball 1990). Therefore, mathematics teachers need professional development and feedback that will enhance their content knowledge. Teacher evaluation systems almost never support this type of work. Because procedural teaching of mathematics is a long-standing tradition in American schools, administrators who have often only learned math and learned to teach math in a procedural way are hard-pressed to move teachers of mathematics toward methods that encourage sense making (Lortie 1975; Steele et al. 2015).

On the other hand, *teaching* evaluation—the study of practice rather than individuals—holds great potential for improving teaching and learning. Lesson study (Lewis and Hurd 2011), peer visitation, and public teaching in a laboratory classroom setting all provide opportunities for teachers to evaluate and implement new teaching practices.

■ What Is Public Teaching?

Public teaching is a new term in the educational literature. In a 2013 American Educational Research Association (AERA) presentation, Deborah Ball and colleagues at the University of Michigan described public teaching as "the work of making one's own teaching practice studyable by observers." In doing so, they noted that public teaching might include pre- and post-class analysis and that teaching in public requires attending to both students and observers. Yet this presentation is the only peer-reviewed work that describes public teaching, and it stopped short of defining the concept. In our view, public teaching occurs any time a teacher performs the work of teaching in front of adults who intend to study teacher practice or the resulting student thinking.

We believe that public teaching is an important missing component of current systems of teacher evaluation and professional development. In the pages that follow, we present one approach to using public teaching as a method for improving mathematics instruction: the creation and implementation of a math lab.

■ The NYC Math Lab: A Study in Public Teaching

Background

The NYC Math Lab spawned from the work of the Math Collective, a group of teachers and schools in New York City engaged in inquiry around children's mathematical thinking. Kate Abell, the founder of the Math Collective, organized a number of lesson study cycles each year. Teachers consistently found lesson study to be a powerful form of professional development. Peter and Kim, the authors of this chapter, were fourth-grade teachers at P.S. 29 who worked regularly with Kate and the Math Collective over several years. As part of our frequent collaboration to plan math instruction, Peter and Kim began to take turns observing a math lesson in each other's classroom every week. These peer visitations and resulting conversations had a deep impact on our growth as teachers of mathematics. Our peer visitations also made us more aware of the power of public teaching, and as a result we became more willing to teach in front of others. Peter, Kim, and Kate came together in the spring of 2015 and decided to create the NYC Math Lab as a way to bring similar experiences to a broader group of teachers.

The University of Michigan's Elementary Math Lab (EML), taught by Deborah Ball, also inspired the creation of the NYC Math Lab. Peter attended a two-week session at the EML in the summer of 2014. Ball framed her teaching of the lab class not as model teaching but as a way to provide participants with a shared experience in math teaching and learning. This framing gave us the conviction that making our practice public could benefit teachers in our district as well. Many of the structures described in this chapter came from the EML.

Creating a Partnership

After some deliberation about how to find students willing to participate in a math lab, we decided to partner with the Hudson Guild, a nonprofit organization that offers support services to low-income families in Manhattan's Chelsea neighborhood. Because we had a negligible budget and no support staff outside of the founding teachers, partnering with the Hudson Guild allowed us to provide two hours of math instruction without needing to develop afternoon programming for students. When approached about the partnership, Hudson Guild staff was excited about the opportunity for their students to have access to summer math instruction within their existing program.

Identifying Values

We began our planning by co-creating a list of instructional values that would guide our work at Math Lab. We decided to orient our lab around the following beliefs:

- Math is about making sense (Hiebert et al. 1997).

- The use of visual representations both deepens students' thinking about math and helps students support their mathematical arguments (NCTM 2014).

- Student ownership is a critical component to teaching mathematical content, and encouraging student talk supports ownership (Yackel and Cobb 1996).

- A mathematical community is one where people can express their ideas and learn from the ideas of others (Hiebert et al. 1997).

- The work of the mathematics teacher is to listen to students as they express their developing ideas and to respond based on their thinking (Hiebert et al. 1997).

Organizing for Instruction

We decided on the following areas of instructional focus: in the first hour of each day's lab class, we would work on (*a*) developing students' math mindset (Dweck 2006; Boaler 2015) through work with materials from YouCubed's Week of Inspirational Math (fig. 1.1) and (*b*) growing students' ability to make generalizations through a Number of the Day routine (fig. 1.2), in which students were given a number and asked to write as many number sentences as they could, using any of the operations, that equaled that number (Russell, Schifter, and Bastable 2011, p. 16).

Day 3: Paper Folding

Paper Folding Gr. 3 - 4
Adapted from Driscoll, 2007

Work with a partner. Take turns being the skeptic or the convincer. When you are the convincer your job is to be convincing! Give reasons for all of your statements. Skeptics must be skeptical! Don't be easily convinced. Require reasons and justifications that make sense to you.

For each of the problems below one person should make the shape and then be convincing. Your partner is the skeptic. When you move to the next question switch roles.

Start with a square sheet of paper and make folds to construct a new shape. Then, explain how you know the shape you constructed has the specified area.

Fig. 1.1. An example of a task from YouCubed's Week of Inspirational Math, and a chart made to accompany this task

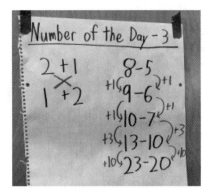

Fig. 1.2. Number of the day routine, with
accompanying observations relating to properties of operations

The second hour would be spent focusing on developing students' conceptual understanding of fractions through a series of inquiry-based, hands-on tasks. We chose fractions for a number of reasons. First, fractions are both vital for future mathematics and often misunderstood by students of all ages (Bezuk and Bieck 1993; Stigler, Givvin, and Thompson 2010; Lortie-Forgues, Tian, and Siegler 2015). Second, fractions are a limited domain within the Common Core State Standards; the Number and Operations—Fractions domain spans grades 3 through 5 only, with foundations in geometry standards in first and second grades and extensions into ratio and proportion in middle school (National Governors Association Center for Best Practices and Council of Chief State School Officers [NGA Center and CCSSO] 2010). We hypothesized that teaching fraction content would allow teacher participants to both deepen their understanding of a challenging content area and see the progression of student understanding develop over the relatively short period of time we had for the Math Lab.

About four weeks before Math Lab, we visited the students who would be attending the program to introduce ourselves, get to know them, and tell them about Math Lab. We returned a few days later to conduct one-on-one interviews with each student, in which we gathered information about their understanding of fraction concepts and their attitudes toward mathematics. What we learned informed our planning; for example, after asking a question about the naming of a fractional piece of a rectangle (fig. 1.3), we determined that students would need more work on the concept of the unit fraction and incorporated that into our plan for the first day of the lab.

What fraction of the large rectangle is gray?

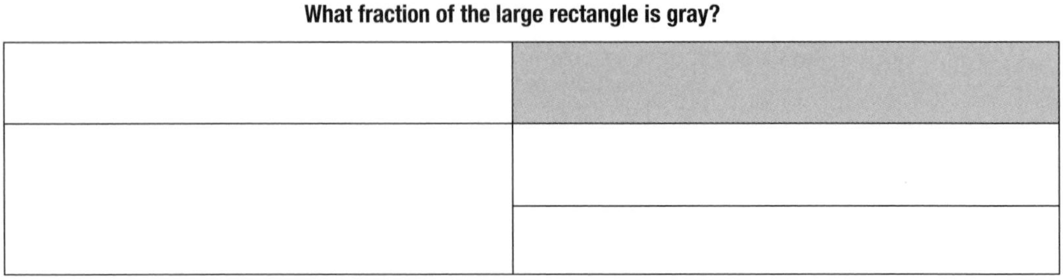

Fig. 1.3. Example of a fraction task used during student interviews

Time + Activity	Task	Details	Commentary/ Anticipations
10:00 – 10:15 **Number of the Day – 5**	Students will write number sentences. These number sentences may include concepts drawn from previous days' work, such as using multiple terms, the commutative property of addition, constant difference, or a concept from the small group the day before. Participants facilitate small-group discussions.	• Students will enter the lab class and begin work on 5, the number of the day, in their notebooks. Teacher will positively reinforce this routine. • Participants will observe the kids they are working with to glean further insights into their mathematical thinking. Particular items to watch for include— → Student uptake of content from previous days → Growth from day 1 of the lab → Areas of continued need	
10:15 – 10:50 **Ant Problem**	Students will try equivalence problems and reason about why the pieces are equivalent in those problems.	• Teacher will introduce the Ant problem. • Students will work with their partners to solve the Ant problem and represent their thinking. • Teacher will lead a discussion to bring out the proportional relationship ("there are three times as many twelfths, so we need three times as many of them to make the same distance"). • Students will generate more equivalent fractions by using Cuisenaire rods.	This work is directly related to the standard 4.NF.A.1: "Explain why a fraction a/b is equivalent to a fraction $(n \times a)/(n \times b)$ by using visual fraction models, **with attention to how the number and size of the parts differ even though the two fractions themselves are the same size.** Use this principle to recognize and generate equivalent fractions."

Fig. 1.4. Part of a lesson plan from day 5 of the NYC Math Lab (following the lesson plan format of the Elementary Math Lab at the University of Michigan) (Source: Elementary Math Lab, University of Michigan)

Structuring the Day with Teacher Learning in Mind

We started Math Lab with the intention of creating a professional development opportunity for teachers that oriented them toward evaluating and learning from live teaching. The first structure that we incorporated to support this goal was a daily "pre-brief." In the pre-brief, which took place for the first hour of the day, we presented the participants with the day's lesson plan (see fig 1.4 on the previous page) and engaged them in a discussion around our instructional considerations and decisions about the enactment of the day's lessons.

We also gave participants the mathematical tasks students would be working with that day (fig. 1.5), and we had them complete the tasks and discuss what challenges they might present for students.

Name _____   Date _____

The Ant Problem

Two ants were bragging about how far they carried a huge leaf. The red ant ran $9/12$ of a boozle. The black ant ran $3/4$ of a boozle. The red ant said, "I ran further because my numbers are bigger."

Is the red ant correct? Use rods to decide who carried the leaf the furthest. Use pictures, numbers, and words to explain your thinking so that someone else can understand it.

one boozle

Fig. 1.5. Student task: The Ant Problem

Following the lab class, we held a daily debrief. As part of our focus on teaching evaluation rather than teacher evaluation, we asked participating teachers to comment on the teaching practices and their effects on student understandings, and not on the teachers themselves. Participants were also invited to give feedback and suggestions for future lessons during the debrief, and we regularly implemented those suggestions into the next day's work with students.

From Observer to Teacher

On the last three days of the week, we also incorporated opportunities for participating teachers themselves to work with students. We paired each teacher with a student and asked him or her to confer with the child about a particular task related to the fraction work. In these one-on-one sessions with students, we first asked teachers to practice just listening to their students and making notes about each child's understandings in relation to the task. During afternoon sessions, teachers talked with their peers about what they observed and how they might further their students' understandings.

■ Discussion: Public Teaching as an Engine for Teacher Growth

There are many ways in which professional development centered on teaching evaluation and public teaching can lead to transferable improvements to practice. In this section, we discuss the ways in which Math Lab may have facilitated teacher growth.

Teacher Math Mindset

We believe public teaching helps teachers shift from a "fixed mindset" to a "growth mindset" (see Dweck 2006) about their own teaching. This is an important first step toward improvements to practice. For teachers, a fixed mindset often sounds like "I'm good at teaching *x*, but not good at teaching *y*" or "I never liked math, so I don't like teaching math." The traditional model of teacher evaluation, in which teachers are given ratings for different areas of competency, can reinforce the fixed mindset teachers may hold about their areas of strength and weakness.

In contrast, public teaching fosters a growth mindset in teachers by forwarding the belief that teaching can be improved with deliberate analysis. At Math Lab we saw a mindset shift take place for a number of participants over the course of the week. Early in the week, participating teachers were sometimes hesitant to share their ideas on the teaching or ask questions about the math in pre-briefs or debriefs, which we interpreted as possible evidence of a fixed mindset or lack of confidence in their mathematical content or pedagogical knowledge. To encourage teachers to view themselves with a growth mindset, we regularly shared our own doubts and questions about the day's work, both before and after the lessons were enacted. By modeling vulnerability for our participants, we sought to communicate that (*a*) teaching is a learnable skill that can be deconstructed and reconstructed collaboratively; and (*b*) the process of studying teaching is messy and offers tremendous potential for growth. On a feedback chart at the end of the week, one teacher wrote, "I used to think that because I was bad at math I would be horrible at teaching it too. Now I think because of my mistakes I can understand and teach math better" (fig. 1.6). Another teacher reflected, "[Teaching] can be scary. You have to be OK with making mistakes."

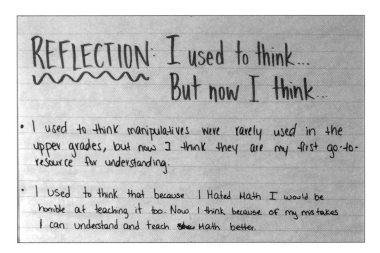

Fig. 1.6. Teachers' reflections on their mindset shifts over the course of the week

Sharing Students, Sharing Ideas

A shared class of students helped participants shift from a stance of evaluating the teacher to evaluating the teaching. On the first day of Math Lab, participants spontaneously applauded for the teacher who had enacted the day's lessons after the students left the room at the end of the lab class. This act reflected the common view that teaching publicly is akin to performance, a belief that we strongly wanted to challenge in the interest of making teachers more comfortable with sharing their practice and learning from one another. It also reflects the sense teachers had at the beginning of the week that they were observers more than active members of a community of practice. Through-out the week, however, as teachers began to get to know the students, the tenor of conversations in pre-briefs and debriefs changed. Instead of talking about the teacher who had enacted the lesson, participants began to talk about the effect of the teaching on the students, saying things such as, "I thought that Elijah understood the unit fraction when he was working with the Cuisenaire rods yesterday, but today his understanding seemed to fall apart. I wasn't sure what to say to help him connect back to what he seemed to get yesterday." The opportunity to speak so specifically about children, their understandings, and the teaching moves that might further their understandings was a unique element of Math Lab that teachers reported finding meaningful. By the end of the week, one teacher reflected, "The big idea [behind public teaching] is cooperation—teachers united around a shared goal."

Talking about Teaching Practices

Teachers began to use more specific language around teaching practices over the course of the week. We highlighted a number of NCTM's Effective Mathematics Teaching Practices (2014) during the lab. In our pre-briefs and debriefs, we encouraged participants to use language that facilitated the discussion of these practices (table 1.1). By orienting the participating teachers toward a study of practices, we worked to shift their gaze from the teacher to the teaching. As a result, many participants were able to describe new practices they would try out in their own classrooms. One teacher said her biggest takeaway was "allowing students to struggle with problems," while another said, "Determining what children know and can do is crucial to being able to celebrate their current level of success and informs us about what next steps we might take." These reflections demonstrate that teachers began to analyze teaching in ways that would be useful to improving their practice once they returned to their own classrooms.

Table 1.1

Language that facilitates discussion of teaching practices

Instead of Saying . . .	Observers Could Say . . .
You really know how to get students interested.	The problem at the start of the lesson really grabbed students' interest.
You have a great way with the kids.	Asking students to explain their thinking during the discussion seemed to make them feel like their ideas matter to the community.
The way you explained that concept was confusing.	I wonder if explaining the concept by . . . would have helped students to see . . . more clearly.

Teacher-Centered Professional Development

Research suggests that professional development is most meaningful and transferable when it is teacher-centered; that is, when it is born out of something the teacher herself wants to learn, study, or get better at (Schoenfeld 2015; Jacob and McGovern 2015; Baldinger and Hu 2016). Just as hands-on and collaborative experiences often yield the most powerful learning for students, teachers improve when they have both agency over what they are working on and immediate opportunities to try new work in the company of colleagues. Because of the practice-based nature of Math Lab, teachers drove their own growth by raising questions and areas of practice for the group to study and work on together. For example, over the course of the week, teachers attending Math Lab became interested in learning more about math conferring—the practice of having a one-on-one conversation with a student about his or her mathematical thinking.

Co-Constructing Innovations in Teaching: Math Conferring

While conferring practices were not a specific area of focus for us going into the week, it quickly became apparent that participating teachers wanted to know how to interact with students one-on-one and in small groups in ways that supported their sense making. As the week progressed, we collaborated with participating teachers to develop a framework for conferring that offered teachers an approach to talking with students about their ideas (fig. 1.7).

As a result of spending a week evaluating and analyzing teaching, participants reported that they would approach the practice of conferring differently in their classrooms going forward. One teacher said she had learned that "[when conferring] . . . struggle is OK. Do not jump to giving kids the answers or prompts. By struggling, they truly build their own understanding." A number of teachers said they would spend more time observing, questioning, and listening to their students in their future math conferences. The opportunity to co-construct a conferring framework and immediately try it out with students increased the likelihood that participants would transfer this new practice to their own classrooms.

Math Conferring to Support Student Understanding

When students make mistakes in their mathematical work, we are offered an opportunity: we can talk with them about misconceptions in a way that acknowledges the sense students have made, supports deepening their understanding, and encourages them to see math as something that requires sense making. But often, in this moment, we feel unsure about how to do this. Should we correct the mistake and explicitly point out the error in process or reasoning? When we do this, it can reinforce a belief that math is about procedural knowledge rather than conceptual knowledge, that the teacher or "expert" holds the keys to that procedural knowledge, and that the ability to access that knowledge may not be inherent within the child but rather something that needs to be "given" to the child by the expert.

Instead of correcting students' mathematical mistakes, we can use a series of conferring prompts to help students develop their understandings and reinforce the belief that sense making is an integral part of mathematics. The following framework may be helpful when approaching students about their mathematical thinking:

• Begin by asking the student to share his/her thinking in a neutral way.

Fig. 1.7. Conferring framework co-constructed by facilitators
and participants at NYC Math Lab

Math Conferring to Support Student Understanding
• Elicit and listen carefully to student thinking, possibly prompting for a visual representation to clarify.
• Begin to address a misconception by referring to a shared/commonly agreed upon math idea—this is the common ground on which you can build the sense making.
• Ask student to consider this idea alongside his/her solution . . . does the solution make sense in light of this idea?
• If a student recognizes that his/her solution doesn't make sense, ask, "What should we do?" This prompts the student to take responsibility for making a new plan to solve the problem.
• If a student doesn't recognize that the solution doesn't make sense, it may mean that the shared belief you started with is not secure for the student. You then have some important information about what foundational pieces you need to work on with that student.

Fig. 1.7. Continued

■ Conclusion

Although evaluating teachers has been a major area of focus in recent years for improving American education systems, research does not suggest that simply evaluating teachers more results in improved teaching and learning. We believe that a shift from *teacher* evaluation to *teaching* evaluation, by increasing opportunities to learn from public teaching, holds potential for improving the quality of math instruction in our schools. Professional development structures like the NYC Math Lab position teachers as knowledgeable observers and agents in their own growth. In addition, the fact that teachers themselves created the NYC Math Lab is notable; it suggests that teachers can play a more active role than previously realized in their own professional learning.

To be effective, teachers of mathematics need more than just ratings from their supervisors with limited actionable feedback. Indeed, without access to meaningful, practice-based, teacher-centered professional development opportunities, feedback from supervisors can serve to deepen teachers' fixed mindsets about deficits in their math teaching skills or content knowledge. Having a shared class to work with and a community of teachers to analyze teaching with can stimulate teacher growth. Further, as teachers collaboratively study the craft of teaching mathematics, they often deepen their content knowledge and their ability to view math from a sense-making perspective.

The NYC Math Lab offers an example of how districts, schools, and teachers themselves can create spaces for the study of teacher practice and children's mathematical thinking. Administrators can play a key role in creating these spaces. For example, districtwide leaders can work together to create networks of schools and teachers who periodically come together to study public teaching. At the school level, principals can develop lab settings by encouraging teachers to open up their classrooms and their practice to colleagues for study or by implementing schoolwide lesson study as a form of professional development. Teachers who want to improve their practice can seek out colleagues to participate in regular peer visitations and debriefs.

For those considering creating a math lab, we offer a few lessons learned from our experience. First, the staging of a math lab can pose considerable organizational challenges. The creation and implementation of a math lab involves tasks as varied as establishing a relationship with community-based organizations, handling administrative tasks, planning and writing lessons and student tasks, teaching the lab classes each day, and recording and collecting artifacts for future study. We suggest recruiting a team to work together on these myriad components of creating a math lab.

Another area for consideration in the creation of a math lab is how to best support teacher learning. As elementary school teachers, we found ourselves primarily focused on the teaching of the students: developing curriculum to use at the lab, creating rich tasks, and working with the individual and collective needs of the students. We found it challenging to also focus our attention on teaching the teachers who participated. For others considering creating a math lab, we suggest that articulating beliefs about teaching teachers or working through university partners might enhance teacher learning at the lab.

A third area of consideration in the creation of a math lab is supporting sustained teacher growth beyond the lab. As noted, research supports the idea that the best professional development involves meaningful follow-up (Fishman, Davis, and Chan 2014) and that the transfer of new teaching practices into the classroom is more likely when teachers are part of a team rather than working in isolation. We selected participants with this in mind: we recruited teachers who would attend the NYC Math Lab in teams, selected teachers working in schools that we knew were supportive of this work, and met throughout the school year to follow up on the work we did in the lab. Yet logistical considerations precluded us from sustaining meaningful collaborations with all participating teachers. We also had little interaction with students in our lab class after the one-week workshop. Those interested in developing a math lab would be wise to build structures from the outset that provide for continued teacher learning and student growth.

Based on the preliminary evidence presented in this article, we believe that observation and analysis of teaching in real time is a powerful learning experience for teachers. Our hope is that initiatives that privilege teaching evaluation over teacher evaluation will spread and that they will play a role in the improvement of mathematics teaching and learning at scale.

References

Baker, Bruce D., Joseph Oluwole, and Preston C. Green. "The Legal Consequences of Mandating High Stakes Decisions Based on Low Quality Information: Teacher Evaluation in the Race-to-the-Top Era." *Education Evaluation and Policy Analysis Archives* 21 (2013): 1–71.

Baldinger, Evra, and Tina Weiting Hu. "Letting Teachers Drive: A Powerful Approach to 'Live' Coaching." Presented at the Annual Meeting of the National Council of Teachers of Mathematics, San Francisco, Calif., April 15, 2016.

Ball, Deborah. "The Mathematical Understandings that Prospective Teachers Bring to Teacher Education." *The Elementary School Journal* 90, no 4 (1990): 449–66.

Ball, Deborah, Lindsey Mann, Meghan Shaughnessy, Kara Suzuka, and Mark Thames. "Designing and Using a Laboratory Approach to the Collective Study of Instruction." Presented at the Annual Meeting of the American Educational Research Association, San Francisco, Calif., April 30, 2013.

Bezuk, Nadine S., and Marilyn Bieck. "Current Research on Rational Numbers and Common Fractions: Summary and Implications for Teachers." *Research Ideas for the Classroom: Middle Grades Mathematics* (1993): 118–36.

Boaler, Jo. *Mathematical Mindsets: Unleashing Students' Potential Through Creative Math, Inspiring Messages and Innovative Teaching*. Hoboken, N.J.: John Wiley & Sons, 2015.

Doherty, Kathryn M., and Sandi Jacobs. *State of the States 2015: Evaluating Teaching, Leading and Learning*. National Center on Teacher Quality. http://www.nctq.org/dmsView/StateofStates2015.

Dweck, Carol. *Mindset: The New Psychology of Success*. New York: Random House, 2006.

Fishman, Barry J., Elizabeth A. Davis, and Carol K. K. Chan. "A Learning Sciences Perspective on Teacher Learning Research." In *The Cambridge Handbook of the Learning Sciences*, pp. 707–25. Cambridge, England: Cambridge University Press, 2014.

Gallimore, Ronald, Bradley Ermeling, William Saunders, and Claude Goldenberg. "Moving the Learning of Teaching Closer to Practice: Teacher Education Implications of School-Based Inquiry Teams." *The Elementary School Journal* 109, no. 5 (May 2009): 537–53.

Green, Elizabeth. *Building a Better Teacher: How Teaching Works (And How to Teach It to Everyone)*. New York: W.W. Norton & Company, 2014.

Hiebert, James. "The Constantly Underestimated Challenge of Improving Mathematics Instruction." In *Vital Directions for Mathematics Education Research*, pp. 45–56. New York: Springer New York, 2013.

Hiebert, James, Thomas P. Carpenter, Elizabeth Fennema, Karen Fuson, Diana Wearne, Hanlie Murray, Alwynn Olivier, and Piet Human. *Making Sense: Teaching and Learning Mathematics with Understanding*. Portsmouth, N.H.: Heinemann, 1997.

Jacob, Andy, and Kate McGovern. "The Mirage: Confronting the Hard Truth about Our Quest for Teacher Development." *TNTP* (2015).

Kane, Cheryl M. *Prisoners of Time: Research. What We Know and What We Need To Know*. Washington, D.C.: U.S. Government Printing Office, Superintendent of Documents, Mail Stop: SSOP, 1994.

LeTendre, Gerald K., David P. Baker, Motoko Akiba, Brian Goesling, and Alex Wiseman. "Teachers' Work: Institutional Isomorphism and Cultural Variation in the US, Germany, and Japan." *Educational Researcher* 30, no. 6 (2001): 3–15.

Lewis, Catherine C., and Jacqueline Hurd. *Lesson Study Step by Step: How Teacher Learning Communities Improve Instruction*. Portsmouth, N.H.: Heinemann, 2011.

Lortie, Dan Clement. *Schoolteacher: A Sociological Study*. Chicago: University of Chicago Press, 1975.

Lortie-Forgues, Hugues, Jing Tian, and Robert S. Siegler. "Why Is Learning Fraction and Decimal Arithmetic So Difficult?" *Developmental Review* 38 (2015): 201–21.

National Council of Teachers of Mathematics (NCTM). *Principles to Actions: Ensuring Mathematical Success for All*. Reston, Va.: NCTM, 2014.

National Governors Association Center for Best Practices and Council of Chief State School Officers (NGA Center and CCSSO). *Common Core State Standards for Mathematics*. Washington, D.C.: NGA Center and CCSSO, 2010. http://www.corestandards.org.

Ronfeldt, Matthew, Susanna Owens Farmer, Kiel McQueen, and Jason A. Grissom. "Teacher Collaboration in Instructional Teams and Student Achievement." *American Educational Research Journal* 52, no. 3 (2015): 475–514.

Russell, Susan Jo, Deborah Schifter, and Virginia Bastable. *Connecting Arithmetic to Algebra: Strategies for Building Algebraic Thinking in the Elementary Grades*. Portsmouth, N.H.: Heinemann, 2011.

Schoenfeld, Alan H. "Thoughts on Scale." *ZDM* 47, no. 1 (2015): 161–69.

Steele, Michael D., Kate R. Johnson, Samuel Otten, Beth A. Herbel-Eisenmann, and Cynthia L. Carver. "Improving Instructional Leadership through the Development of Leadership Content Knowledge: The Case of Principal Learning in Algebra." *Journal of Research on Leadership Education* 10, no. 2 (2015): 127–50.

Stigler, James W., Karen B. Givvin, and Belinda J. Thompson. "What Community College Developmental Mathematics Students Understand about Mathematics." *MathAMATYC Educator* 1, no. 3 (2010): 4–16.

Stipek, Deborah J., Karen B. Givvin, Julie M. Salmon, and Valanne L. MacGyvers. "Teachers' Beliefs and Practices Related to Mathematics Instruction." *Teaching and Teacher Education* 17, no. 2 (2001): 213–26.-

Yackel, Erna, and Peter Cobb. "Sociomathematical Norms, Argumentation, and Autonomy in Mathematics." *Journal for Research in Mathematics Education* 27, no. 4 (1996): 458–77.

CHAPTER 2

Decomposing Mathematical Proof with Secondary Teachers

Michelle Cirillo, *University of Delaware, Newark*

Neil McCall, *Archmere Academy, Claymont, Delaware*

Zack Murtha, *The Haverford School, Haverford, Pennsylvania*

Samuel Walters, *The Haverford School, Haverford, Pennsylvania*

"Pointlessly complicated," "a wolf in sheep's clothing," "rigid," and "dogmatic" are words and phrases that have been used to describe the traditional high school geometry curriculum (Lockhart 2009). Historically, high school geometry is the place where students first encounter deductive proof. However, the fact that students struggle with geometry proof is well documented (Senk 1985), and proof has also been identified as a difficult topic to teach (Sinclair, Pimm, and Skelin 2012). Even some experienced teachers with excellent mathematics knowledge for teaching claim that they do not have good strategies for introducing geometry proof (Cirillo 2011).

Yet, because proof is considered fundamental to the *field* of mathematics, the research community has issued calls to better support the teaching of proof. For example, in his study of student engagement with two-column proof, Herbst (2002) concluded, "The mandate to involve students in proving is likely to be met with the development of tools and norms that teachers can use to enable students to prove and to demonstrate that they are indeed proving" (p. 200). As is the case with all mathematics teaching endeavors, involving students in the study of geometric proof is best supported when teachers can anticipate students' perplexities, help them avoid known pitfalls, and recognize and dispel misconceptions (Sinclair, Pimm, and Skelin 2012).

To better understand these issues, we collaborated on a three-year qualitative study to explore the following questions:

- What are some challenges of introducing proof in the high school geometry course?

- What new approaches can address these challenges, and how might they support student learning?

Here, we provide some answers to these questions and introduce the Geometry Proof Scaffold (GPS), a pedagogical framework for introducing proof. First, we describe the project and the people involved in the work.

■ The Project and the People

This chapter's author team consists of a university researcher (Michelle) and three classroom teachers (Neil, Zack, and Sam). Prior to the start of the Geometry Proof Project (GPP), all of us had taught geometry with conventional textbooks that treated proof as a stand-alone topic to be covered over a semester. After reflecting on her own struggles with teaching proof in geometry and then studying the topic for her doctoral dissertation (Cirillo 2008), Michelle designed a collaborative research project that allowed her to further explore the issue.

Michelle collected baseline data in teachers' classrooms in fall 2010. Specifically, classroom observations were conducted over two nonconsecutive weeks in one target geometry class of each teacher. Beginning in spring 2011, our group met for eighteen professional development sessions consisting of more than sixty-five meeting hours. These sessions were designed to assist the project teachers in engaging with research literature on proof and reflecting on and considering alternative approaches to teaching proof. These sessions took place over the course of a year.

In fall 2011, additional classroom data were collected to observe changes made to the teachers' practices. Originally part of a group of six teachers, the three teacher-authors were able with supplemental funding to continue working with Michelle for a third year. About ten observations in one target class were conducted every year of the project. Interviews were conducted annually to help Michelle understand what she observed in the lessons.

Text for this chapter was generated from several sources: the research literature, classroom data and analysis, and the three teacher-authors' written responses to a series of prompts. The prompts focused on how we taught prior to participating in the GPP, how our participation in the project influenced our teaching and our students' learning, and so forth. The teachers-authors' written responses are woven throughout this chapter because the project was a collaborative endeavor rather than a study *about* teachers. Because a main focus of the chapter is on how the research partnership impacted practice, we continue by exploring what teaching proof looked like in Year One.

■ Introducing and Doing Proofs in Geometry in Year One

To describe what teaching proof looked like in our classrooms before the professional development, we draw from Herbst and Brach's (2006) descriptions of "doing proofs" in secondary geometry classrooms. Similar to findings from student interviews reported in their study, teaching proof in our classrooms began by providing "Given" and "Prove" statements. We always made clear to students what statement was to be proved, and there was never any doubt about the truth of these statements. We would ease students into this work by providing a diagram that displayed the "Given" information clearly, and the diagram would convey ideas to be used in the two-column proof. For students, doing proofs in class likely did not demand too much effort on their part because we heavily guided them through the proofs on the board. Introducing proof in the beginning of the semester was particularly challenging for us, however, because, like the teacher in Cirillo's (2011) study, the only way we knew how to cultivate proving was through a show-and-tell approach.

To better understand how proof was first *introduced* in Year One, we look into Zack's classroom because this episode was instrumental to the development of the GPS presented later in this chapter. Zack's introduction to proof began with a discussion of triangle congruence and a first proof that made use of the side-side-side postulate (see fig 2.1).

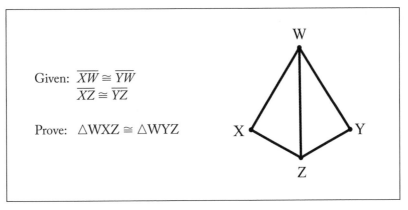

Given: $\overline{XW} \cong \overline{YW}$
$\overline{XZ} \cong \overline{YZ}$

Prove: $\triangle WXZ \cong \triangle WYZ$

Fig. 2.1. Zack's first proof in Year 1

After demonstrating this simple proof, Zack started a second proof, saying:

Zack: This is a proof. Here we go. So proofs are tough. You know, one thing about proofs is, there's no easy way . . . there's no shallow end. You can't wade into the proof pool. You gotta jump right in the deep end with these tough ones.

Student: I would drown.

Zack: You would drown? I hope not.

The next day, students came to class with incomplete homework proofs. One student commented, "I pretty much have no idea what to do on 'em." Zack responded:

> You pretty much have no idea what to do? So that's okay. These proofs are really hard, and . . . there's no real easy way to start proofs. It's not like algebra where you could start with easy problems and work to more difficult problems . . . The proofs start and they're immediately difficult . . . so you'll learn how to do 'em by sort of trying them.

After going over and making significant corrections to the students' homework proofs, Zack discussed answers to students' questions including:

* How big should I make the T [in two-column proof]?

* What reasons am I allowed to use?

* How many steps do I need to write?

We highlight this episode for several reasons. First, Zack's words resonated with all of us. Even though we had all taught geometry proof before the project, none of us believed that we had developed successful strategies for introducing it. Second, the students' questions indicated that they were more focused on the form over the reasoning in the argument. Last, Zack's claim that there was no shallow end to the proof pool provided food for thought, and the group revisited this episode and hypothesis throughout the project.

■ Connecting Research and Practice

Simultaneous engagement with the research literature and ongoing research activities within the project influenced our thinking about our practice. The professional development component began with reading research conducted on proof in geometry. We read about van Hiele level theory in Cirillo's (2009) article, "Ten Things to Consider When Teaching Proof." Citing Senk (1985), Cirillo highlighted how the van Hiele model (see table 2.1) has been used to explain some of the difficulties students have with proof in geometry. Neil recalled the impact this article had on his thinking:

> We learned that the van Hiele levels may be the reason we felt our students weren't developmentally ready for proof. If students had not had prior experiences with discovering relationships empirically, they would not be able to move to formal deduction. We were taking students at Level 2 [Analysis] and trying to force them into Level 4 thinking [Deduction].

This experience motivated us to seek out and develop different mathematics tasks to scaffold the introduction to proof the following year (i.e., navigate the shallow end of proof).

Table 2.1

Summary of van Hiele levels and their characteristics (Crowley 1987; Burger and Shaughnessy 1986) as summarized in Cirillo (2009)

Levels	Characteristics
1 Visualization	The student identifies, names, compares, and operates on geometric figures (e.g., triangles, angles, intersecting, or parallel lines) according to their appearance.
2 Analysis	The student analyzes figures in terms of their components and relationships among components and discovers properties/rules of a class of shapes empirically (e.g., by folding, measuring, using a grid or diagram).
3 Informal Deduction	The student logically interrelates previously discovered properties/rules by giving or following informal arguments.
4 Deduction	The student proves theorems deductively and establishes interrelationships among networks of theorems.
5 Rigor	The student establishes theorems in different postulational systems [i.e., non-Euclidean] and analyzes/compares these systems.

In spring 2011, after the baseline data collection, Michelle interviewed some of Sam's and Zack's students by using alternative proof tasks presented in Cirillo and Herbst's (2012) paper. For example, rather than explicitly provide students with a statement to prove, students were asked to draw conclusions based on simple "Given" statements and diagrams (see fig. 2.2). Sam recalled the impact the findings had on him: these tasks showed us that even after completing the proof semester earning decent grades, the sampled students were not good at drawing valid conclusions, and they often made erroneous assumptions based on a diagram. These experiences contributed to our interest in trying a new approach to teaching proof. This approach evolved over time as we connected research to practice and practice back to research.

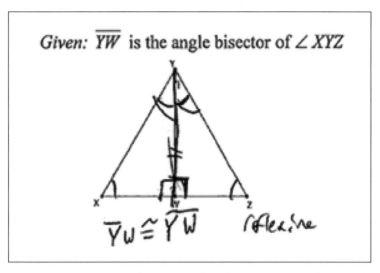

Fig. 2.2. "Drawing Conclusions" task with erroneous student work

■ Developing the Geometry Proof Scaffold

Analyzing baseline data and reflecting on her dissertation study and Zack's shallow-end metaphor helped Michelle realize that when the teachers introduced proof, they attempted to teach many important mathematical competencies at the same time. Michelle summarized:

> After observing and analyzing about forty hours of teachers introducing proof in geometry, I realized that there is a set of competencies that teachers were *implicitly* attempting to teach during these show-and-tell presentations. When students are introduced to proof in geometry, they must learn the following simultaneously: (*a*) particular postulates, definitions, and theorems; (*b*) how to *use* definitions and theorems to draw conclusions; (*c*) how to work with diagrams; (*d*) a variety of sub-arguments and classroom norms for writing them up; and (*e*) how sub-arguments come together to construct a larger argument. Based on the shallow-end proof pool metaphor suggested by Zack, I hypothesized that perhaps there were practices that students needed to develop proofs that could be ramped up over time. The professional development sessions and subsequent observations gave us a way to test this hypothesis.

Michelle presented these findings early in the professional development. After considering the list of proof subgoals that were all being taught simultaneously without making these things *explicit* to our students, we thought that we might be on to something. The problem and the solution, which had bewildered us all for years, now seemed so obvious. Zack reflected on these findings, writing: We needed some way to effectively scaffold these foundational skills so that when we ask students to write a proof, they are ready for it.

What happened next was a series of teaching experiments (see Hiebert, Morris, and Glass 2003 for more on this idea). Michelle would present some written tasks that she also piloted in a geometry class for preservice teachers. These tasks included different kinds of problems inspired by the earlier work of Cirillo and Herbst (2012) that attempted to isolate some of the compentencies listed above. The project teachers would try out and build on these tasks, developing new tasks on their own. Sam and Zack went as far as writing a new curriculum based on the GPS (Cirillo 2014). The list of subgoals and their associated competencies was continuously revised. Neil found the list to be a useful tool that he laminated and consulted daily when planning his lessons. After conducting a thorough analysis of the corpus of data from the project, the list has evolved into what we now call the GPS.

■ The Geometry Proof Scaffold

The GPS is organized around the subgoals of teaching proof, and it describes the competencies that students must understand and be able to exhibit to ultimately be successful with proving. It simplifies the task of proving so that understanding can be built in progressive steps toward the larger goal. The GPS is summarized next (see table 2.2), and some examples from the curriculum developed by Zack and Sam are provided. Additional examples are provided on this book's page at NCTM's More4U site.

The **Understanding Geometric Concepts** subgoal highlights the importance of understanding the building blocks of geometry. This includes developing and refining students' *concept images*, that is, the total cognitive structure associated with a concept (including the mental pictures), and their *concept definitions*, the form of words used to specify that concept (Tall and Vinner 1981). Ultimately, students should be able to use *formal concept definitions*—those that are accepted by the mathematical community (Tall and Vinner 1981). This is important because definitions of mathematical terms play a central role in mathematical proof.

The **Coordinating Geometric Modalities** subgoal supports students in communicating geometric objects through the use of a diagram, notation, or a verbal description of that particular object. To address this subgoal, for example, Zack developed a task asking students if it was possible to draw a diagram in which $\overline{DF}$ *bisects* $\overline{PO}$, *but* $\overline{PO}$ *does not bisect* $\overline{DF}$. Students were expected to explain their answers. Spending time developing such competencies is important because working with diagrams is central to geometric thinking (Sinclair, Pimm, and Skelin 2012). Additionally, working with diagrams and mathematical notation has been likened to learning a new language (Sinclair et al. 2012; Usiskin 1996).

Defining highlights the logical structure of definitions, how definitions are developed, and how they are used in mathematical proof. An example from the curriculum is: "Write the two conditional statements that comprise the biconditional: *Two angles are complementary if and only if their measures sum to 90 degrees.*" Helping students understand that definitions "work both ways" and having them attempt to write their own definitions before trying to construct a proof helped scaffold the introduction to proof because students were already familiar with these competencies before they began working on proofs.

The **Conjecturing** subgoal recognizes that conjecturing is an important part of mathematics and of proving. Conjecturing seems nearly lost in the modern version of "doing proofs" in school math where the "Given" and the "Prove" statements tend to be provided to the students. Yet, engaging students in opportunities to conjecture is important because conjecturing about relationships "is at the heart of mathematical practice" (Lampert 1992, p. 308).

Table 2.2

The Geometry Proof Scaffold (GPS) framework

Subgoals	Descriptions	Competencies
Understanding Geometric Concepts	This subgoal highlights the importance of understanding the building blocks of geometry.	1. Having accurate "mental pictures" of geometric concepts (i.e., having a concept image)
		2. Being able to verbally describe geometric concepts; ideally, being fluent with one or more definitions of the concept (i.e., having or developing a concept definition)
		3. Determining examples and non-examples
		4. Understanding connections among classes of geometric objects, where they overlap, and how they are contained within other classes (i.e., understanding mathematical hierarchy)
Coordinating Geometric Modalities	This subgoal highlights the ways in which the mathematics register draws on a range of modalities.	1. Translating between language and diagram
		2. Translating between diagram and symbolic notation
		3. Translating between language and symbolic notation
Defining	This subgoal highlights the nature of definitions, their logical structure, how they are written, and how they are used.	1. Writing a "good" definition (includes necessary and sufficient properties)
		2. Knowing definitions are not unique (i.e., geometric objects can have different definitions)
		3. Understanding how to write and use definitions as biconditionals
Conjecturing	This subgoal recognizes that conjecturing is an important part of mathematics and proving.	1. Understanding that empirical reasoning can be used to develop a conjecture but that it is not sufficient proof of the conjecture
		2. Being able to turn a conjecture into a testable conditional statement.
		3. Seeking out counterexamples to test conjectures and knowing that only one counterexample is needed to disprove a conjecture
		4. Understanding that when testing a conjecture, you are testing it for every case so you might begin by writing: "All," "Every," or "For any"

Continued on next page

Table 2.2 continued

Subgoals	Descriptions	Competencies
Drawing Conclusions	This subgoal presents the idea of an open-ended task that leads to conclusions that can be drawn from given statements and/or a diagram.	1. Understanding what can and cannot be assumed from a diagram
		2. Knowing when and how definitions and/or "Given" information can be used to draw a conclusion from a statement about a mathematical object
		3. Using postulates, definitions, and theorems (or combinations of these) to draw valid conclusions from some given information
Understanding Common Sub-Arguments	This subgoal recognizes that there are common short sequences of statements and reasons that are used frequently in proofs and that these pieces may appear relatively unchanged from one proof to the next.	1. Recognizing a sub-argument as a branch of proof and how it fits into the larger proof
		2. Understanding what valid conclusions can be drawn from a given statement and how those make a sub-argument (i.e., knowing some commonly occurring sub-arguments)
		3. Understanding how to write a sub-argument using notation and acceptable language (where "acceptable" is typically determined by the teacher)
Understanding Theorems	This subgoal highlights the nature of theorems, their logical structure, how they are written, and how they are used.	1. Interpreting a theorem statement to determine the hypothesis and conclusion and, if needed, providing an appropriate diagram
		2. If applicable, marking a diagram that satisfies the hypothesis of a proof
		3. Understanding that a theorem is not a theorem until it has been proven
		4. Understanding that one cannot use the conclusions of the theorem itself to prove the conclusions of that theorem (i.e., avoiding circular reasoning)
		5. Understanding that theorems are mathematical statements that are only sometimes biconditionals
		6. Understanding the connection between logic and a theorem; for example, how to write the contrapositive of a conditional statement

Continued on next page

Table 2.2 continued

Subgoals	Descriptions	Competencies
Understanding the Nature of Proof	This subgoal highlights the nature of proof, proof structure, and how the laws of logic are applied.	1. Understanding that the only way to sanction the truth of a conjecture is through deductive proof (rather than empirical reasoning)
		2. Exploring a pathway for constructing a proof (i.e., the problem-solving aspect of proving)
		3. Understanding that proofs are constructed by using axioms, postulates, definitions, and theorems and that they follow the laws of logic
		4. Knowing what language is acceptable to use and how to write up a proof
		5. Recognizing that if you prove that something is true for one particular geometric object, then it is true for all of them

Drawing Conclusions presents the idea of open-ended tasks that ask students to draw conclusions from given statements (see fig. 2.3). One benefit of engaging students in such tasks is that they help teachers correct some common errors students make when they draw erroneous conclusions from diagrams rather than from given information. For example, figure 2.2 shows a diagram where a student concluded that there were right angles and a second pair of congruent angles simply because they *appeared* to be so. Other students also concluded that line segments were congruent even though they were only "Given" that there was an angle bisector. Neil claimed that developing this subgoal had the biggest impact on how he taught geometry. After developing students' abilities to draw (valid) conclusions, his students viewed proof as an extension of this set of competencies, rather than a mysterious, unconnected new concept.

The **Understanding Common Sub-Arguments** subgoal presents the idea that there are common short sequences of statements and reasons frequently used in proofs that may appear relatively unchanged from one proof to the next. The subgoal helps students recognize regularity in repeated reasoning. The sub-arguments come together to make up the central proof idea (e.g., two triangles are congruent). An example of a common sub-argument is a proof of the proposition: If two lines are perpendicular, then congruent angles are formed (see fig. 2.4). Zack argued that the Sub-Arguments tool was instrumental in helping students wade through the shallow end of the proof pool because it was a bridge between drawing valid conclusions and constructing proofs.

Finally, the **Understanding Theorems** and **Understanding the Nature of Proof** subgoals support students in proving theorems and understanding proving. More detail is provided at this book's page on NCTM's More4U site.

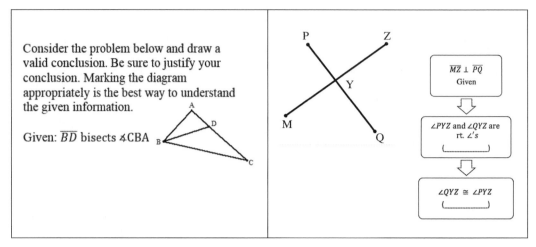

Fig. 2.3. Drawing Conclusions example   Fig. 2.4. Sub-Arguments example

■ Evidence from Practice

The development of the GPS profoundly affected the way we think about teaching proof in geometry. Rather than present proof as an exercise in show-and-tell, we now know that instead of throwing students into the deep end of the proof pool we can cultivate important competencies that allow us to scaffold the introduction to proof. Laying this groundwork, which often includes attending to van Hiele levels below level 4, takes additional time. However, once we developed the competencies required for doing proofs, the transition from the shallow to the deep end of proof is remarkably smooth. Zack reflected:

> I no longer feel like proofs begin by throwing students in the deep end and expecting them to flail around until they hopefully begin to copy my work well enough. My students now see proofs the way I do—as a sequence of logical steps. Since the proofs make sense, they are not hung up on the length of proofs or the number of steps.

All of us concluded that more than ever before, with this approach, far more students seemed to actually understand proof. Sam reported that breaking it into pieces made it easier for students to digest and understand the material and see how it fits together. Prior to the intervention, we heard complaints from many students about doing proofs; after it, all the teachers reported that the students' grades and dispositions toward doing proofs improved through this method. Students who learned proof in this way have said things like: "These are neat," "These just make sense," and "That was fun!" In fact, Neil had students *ask* to write a proof in a later unit in order to better understand *why* something was true. Sam and Zack reported that students were sometimes disappointed when the proof units were completed. This group's work offers promising evidence that perhaps teachers can, in the words of Herbst (2002), use new tools and norms to enable students to prove and demonstrate that they are indeed proving.

■ Conclusion

The work described in this chapter connects to the idea of decomposing practice described by Grossman and colleagues (2009), which involves breaking down practice into its constituent parts for teaching and learning. Engaging in this collaborative research has been a highlight of our careers as mathematics educators. We no longer have concerns about how to introduce proof. The GPP helped us feel empowered and provided a new lens to look more critically at the other courses that we teach. Current work involves the development of lesson plans, based on the GPS, that will be revised through cycles of lesson study and that will be shared with others. Additional research is being conducted to further document the effectiveness of this approach. We encourage you to consider engaging in studies that decompose proof in other domains or that decompose other mathematical practices.

Acknowledgments

The research reported in this paper was supported with funding from the Knowles Science Teaching Foundation (KTSF) and the National Science Foundation (NSF award #1453493). Any opinions, findings, and conclusions or recommendations expressed in this material are those of the authors and do not necessarily reflect the views of the KSTF or NSF.

References

Burger, William F., and Michael Shaughnessy. "Characterizing the van Hiele Levels of Development in Geometry." *Journal for Research in Mathematics Education* 17, no. 1 (1986): 31–48.

Cirillo, Michelle. *On Becoming a Geometry Teacher: A Longitudinal Case Study of One Teacher Learning to Teach Proof.* PhD dissertation, Iowa State University, 2008.

———. "Ten Things to Consider When Teaching Proof: What I Wish I Had Known about Teaching Proof before I Taught Geometry." *Mathematics Teacher* 103, no. 4 (2009): 251–57.

———. "'I'm Like the Sherpa Guide': On Learning to Teach Proof in School Mathematics." In *35th Conference of the International Group for the Psychology of Mathematics Education Proceedings*, edited by B. Ubuz, pp. 241–48. Ankara, Turkey: PME, 2011.

———. "Supporting the Introduction to Formal Proof." In *Proceedings of the Joint Meeting of Psychology of PME 38 and PME-NA 36*, edited by C. Nicol, P. Liljedahl, P. Oesterle, and D. Allan, pp. 321–28. Vancouver, Canada: PME, 2014.

Cirillo, Michelle, and Patricio Herbst. "Moving toward More Authentic Proof Practices in Geometry." *The Mathematics Educator* 21, no. 2 (2012): 11–33.

Crowley, Mary L. "The van Hiele Model of the Development of Geometric Thought." In *Learning and Teaching Geometry, K–12*, 1987 Yearbook of the National Council of Teachers of Mathematics (NCTM), edited by Mary Montgomery Lindquist. Reston, Va.: NCTM, 1987.

Grossman, Pam, Christa Compton, Danielle Igra, Matthew Ronfeldt, Emily Shahan, and Peter W. Williamson. "Teaching Practice: A Cross-Professional Perspective." *Teachers College Record* 111, no. 9 (2009): 2055–100.

Herbst, Patricio G. "Engaging Students in Proving: A Double Bind on the Teacher." *Journal for Research in Mathematics Education* 33, no. 3 (2002): 176–203.

Herbst, Patricio G., and Catherine Brach. "Proving and Doing Proofs in High School Geometry Classes: What Is It That Is Going on for Students?" *Cognition and Instruction* 24, no. 1 (2006): 73–122.

Hiebert, James, Anne K. Morris, and Brad Glass. "Learning to Learn to Teach: An 'Experiment' Model for Teaching and Teacher Preparation in Mathematics." *Journal of Mathematics Teacher Education* 6 (2003): 201–22.

Lampert, Magdalene. "Practices and Problems in Teaching Authentic Mathematics." In *Effective and Responsible Teaching: The New Synthesis,* edited by Fritz K. Oser, Andreas Dick, and Jean-Luc Patry, pp. 295–314: San Francisco, Calif.: Jossey-Bass, 1992.

Lockhart, Paul. "High School Geometry: Instrument of the Devil." In *Mathematician's Lament,* edited by Paul Lockhart, pp. 67–88. New York: Bellevue Literary Press, 2009.

Senk, Sharon L. "How Well Do Students Write Geometry Proofs?" *The Mathematics Teacher* 78, no. 6 (1985): 448–56.

Sinclair, Nathalie, David Pimm, and Melanie Skelin. *Developing an Essential Understanding of Geometry for Teaching Mathematics in Grades 9–12.* Reston, Va.: NCTM, 2012.

Tall, David, and Shlomo Vinner. "Concept Image and Concept Definition in Mathematics with Particular Reference to Limits and Continuity." *Educational Studies in Mathematics* 12 (1981): 151–69.

Usiskin, Zalman. "Mathematics as a Language." In *Communication in Mathematics: K–12 and Beyond,* edited by Portia C. Elliott and Margaret J. Kenney, pp. 231–43: Reston, Va.: NCTM, 1996.

CHAPTER 3

Educators Learning from Middle School Students' Views of Mathematical Strengths

Dorothy Y. White, *University of Georgia, Athens*

Carlos Nicolas Gomez, *Clemson University, Clemson, South Carolina*

Kristina Patel, *Clarke Middle School, Athens, Georgia*

Nicholas Hussain, *Hilsman Middle School, Athens, Georgia*

Robert Simpson, *Clarke Middle School, Athens, Georgia*

Fredric Rushing, *Coile Middle School, Athens, Georgia*

Jason Pratt, *Hilsman Middle School, Athens, Georgia*

Creating equitable classroom environments where every student is valued and respected requires teachers to work collaboratively while they plan instruction, resolve problems of practice, and support each other to take responsibility for their students' mathematics learning (National Council of Teachers of Mathematics [NCTM] 2014). Research on professional learning communities (PLCs) suggests that these communities can provide teachers with opportunities to work collaboratively, communicate with colleagues, and continuously learn together (Vescio, Ross, and Adams 2008). Paramount to these communities is teacher engagement in professional conversations, defined as "discussions among those who share a complex task or profession in order to improve their understanding of and efficacy in what they do" (Britt, Irwin, and Ritchie 2001, p. 31). These conversations can promote professional learning and instructional improvement when teachers reflect on problems of practice (Little and Horn 2007). Problems such as motivating students, differentiating instruction for diverse learners, and navigating new curricular resources and district mandates are more likely to be resolved when teachers collaborate with colleagues. In our PLC, we have found that focusing our conversations on students' mathematical strengths has fostered new perspectives of our students' potential and success in mathematics classrooms.

Featherstone and colleagues (2011) have suggested that every student has mathematical strengths and that it is the teacher's responsibility to set norms in the classroom that highlight these strengths. Students' strengths extend beyond rapid computation and other attributes traditionally seen as displays of intelligence and understanding in mathematics. These strengths include students' reasoning skills, communication skills, motivation, and other mathematical practices. Teachers who focus on mathematical strengths look beyond students' behaviors and recognize the contributions students bring to the classroom (e.g., how students do mathematics). By acknowledging students as doers of mathematics, the teacher considers the multiple identities (race, ethnicity, class, etc.) students use to make sense of mathematics, thereby having to rethink what equitable practices mean in the classroom and the purposes of learning mathematics (Aguirre, Mayfield-Ingram, and Martin 2013). Considering strengths in mathematics can change what it means to do mathematics and increase students' development of productive dispositions toward mathematics. Productive disposition is one piece of mathematical proficiency that influences the intrinsic motivation of the student (National Research Council 2001). Furthermore, by redefining what it means to do mathematics, students' perspectives of each other as doers of mathematics shift and can raise the status of students' mathematical ideas that previously might have been ignored (Featherstone et al. 2011). Therefore, by affirming students' mathematical strengths, we acknowledge their identities as doers of mathematics (Aguirre, Mayfield-Ingram, and Martin 2013), help them develop a productive disposition toward mathematics, and empower students mathematically in the classroom (Cohen and Lotan 2014; Featherstone et al. 2011). As educators, however, focusing on students' strengths can be difficult, because we have been taught to look for students' errors and misconceptions in order to correct them (Jilk 2016). A focus on mathematical strengths aids teachers in highlighting what a student can do rather than an endless remediation of weaknesses.

Our PLC, the Mathematical Pedagogical Problem Solvers (MPPS), is made up of five middle school mathematics teachers and two mathematics teacher educators. For the previous three years, we have worked to identify students' mathematical strengths while we collaborate on solving our pedagogical problems of practice. The teachers teach at three different middle schools in the county, and the teacher educators teach at a local university. Through monthly meetings and by observing one another's classrooms, we developed the Taxonomy of Students' Mathematical Strengths (TMS) as a tool to consider the mathematical strengths students display in the classroom (see fig. 3.1). The Common Core Standards for Mathematical Practice (SMP; National Governors Association Center for Best Practices and Council of Chief State School Officers [NGA Center and CCSSO] 2010) implicitly influenced our consideration of student strengths as a means for a better understanding of the ways students can demonstrate certain practices. For example, the TMS strength "explains ideas to other students well" is a communication strength that supports the SMP that has students "construct viable arguments and critique the reasoning of others." Though we did not at the time directly connect the TMS with the SMPs, we believe that there is a strong connection between the two.

We chose to focus on strengths because we realized that we spent most of our meeting times voicing our students' problems instead of solving problems. The TMS enables us to look beyond our students' off-task behaviors and to understand the various ways students engage in mathematics lessons. In order to improve the TMS, including its sensitivity to student perspectives, we designed action research projects to learn how our students think about mathematical strengths. In this chapter, we explore how we worked together to create classroom activities to solicit middle school students' perceptions of mathematical strengths. Sharing our work as a PLC can provide insight into the power of teacher collaboration and ways to incorporate students' views into the mathematics classroom.

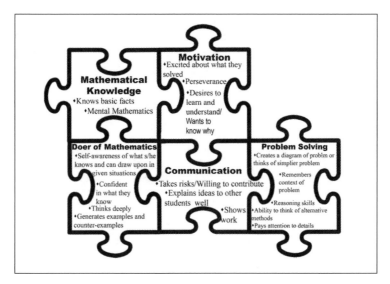

Fig. 3.1. Taxonomy of Students' Mathematical Strengths

■ Context

One of the most important ideas underlying both PLCs and teacher inquiry is recognizing the central role of teachers as agents in transforming the work of schools (Cochran-Smith and Lytle 2009). We chose to explore students' perspectives on mathematical strengths by engaging in inquiry or action research projects in our individual classrooms. Action research is systematic inquiry by practitioners who examine teacher, classroom, or school operations and practices (Nolan and Vander Putten 2007). Teachers who participate in these projects are reflective practitioners who make contributions to instructional improvements and advocate for change within the mathematics education research community. PLCs can be the catalyst for teacher inquiry and change.

■ Setting

Kent County (a pseudonym) School District enrolls a diverse student body across twenty-one schools. During the 2015–2016 school year, the district enrolled approximately 13,600 students; these were reported by the district as 49 percent African American, 24 percent Hispanic, 21 percent white, 4 percent multiracial, and 2 percent Asian, with approximately 78 percent of students eligible for free or reduced-price lunch. The district includes four middle schools with approximately 2,800 students in grades 6–8.

■ Inquiry Projects

The overall goal of our inquiry projects was to answer the question: What are middle school students' views of mathematical strengths? The objectives of the MPPS for the 2015–2016 school year were to plan instructional strategies around our TMS and to examine its influence on students' thinking and class participation. We realized, however, that our activities would be more relevant if we could engage our students with the construct of strengths. Therefore, we decided to share the TMS with our students and spent the MPPS meetings focused on designing, implementing, and analyzing teacher inquiry projects. Each of the five classroom teachers conducted projects in their classes that allowed us to explore students' perspectives across schools, classes, and data collection methods. In this chapter, we present four of the five projects. Table 3.1 gives a breakdown of the inquiry projects that are discussed by each teacher in the next section.

Table 3.1

Breakdown of teacher inquiry projects

Teacher	Number of Students	Grade	Number of Classes	Collection Methods
Kristina	26	8th	2	Class discussions
Nick	37	7th	2	Survey and class bulletin board
Rob	50	6th	2	Surveys and class discussion
Fred	110	7th	4	Surveys and class discussions

■ What We Learned about Our Students

Kristina's Project

I am an eighth-grade mathematics teacher with five years of teaching experience. I chose to survey the two classes ($n=26$) where many of my students struggle in mathematics and do not see themselves as good at it. I wanted to empower them in mathematics with a strength-identifying activity, and if it was successful use it to empower the students in all of my classes. I began the activity by asking the class to identify what it means to have a mathematical strength. Students came up with a short list of characteristics such as "gets the answer right," "shows work," "explains thinking," and "works hard." We then compared their list with those on the TMS, and I clarified the meanings for strengths on the TMS that were not on the students' list. Next, I asked them to choose one of the mathematical strengths they thought they displayed in class. They seemed to struggle, so as a class we worked together to identify at least one strength for every student. Thereafter, the students were tasked with paying attention and noting when they used one of their self-identified strengths throughout the next week. When we discussed these examples the following week, three to four students in each class had a story ready to share (see table 3.2). These students were very proud of their stories, while other students seemed less confident with sharing their examples and were quick to say, "I changed my mind" or "I don't think it is my strength." Therefore, we had a second class conversation and came up with examples of mathematical strengths for each student. Some examples were self-identified, others teacher-identified, and a few were peer-identified.

Table 3.2

Samples of student stories

Student	Identified Strength	Story of Strength
S11	Draw upon what you know	When solving systems of equations algebraically, student made explicit connections to solving linear equations and using inverse operations.
S16	Mental math	Finding solution to a linear equation, student was able to generate examples quickly by manipulating the equation mentally.
S23	Thinks deeply Takes risks and willingness to contribute	When creating a system to compare pizza companies, this student thought through the problem (given price per pizza and delivery fees) to decide which was cheaper. Shared thinking in conversation.

Overall, I found students were quick to identify strengths when making a general list but much more hesitant to identify their own strengths. I knew this activity might be challenging for my students because many of them struggle to understand and think through mathematics topics. They also tend to believe that there is a single right way to do a problem. Students were surprised to hear that we considered "excited about what they solved" and "remembers context of the problem" to be strengths. Once students were able to think of strengths in a new way using those listed in the TMS, they became more invested. After we discussed examples of mathematical strengths, students took more ownership of their strengths. For instance, one student who was listening, but not actively participating in the conversation, suddenly spoke up and asked, "So being excited about math is a strength, even if I miss the answer?" As a class we discussed that being excited and engaged is an important strength. Students then led the conversation to another strength—perseverance in problem solving and its relationship to being excited. I learned that students also wanted to share and support one another in this strength-finding activity. For example, when students shared examples of their strengths, one student expressed that he changed his mind and no longer believed that his strength was "using reasoning skills." Instead of validating this thinking, his class partner reminded him of a task they worked on the day before in which the student used reasoning to solve a system represented with pictures. In the future, I will start the year with this activity and acknowledge alternative methods of doing mathematics, because I think it helps students value their own ways of thinking. Sharing specific examples of student strengths as a class will be a recurring part of our classroom discussions.

Nick's Project

I teach seventh-grade social studies and mathematics classes. My inquiry project was based on the assumption that acknowledging mathematical strengths among my students would help them recognize the many mathematically good things that happen each day and would increase their mathematical self-efficacy because their classmates and I would be looking for each student's strengths. I chose to administer a survey on mathematical strengths to the students in both of my mathematics classes (*n*=37; see appendix A). The survey asked students to read the TMS and to select the mathematical strength they thought was their greatest strength, and also to select a strength they most wanted to improve (see table 3.3). I noticed that the top responses for students' self-selected strengths were "good at mental math" and "perseverance," while their top responses for strengths to improve were "shows work" and "perseverance."

Table 3.3

Survey responses

Strength	What is one of YOUR math strengths?		Choose a math strength that you want to get BETTER at this year in math.	
	Number	Percent	Number	Percent
Knows basic facts	5	14%	4	11%
Good at mental math	8	22%	4	11%
Excited about what you solved	2	5%	2	5%
Perseverance (keeps trying even when it's hard)	6	16%	6	16%
Desires to learn and understand—wants to know WHY	4	11%	0	0%
Explains ideas to other students well	1	3%	2	5%
Takes risks—willing to contribute	3	8%	3	8%
Shows your work	4	11%	7	19%
Creates a diagram of a problem or thinks of a simpler solution	2	5%	0	0%
Remembers the context of a problem	0	0%	1	3%
Ability to think of alternate methods	0	0%	4	11%
Has reasoning skills	2	5%	0	0%
Pays attention to details—distinguishes between important/extraneous data	0	0%	4	11%

After I reviewed the survey data and discussed it in an MPPS meeting, I decided to incorporate mathematical strengths in my mathematics lessons to increase students' awareness of their own strengths. I created a bulletin board in my classroom with each TMS category written in student-friendly language ("I have mathematical knowledge," "I am motivated," "I do mathematics," "I communicate," and "I am a problem solver") and accompanying strengths printed on colored pieces of paper. Figure 3.2 shows the board after a few days of class. This was an easy way to visually highlight the strengths, making the students and me more aware of them.

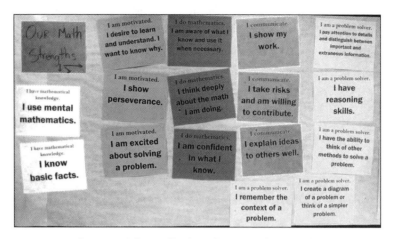

Fig. 3.2. Nick's wall of mathematical strengths

As I taught mathematics, I intentionally looked for students using the strengths either in their three- to four-person group or during a class discussion. Then I recognized the strength publicly by announcing it to the class, explaining the example I witnessed, and having the student place a star sticker on that strength's page. For example, one student placed a star on the board for displaying the strength "I explain ideas to others well." In this instance, he explained to the class how his group had used measures of center from a sample of data to conclude whether a lone data point could reasonably belong to the same population from which the sample had been taken. As students saw me acknowledge strengths from the TMS, I saw some students begin to pay close attention to their peers who were being acknowledged; some began to attempt to emulate those peers.

As I reflect on my project, my views on students' mathematical strengths and my role as a teacher have expanded. I learned that my students were more likely to recognize and value strengths that are traditionally mathematical, such as "good at mental math" or "explains ideas to other students well." I also saw that my teaching affected some of my students' perceptions of the need to develop strengths in these areas. For example, most students selected to improve upon the strength of "showing work," and I think that was because I reminded them frequently throughout the year of the value of recording their work as a strength in our classroom. I saw students begin to emulate their peers as they developed an understanding of the strengths in the TMS. The project increased the positive environment in my classroom and thus helped me focus explicitly on my students' strengths. I see this as evidence of students' increasing status and self-efficacy in the mathematics classroom. Although my results were limited by the short time I was able to implement the project, in the future I would implement this project at the beginning of the year to learn about my students and to create a norm where mathematical strengths are publicly addressed.

Rob's Project

As a second-year sixth-grade mathematics teacher and the newest member of the MPPS, I wanted to get a sense of my students as individuals before introducing them to the TMS. I thought it would be easier for me to work on this with students who were reflective and quite open in sharing their views. To gather my data, I gave two rounds of surveys as a Google Form to two of my classes (*n* = 50). The first survey was open-ended with one item focused on the question "What is your greatest strength as a student?" (see appendix B). Figure 3.3 represents the students' responses to this question from the first survey. There were five answers to choose from on this question: (1) consistency, (2) critical thinking, (3) focus, (4) organization, and (5) other. The last option was for them to write in their own strength as they saw it. The students' responses showed me that they saw themselves primarily as critical thinkers, able to think analytically about math problems. The "other" option was chosen by nearly a fifth of the students and yielded responses such as, "happiness," "hard work," "I honestly don't know," and "NONE OF UR BUSNESS," all of which helped further my understanding of these students.

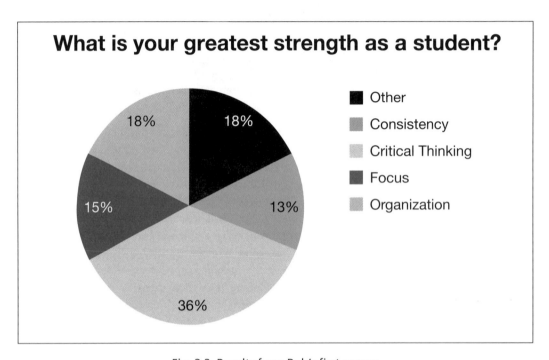

Fig. 3.3. Results from Rob's first survey

After reconvening with the MPPS group, I was able to refine the direction of my inquiry project. I introduced the TMS at the beginning of a new unit by having my students look it over as I explained the different components. Over the next week, I had the students refer back to the TMS briefly to identify which characteristics they may have used that particular day. After a week and a half, I had my students take a second survey in which they answered the following questions (see appendix B): (*a*) Which of the five characteristics outlined above do you most identify with as a math student? and (*b*) Why did you choose that strength? The results of this survey are found in fig. 3.4. I was most surprised to see that "problem solving" was chosen by so few students, considering they had overwhelmingly chosen "critical thinking" as their mathematical strength in the first survey.

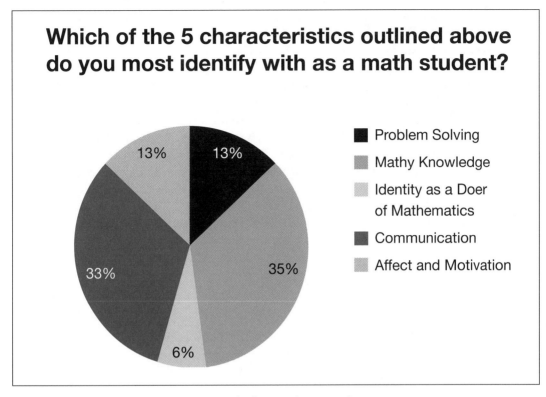

Which of the 5 characteristics outlined above do you most identify with as a math student?

- Problem Solving
- Mathy Knowledge
- Identity as a Doer of Mathematics
- Communication
- Affect and Motivation

13% 13% 35% 6% 33%

Fig. 3.4. Results from Rob's second survey

In my classroom I use the word "mathy" to encapsulate the idea that students think logically and analytically in their applications of numbers and processes. My students understand that I expect them to be "mathy," so I was pleased to see that many of them identified with that strength. As I reflect on my students' survey responses, I perceive trends in how the students saw themselves and whether their responses match how I perceived them. Question B in particular—"Why did you choose that strength?"—requires me to think about these differences and try to reconcile the recurring themes of self-satisfaction and genuine curiosity with parental pressure and peer approval. It reminds me to consider the various factors that motivate each student. As a member of the MPPS, I know it is also important that I collaborate to continue to develop a deeper understanding of how looking for strengths in my students can influence the way I see them and interact with them for the better, thereby increasing their sense of mathematical self-efficacy. This project allowed me to see not just one large class but to see twenty-six individual voices. Our MPPS discussions, where all of our members' experiences were shared, have allowed me to better understand how I could use this information to tailor my teaching in each class to more meaningfully engage my students.

Fred's Project

As a seventh-grade mathematics teacher, I chose to include all of my students ($n=110$) in my inquiry project because I recognize each child is different, and therefore they may feel differently about the strengths they display. For this project, I decided to focus two surveys on students' mathematical strengths by including the question "What is/are your mathematical strength(s)?" at the end of my weekly content assessments (see appendix C). The initial survey asked students to select as many strengths as they believed they possessed from a list of ten strengths from the TMS. I selected the ten strengths instead of the full TMS because I felt those were more familiar to the students given how I highlighted particular Standards of Mathematical Practice. As students completed the assessment, several of them had questions when they got to the last question on mathematical strengths, such as, "Are we getting graded on this?" and "Is there a right or wrong answer?" I reassured them that their answers were a way for me to understand their thinking and that the results would not be part of their grade. Table 3.4 shows the number of students who chose each strength on the initial survey in all four classes. The results were difficult to interpret because students' responses ranged from selecting one strength to all ten strengths. There were four strengths that stood out in the number of responses: (1) knows basic facts, (2) knows mental mathematics, (3) desires to learn and understand, and (4) shows work. I believe these were the most selected strengths because they are commonly used to characterize a student who is good at mathematics. Although some may be surprised that many students selected desires to "learn and understand," I was not surprised because I believe all students want to learn.

Table 3.4

Number of students who chose each strength in Survey 1

	Number of Students
Knows basic facts	100
Knows mental mathematics	99
Excited about what I solved	63
Desires to learn and understand	110
Confident in what I know	50
Thinks deeply	19
Self-aware of what I know and can use it in situations	43
Explains ideas to other students	22
Shows work	110
Ability to think of alternate methods	45

While sharing the TMS with the students, we discussed examples for each of the ten mathematical strengths. One student asked, "Can a person show all of the strengths in one class?" I explained to them that everyone has strengths and sometimes you can recognize them right away and other times it is not so easy. To help familiarize students with seeing the strengths in action, I asked them if they could identify the strengths I displayed in the classroom during the lesson. The students watched as I modeled how to find the measures of central tendencies (mean, median, mode) and measure of variation. I asked the class if anyone would like to volunteer to explain how to get the measures of center of a list of numerical data. After the students completed the task, we talked about the strengths I displayed. Students recognized that I was "confident in what I knew" and that I "knew basic facts," especially when I performed operations on the data set. I asked if anyone could tell me the strengths they displayed themselves. They told me they "showed the ability to explain to others" when presenting their procedures for finding the measures of central tendencies. At the end of the next assessment, I gave the survey again, but limited students to choosing two strengths that they most often displayed. The only two strengths selected were "knows basic facts" and "confident in what I know."

Looking back on this project, I believe the students only selected the two strengths because these were the ones they saw me model and therefore recognized when they displayed them in class. I believe I unintentionally biased the results of the survey based on the way the strengths were introduced to them. I thought it was a good idea to help students see me display various strengths, but I think the students tried to reproduce my strengths instead of recognizing their own. If I had taught other content (e.g., unit rates, ratios and proportions), I wonder if the students would also have selected these strengths or would they have been able to find evidence for other strengths. For future classes, I will attempt to take more time to model other strengths for students and provide them with experiences where those strengths can be discussed. Another thing I would do differently is I would not include the survey in assessments. Instead I would use a daily ticket out the door or some sort of electronic data tracker. By using it daily, the students will most likely become more fluent in the use of the TMS and will increase their status within the class. From this project, I learned the students are able to recognize mathematical strengths and the TMS provides a way for students to expand their own understandings of strengths. It allowed me to create a positive atmosphere in my classroom where strengths are emphasized.

■ Summary of Students' Views of Mathematical Strengths

We purposefully conducted our inquiry projects across various grade levels and classrooms. We know that every student has mathematical strengths; and as teachers we can learn more when we include the perspectives of students who have been successful in mathematics, as well as those who have not. We found that all students consider speed and accuracy as mathematical strengths, and we were surprised to learn they rarely thought about many of the strengths we identified on the TMS. Some students were resistant to these new strengths when we first presented them and made comments like, "I don't think I have one" or "This is easy for you [the teacher] because you know this stuff." Students welcomed the opportunity to broaden their views on strengths; and as one student noted, "it was freeing to know that there were many ways to be successful beyond being textbook smart." Some students felt that most people in the world were good at mathematics, something we had not expected.

We began this project late in the school year, which limited the amount of time available for working on these ideas in class with students. However, we began to see a shift in the way students talked about strengths and interacted with one another. They began to pay attention to the way their peers solved problems and provided justifications. We saw students' willingness to try, to reach outside of their comfort zone, to take chances, and to seem vulnerable in front of their peers. Helping students recognize, develop, and use specific mathematical strengths enables them to become mathematically powerful by helping them understand what they are good at and providing them a toolbox of skills to use in future mathematics experiences. More important, it helps students see themselves as mathematical doers and raises their self-esteem. If strengths are a focus of a classroom and referenced continually throughout a school year, it seems likely that student attitudes toward their own strengths may change.

As we shared our concerns in our MPPS meetings, we realized our middle schoolers have spent a lot of time with teachers, including ourselves, who have communicated to them a limited view of strengths. A major lesson we learned from our students' perspectives is that we must be mindful of the subtle messages we communicate to our students. For example, we noticed some students began to emulate the strengths that we acknowledged in the classroom, which suggests that their understanding of mathematical success was framed by our acknowledgment of their strengths. We learned to not only include their answers and explanation to mathematical problems but also to encourage them to help us identify the myriad of strengths they and their peers exhibit as they solve problems.

■ Conclusion: The Power of Reflection and Collaboration

In the MPPS, our goal as a PLC is to identify students' mathematical strengths while we collaborate on solving our pedagogical problems of practice. Over the years, we have worked to develop the TMS and tried to use it in our classrooms. We agree with Featherstone and colleagues (2011) that every student has mathematical strengths that can be displayed in many ways. We are still challenged, however, to find ways to share our thoughts with the students we teach. We decided our work could be strengthened with the help of our middle school students.

In this chapter, we have shared our attempts to solicit our students' perspectives on their own and their classmates' mathematical strengths. Each teacher engaged in an inquiry project and approached our goal in different ways. These differences were across classrooms, grade levels, and data collection methods. The MPPS provided the motivation and accountability to learn about implementing inquiry projects. We continuously encouraged one another because we found it challenging to incorporate the projects into our existing class routines. For example, we were concerned about not having enough time to consistently address strengths with our students. Timing was particularly challenging as we started state testing and had to modify our classroom routines. Another challenge for one of our members was working in a collaborative classroom with a teacher who was not willing to include strength-based activities in the lessons. These challenges showed us the importance of starting these activities early in the school year to establish a classroom culture grounded in mathematical strengths and to share our ideas with our school colleagues. Overall, our inquiry projects helped us "study and analyze classroom practice to develop either a deeper understanding or a plan for action or change" (Nolen and Vander Putten 2007). We hope our continued development as individuals will affect the other teachers in our schools because of the interdependence we have as colleagues (Horn 2008).

We all agreed that the inquiry projects were worthwhile exercises and that we learned a lot from our students. We doubt we would have learned as much if we had conducted these projects on our own. Vescio, Ross, and Adams (2008) found "that successful collaborative efforts include strategies that 'open' practice in ways that encourage sharing, reflecting, and taking the risks necessary to change" (p. 84). Our PLC provided a supportive space for us to collaboratively resolve problems of practice and to try new approaches in our classrooms as we held each other accountable for our students' mathematical learning. The professional conversations in the MPPS allowed us to think more deeply about students' mathematical strengths and how to incorporate our students into these conversations. The conversations also taught us different methods for learning from our students. As a result, we modified our projects and began to think deeper about our practice. Another benefit was that we found all students, regardless of their mathematics and academic performances, are willing to participate in these strength-identifying activities. They could identify academic and mathematical strengths in general or in their peers, even though they often struggled to see their own mathematical strengths. This was contrary to what we initially expected, yet we consistently noticed this willingness across schools, contexts, and classrooms.

We believe the TMS also improved our teaching. Our knowledge of students' strengths gave us a strong framework to isolate and focus on individual student mathematical strengths. We began to reference mathematical strengths more frequently as we taught and as we planned mathematics lessons. For example, when planning a lesson or activity, we thought about how to capitalize on particular students' strengths. Additionally, the knowledge of students' strengths allowed us to highlight the positive mathematical habits and characteristics of our students, thereby creating a more positive learning environment. Our teaching of mathematics is beginning to redefine doing mathematics, shift students' perspectives of one another as doers of mathematics, and raise the status of students' mathematical ideas that previously would have been ignored (Featherstone et al. 2011).

Our work has not ended—we will continue to modify the TMS to identify strengths, think deeply about what it means to have a mathematical strength, and encourage mathematical strengths in our students in years to come. We also want to explore students' out-of-school strengths and find ways to acknowledge and incorporate them in our mathematics classes. As we shared in our findings, we learned that middle school students are willing to share their perspectives on mathematical strengths. This is important because we can take this information into our future classrooms as a tool to encourage recognition and promotion of mathematical strengths by and from all students.

Acknowledgments

This work was supported by the University of Georgia Office of Stem Education. The authors would like to thank all the students who participated in this project.

References

Aguirre, Julia M., Karen Mayfield-Ingram, and Danny B. Martin. *The Impact of Identity in K–8 Mathematics Learning and Teaching: Rethinking Equity-Based Practices.* Reston, Va.: National Council of Teachers of Mathematics, 2013.

Britt, Murray S., Kathryn C. Irwin, and Garth Ritchie. "Professional Conversations and Professional Growth." *Journal of Mathematics Teacher Education* 4, no.1 (2001): 29–53.

Cochran-Smith, Marilyn, and Susan L. Lytle. *Inquiry as Stance: Practitioner Research for the Next Generation.* New York: Teachers College Press, 2009.

Cohen, Elizabeth G., and Rachel A. Lotan. *Designing Groupwork: Strategies for the Heterogenous Classroom.* 3rd ed. New York: Teachers College Press, 2014.

Featherstone, Helen, Sandra Crespo, Lisa M. Jilk, Joy A. Oslund, Amy Noelle Parks, and Marcy B. Wood. *Smarter Together! Collaboration and Equity in the Elementary Math Classroom.* Reston, Va.: National Council of Teachers of Mathematics, 2011.

Horn, Ilana Seidel. "The Inherent Interdependence of Teachers." *Phi Delta Kappan* 89, no. 10 (2008): 751–54.

Jilk, Lisa M. "Supporting Teacher Noticing of Students' Mathematical Strengths." *Mathematics Teacher Educator* 4, no. 2 (2016): 188–99.

Little, Judith W., and Ilana S. Horn. "'Normalizing' Problems of Practice: Converting Routine Conversation into a Resource for Learning in Professional Communities." In *Professional Learning Communities: Divergence, Depth and Dilemmas*, edited by Louise Stoll and Karen Seashore Louis, pp. 79–92. Maidenhead, England: Open University Press, 2007.

National Council of Teachers of Mathematics (NCTM). *Principles to Actions: Ensuring Mathematical Success for All*. Reston, Va.: NCTM, 2014.

National Governors Association Center for Best Practices and Council of Chief State School Officers (NGA Center and CCSSO). *Common Core State Standards for Mathematics*. Washington, D.C.: NGA Center and CCSSO, 2010. http://www.corestandards.org.

National Research Council. *Adding It Up: Helping Children Learn Mathematics*. Washington, D.C.: National Academies Press, 2001.

Nolan, Amanda L. and Jim Vander Putten. "Action Research in Education: Addressing Gaps in Ethical Principles and Practices." *Educational Researcher* 36, no. 7 (2007): 401–7.

Vescio, Vicki, Dorene Ross, and Alyson Adams. "A Review of Research on the Impact of Professional Learning Communities on Teaching Practice and Student Learning." *Teaching and Teacher Education* 24, no.1 (2008): 80–91.

Appendix A
Nick's Survey Questions

1. What is one of YOUR math strengths? (choose one)

   - ❏ Knows basic facts
   - ❏ Good at mental math
   - ❏ Excited about what you solved
   - ❏ Perseverance (keep trying even when it's hard)
   - ❏ Desires to learn and understand—want to know WHY
   - ❏ Explains ideas to other students well
   - ❏ Takes risks—willing to contribute
   - ❏ Shows your work
   - ❏ Creates a diagram of a problem or thinks of a simpler solution
   - ❏ Remembers context of a problem
   - ❏ Ability to think of alternative methods
   - ❏ Has reasoning skills
   - ❏ Pays attention to details—distinguishes between important/extraneous data

2. Choose a math strength that you want to get BETTER at this year in math. (choose one)

    ❏ Knows basic facts

    ❏ Good at mental math

    ❏ Excited about what you solved

    ❏ Perseverance (keep trying even when it's hard)

    ❏ Desires to learn and understand—want to know WHY

    ❏ Explains ideas to other students well

    ❏ Takes risks—willing to contribute

    ❏ Shows your work

    ❏ Creates a diagram of a problem or thinks of a simpler solution

    ❏ Remembers context of a problem

    ❏ Ability to think of alternative methods

    ❏ Has reasoning skills

    ❏ Pays attention to details—distinguishes between important/extraneous data

3. What are your thoughts about this puzzle of math strengths?

Appendix B

Rob's Survey Questions

Survey #1

Question 1: How many hours a night do you spend relaxing?

Question 2: How many hours of sleep do you get a night?

Question 3: How many hours a night do you spend studying?

Question 4: Suppose you missed a quiz. What do you do?

      A. Make arrangements to make up the quiz.

      B Try to pull your grade up with the next quiz.

      C. Try not to think about it.

      D. Other _____.

Question 5: What is your greatest strength as a student?

      A. Critical thinking

      B. Focus

      C. Organization

      D. Consistency

      E. Other _____.

Survey #2

Question 1: Which of the five characteristics outlined above do you most identify with as a math student?

      A. Problem solving

      B. Mathy knowledge

      C. Identity as a doer of mathematics

      D. Communication

      E. Affect and motivation

Question 2: Why did you choose that?

Question 3: What motivates you to do well in school?

Appendix C

Fred's Survey Questions

Survey #1

What is/are your mathematical strength(s)? Choose all that apply.

A. Knows basic facts

B. Knows mental mathematics

C. Excited about what I solve

D. Desires to learn and understand

E. Confidant in what I know

F. Thinks deeply

G. Self-aware of what I know and can use it in situations

H. Explains ideas to other students

I. Shows work

J. Ability to think of alternative methods

Survey #2

What is/are your mathematical strength(s)? Choose two.

A. Knows basic facts

B. Knows mental mathematics

C. Excited about what I solve

D. Desires to learn and understand

E. Confident in what I know

F. Thinks deeply

G. Self-aware of what I know and can use it in situations

H. Explains ideas to other students

I. Shows work

J. Ability to think of alternative methods

CHAPTER 4

Teachers' Voices:
How Collaboration Helps Us Put Research into Practice

Michelle Martin, Gabriel Meerts, Cathy Oehmke,
and Simon Tyler, *Prairie Creek Community School, Castle Rock, Minnesota*
Ryota Matsuura, *St. Olaf College, Northfield, Minnesota*
Sarah Sword, *Education Development Center, Inc., Waltham, Massachusetts*

Teachers must be the primary driving force behind change. They are best positioned to understand the problems that students face and to generate possible solutions. (Stigler and Hiebert 1999, p. 135)

We've come on this journey together: this is professional development that we design ourselves. We are immediately responsive to our own needs, and we bring in all the resources that we have. (Teacher reflection)

Prairie Creek Community School is a progressive public school in Castle Rock, Minnesota. Students are in mixed-grade classrooms: K–1, 2–3, and 4–5. We have a strong teacher community, and our school director is deeply involved in teaching with us. We face the same questions all elementary schools face: How do we deepen our own understanding of mathematics? How do we deepen our understanding of students' thinking to help them deepen their understanding of mathematics? How do we deal with the tension between covering more material superficially and covering less material more deeply?

Like many teachers, our resources for investigating these questions are limited to our own time and efforts. Research is constantly emerging to address these questions, and we rely on our combined efforts to read, interpret, and implement the fruits of education research. What we can do as individuals is somewhat limited; what we can do together is far less so.

Prairie Creek is a rural school. In 2015–2016, we had 180 students, with 11 percent minority, 17 percent free and reduced-price lunch, and 18 percent special education students. In philosophy and practice, our progressive curriculum invites students to delve into learning that recognizes their lives as intriguing and collaborative adventures. Prairie Creek is also a charter school that is true to the original twin missions of charter schools: that we experiment with educational practices and share the results with the broader community (Kahlenberg and Potter 2014). In this article, we share our perspective on how collaboration empowers us to experiment with research practices.

We illustrate how teachers can implement research ideas by working together through an intentional process of self-driven professional development. Our primary goal here is to provide teachers in similar circumstances with a model for our collaboration and a vision for what can be accomplished when teachers work together. As classroom teachers, we have not conducted formal research about the efficacy of our collaboration. But we know that our collaboration enables us to implement research ideas in our classrooms, and we believe this has value for other teachers. A secondary goal is to provide motivation for education researchers to continue to structure dissemination so that teachers like us can implement ideas from current research.

The article is written by three grades 4–5 teachers (Michelle, Gabriel, and Cathy), two school parents (Ryota and Sarah), and the school director (Simon). (The two parents are mathematics educators who were invited by the teachers to participate as community members in discussions about teaching elementary school mathematics.) We describe what collaboration affords us, illustrate how collaboration works in practice through a detailed example of how we implemented Lesson Study, and end with remarks about the adventure of teaching together.

■ What Collaboration Affords Us

> That tension between covering more material and covering material well always underlies my math teaching—I fight against moving too fast, but it's easier to fight when I have the support of my teacher community. (Teacher reflection)

For years we struggled with how to meet the mathematical needs of every child in our classroom. We did not want to "track" students into high or low groups for the year—especially since mathematical understanding does not follow a prescribed trajectory for every student (National Research Council 2001). Some excel at geometry, others at prealgebraic puzzling. But in a mixed-grade classroom, having everyone together for every lesson meant some students never spoke and thought they were "bad" at math because students around them responded to questions more quickly. How could we meet everyone's needs?

Collaboration has provided some answers. Instead of each of us teaching mathematics to only our own students, we pool all students and teach as a team. Before beginning each unit, we choose groups from the entire collection of grades 4–5 students. Throughout the year, each of us works with every student. To do this, we collaborate closely in planning and teaching. Three common planning periods each week enable us to share insights or ask questions about particular students. These meetings are invaluable for reflection as we share our experiences teaching and observing students. Through our work together we have developed deep trust.

Our conversations veer into pedagogy—What were we teaching? Why were we teaching it? Where did our students struggle? Why were they struggling? We often notice that many struggling students have memorized algorithms that make no sense to them. They can get the right answers to familiar-looking problems, but they can't *use* mathematics. We want our instruction to help students learn concepts deeply. We are not satisfied to teach superficial procedures; we want students to understand the underlying structure of the ideas, as well as to make meaningful connections among them (National Governors Association Center for Best Practices and Council of Chief State School Officers [NGA Center and CCSSO] 2010; National Council of Teachers of Mathematics 2000).

Below, we describe how collaboration allows us to group students flexibly, to teach mathematics deeply, and to bring research-based practices into our school.

Flexible Grouping

Collaboration allows us to group students flexibly. For every topic, we create new instructional groups. We develop formative assessments or use data from Measures of Academic Progress assessments (Northwest Evaluation Association 2008) to determine groups for that topic. We create myriad groupings throughout the year so that students sometimes have a learning space with students at a similar developmental stage. At other times, they are in mixed groups so they have the opportunity to teach others or see mathematics being discussed and modeled in new ways. We believe that fluid groupings help students see instruction as something that meets their needs.

Mile-Deep Teaching

Collaboration gives us power: we can fight perceived external pressure to teach "mile wide" instead of "mile deep" (Schmidt, McKnight, and Raizen 1997). We support one another's instincts to spend more time on topics when our students need that time. Communication, trust, and shared ownership of students' achievement allow us to agree about what achievement *means* in our progressive environment, and they allow us to work together to push students toward that goal. In a later section of this chapter ("Our Collaboration in Practice: Lesson Study"), we share an example of how collaborating on lesson study allowed us to dig into students' number sense.

Research-Based Practices

Above all, collaboration allows us to bring research-based practices into our school. This effort has taken many forms—experimenting with number talks (Math Perspectives 2007), Developing Mathematical Ideas (DMI; Schifter, Bastable, and Russell 2016), Jo Boaler's MOOC (Stanford University 2014), and the Think Math! resource website (Education Development Center, Inc. [EDC] 2016b), to name a few. As individual teachers, we could not explore emerging research to the extent that we can as a group. We continue to learn from the field and from one another, to push one another, and to grow together. In another section of this chapter ("Connecting Collaboration and Lesson Study"), we elaborate on the process through which we identify a research-based practice, how we implement that practice, and how we assess that implementation.

We focused our collaboration in the form of professional development that deepened our instruction. We began by articulating our professional needs. For example, some students were taking formulaic approaches to various place-value concepts, without deep understanding. We were unsure what underlying number-sense issues existed or how to fix them, but we needed to make a change. Next, we describe how we used lesson study to focus our work.

■ Our Collaboration in Practice: Lesson Study

A teacher committee within the school, researching how to tackle some of the questions we raised at the beginning of this chapter, proposed lesson study as a formal, strategic, and collaborative approach. Initially, this wasn't very appealing to us: we weren't interested in "perfect lessons" as petrified objects we would return to every year. Still, we continued research, including reading Hurd and Lewis (2011), and we decided we could try anything *once*.

Our willingness to try lesson study paid off so much that we have done four cycles in the past three years. We continue to use lesson study not to create perfect lessons but as a tool for uncovering student thinking *and* "big ideas" of elementary mathematics. We now describe one example of how the experience unfolded for us.

Background and Purpose

Some students in our school can estimate numbers in real-world contexts but have difficulty rounding a number to a specific place value and even more difficulty rounding the same number to various place values. Some of those students have memorized procedures but cannot execute the procedures with understanding. For example, when asked to round 1,005 to the nearest thousand, some might answer 2,000, because "five means round up."

In addition to the need to meet a common standard (such as, in this case, Common Core State Standard 3.NBT.A.1 [NGA Center and CCSSO 2010]), this misuse of a procedure led us to wonder about students' underlying number sense. What sense were they making of place value, for example? Problems with rounding felt like a symptom of a larger number-sense issue. We suspected that a lesson on rounding would both illuminate those underlying issues and offer students insight about numbers. So we started a lesson-study cycle focused on rounding—not because we wanted to reinforce previously learned procedures, but because we wanted to better understand students' sense of number relationships.

For the lesson study lesson, we chose eighteen students from our collective grades 4–5 classrooms whom we had seen struggle with rounding. We preassigned them to pairs based on the difficulty they had with previous assignments.

The following questions guided the planning, teaching, and reflecting of this lesson.

- How do students make decisions about rounding?

- How can we help students identify the "target" rounding interval?

- What common misconceptions do students exhibit when they try to place numbers on a number line? How can we counter those misconceptions?

Lesson Synopsis

Before the lesson, we investigated existing research on the teaching and learning of numbers. Paul Goldenberg's work with number lines (EDC 2016a) appealed to us, so we made three large number lines:

1. From 1,000 to 4,000 in increments of 1,000.

2. From 1,900 to 3,100 in increments of 100.

3. From 2,000 to 2,700 in increments of 10.

These number lines were placed on three tables in the classroom.

To start the lesson, we gave each pair of students three sticky notes with the same number on them, with the following instruction:

Take your number to each table and decide where you would place the number on the number line. Draw an arrow to show where you would round that number on the number line. Above the arrow, explain your reasoning.

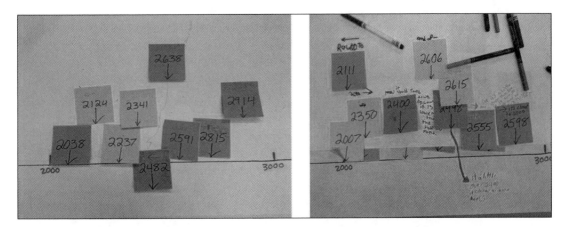

Fig. 4.1. Students placed numbered sticky notes onto number lines

Two rounds of this activity were completed (see fig. 4.1), with whole-class discussion after each round. Some numbers, such as 2,400, were chosen because of common student errors we had seen (not knowing how to round a number that was already on a century, for example). We had several students who had shown some competence in rounding but were unsure how to round a number in the middle of a decade (2,815, for example). We gave such numbers to those students.

Through the activity and the whole-class discussions, we sought to understand the criteria students used to determine where to place their number on the number line and how to round it. We also asked students how they would explain their strategies.

Earlier in this chapter, we mentioned that some students, when rounding 1,005 to the nearest thousand, would answer 2,000, because "five means round up." Using different number lines encouraged students to consider what the number 5, for instance, means relative to 10, to 100, and to 1,000. In placing the number 2,315 between 2,310 and 2,320, they saw that it is halfway between the two. In placing the same number on the number line labeled with 100s, students saw that 2,315 is close to 2,300; and in placing it on the 1,000s number line, they saw that 2,315 is close to 2,000. As students moved between the number lines, they saw the different role that "5" plays, depending on the place value of interest.

In the lesson study spirit of collecting data, we built a more formal assessment. For 8,379 and 45,012, we asked students to round each number —

- to the nearest ten;

- to the nearest hundred; and

- to the nearest thousand.

Students did well with 8,379. However, even after working with number lines and creating a general procedure as a group, 45,012 proved difficult for some. Most students were comfortable rounding when using provided number lines. However, some students didn't build their *own* number lines, even when that representation would have been useful.

Teacher Reflection

> Making the number lines made me realize what a rich process it is — how to represent different place values . . . what "scale" to use . . . how the whole number system is structured. We round because we want to be able to conceive of numbers more easily. (Teacher reflection after lesson study)

To support students' mathematical growth, we concluded that they need more experience with number lines, while also developing their independence (i.e., not relying on the number lines provided by the teacher). We could, for example, provide students with a blank number line to fill in on their own with appropriate benchmark numbers.

Based on this lesson, we decided to put more emphasis on number lines. We redesigned the introductory rounding lessons, applying what we learned through lesson study. (See this book's page at NCTM's More4U website for the redesigned lesson plan.) Our whole school teaching staff then talked concretely about when to introduce and use number lines across grades.

We re-emphasize that the questions we were asking weren't *really* about rounding — at least not about memorizing rounding procedures. When we started using number lines, we were excited to have something that students could use to connect rounding to number sense. We wanted them to be flexible enough to put numbers on different number lines, and this is why the lesson felt effective: students had to use the geography of the number line more practically. They consequently learned something about *numbers*.

The research structure of lesson study, particularly observing and assessing, illuminated students' need for more opportunity to work with number lines. Observing together provided multiple perspectives on the same event. Reflecting — treating student work as "data" — encouraged an experimental, nonjudgmental approach, as the lesson study process requires intentionally postponing analysis until after observers share observational data (Hurd and Lewis 2011). Each observer saw many student interactions; from those collective observations, an accurate picture of classwide student thinking emerged. (For the mechanics of our lesson study implementation, see the More4U site.)

■ Connecting Collaboration and Lesson Study

Collaboration is at the heart of all we do. We have a teacher mathematics committee with one teacher from each grade band. The committee uses the following criteria for evaluating whether to bring particular research-based practices into our school:

- Does the work fit with our school's progressive philosophy?

- Does the work build our knowledge over time?

With input from the whole staff, the committee makes these decisions and does the logistical work. As mentioned previously, lesson study was initially not met with enthusiasm. Without the work of the committee, we would not have seen those benefits! This exemplifies the power of collaboration in bringing in external resources and relying on many perspectives.

How do we know if our work with students is successful? We use these criteria for deciding whether something worked for us:

- Did students seem to have a deeper understanding of the concepts?

- Did it allow students to deeply engage with ideas and with each other?

- Did it help us understand students' thinking better?

The Upward Spiral

We are able to engage in lesson study because of our collaborative relationships, and lesson study also serves to strengthen our collaboration. In conducting lesson study, we shift the focus from our *individual* work to our *collective* work. The lesson study process (Hurd and Lewis 2011) requires that we refer to the lesson as "our" lesson. The focus is on *our* learning rather than any individual learning. We focus on *all* students, rather than any one set of students. By sharing responsibility, we share risk. It then becomes far less scary to try new things. We share success, too. The more we collaborate, the better we are at lesson study; the better we become at lesson study and other collaborative efforts, the stronger our collaborations. It's an upward spiral.

■ Structures That Help Us Implement Research

Lesson study is a natural example for this chapter because it has structures that make research usable for teachers working together without external facilitation. While not easy, the process is clear. For example, we knew to begin by formulating a long-term goal for student learning and development. While we initially perceived the lesson study structure as too prescriptive, having this structure let us put aside questions about what to do and how to do it and focus on what really mattered: the mathematics content and how students were learning.

The lesson study literature is extensive; we relied on a book that laid out the process (Hurd and Lewis 2011) and teacher-oriented articles from the NCTM journal *Teaching Children Mathematics* such as Takahashi and Yoshida (2004). We weren't so much interested in how lesson study changes students' test scores, but in how it could change their thinking and ours about mathematics.

More broadly, we look for ideas we can implement ourselves: as another example, one summer we implemented a week of the Developing Mathematical Ideas (DMI) program (Schifter, Bastable, and Russell 2016). One teacher used the facilitator materials to guide the work, and the key for us was that the available material from that program included all the tools we needed to conduct the work. Our experience in implementing ideas is consistent with findings in the field about bringing research to practice (Hurd and Lewis 2011, p. 12).

■ Collaboration Raises Hard Questions

When we observe each other's classrooms, we gain new perspectives on students' knowledge. Consequently, collaboration forces us to confront difficult questions. For example: we are committed to progressive education, to mathematical exploration, and to meeting each student where he or she is rather than at some prescribed "fourth-grade level." Given these commitments, how do we ensure that all students cover the ground they need to cover in preparation for future mathematics? Similarly, as we deepen our own understanding of the importance of underlying mathematical structure, we want to foster similar understanding in our students. But what counts as evidence of that understanding? How can we assess it? These are questions with which we continue to grapple; we are grappling with them together.

■ Final Thoughts: The Adventure of Collaboration

What's the adventure in collaboration? For us, the adventure comes from learning about our students, mathematics, and teaching. We push students to not simply accept that something works but to figure out *why* it works, to understand ideas deeply. Similarly, with mathematics instruction we don't take lessons at face value. We want to know more than whether "they work well" or do not work well. We want to know the student thinking that those lessons support and why and how they support it.

Working together, coupled with professional reading, enables us to look under the hood and understand *what* makes a lesson work. We can see student thinking more clearly and how a successful lesson moves that thinking forward. It is so empowering. We can look at a series of problems and think, "We know why they chose those numbers (or activity). We know the student conceptions (or misconceptions) those elements may expose."

Similarly, we constantly learn about mathematics as a discipline. We see the importance of developing certain ways of thinking about mathematics in students—that search for structure (like using number lines!) and the clear articulation of mathematical ideas, "practices, dispositions, sensibilities, habits of mind" (Bass 2011, p. 4).

We are not simply transmitters. Instead, we are co-creators. We share knowledge and understanding that enable us to amplify lessons and change them to respond to students' needs. We *understand* what we are doing, thanks to having the opportunity to work and reflect together.

References

Bass, Hyman. "Vignette of Doing Mathematics: A Meta-Cognitive Tour of the Production of Some Elementary Mathematics." *The Montana Mathematics Enthusiast* 8, no. 1 & 2 (2011): 3–34.

Education Development Center, Inc. (EDC). "Number Line | Think Math!" (2016a).

———. "Welcome to the ThinkMath! Website" (2016b). http://thinkmath.edc.org/.

Hurd, Jacqueline, and Catherine Lewis. *Lesson Study Step by Step*. Portsmouth, N.H.: Heinemann, 2011.

Kahlenberg, Richard D., and Halley Potter. "Restoring Shanker's Vision for Charter Schools." *American Educator* 38, no. 4 (2014): 4–13.

Math Perspectives. "Number Talks" (2007). http://www.mathperspectives.com/pdf_docs/number_talks.pdf.

National Council of Teachers of Mathematics (NCTM). *Principles and Standards for School Mathematics.* Reston, Va.: NCTM, 2000.

National Governors Association Center for Best Practices and Council of Chief State School Officers (NGA Center and CCSSO). *Common Core State Standards for Mathematics.* Washington, D.C.: NGA Center and CCSSO, 2010. http://www.corestandards.org.

National Research Council. *Adding It Up: Helping Children Learn Mathematics.* Washington, D.C.: National Academies Press, 2001.

Northwest Evaluation Association. "Teacher Handbook: Measures of Academic Progress (MAP)" (2008). http://www.nwea.org/sites/www.nwea.org/files/resources/Teacher%20Handbook_0.pdf.

Schifter, Deborah, Virginia Bastable, and Susan Jo Russell. *Developing Mathematical Ideas: Number and Operations, Part 1: Building a System of Tens Casebook*. Reston, Va: NCTM, 2016.

Schmidt, William H., Curtis McKnight, and Senta Raizen. *A Splintered Vision: An Investigation of U.S. Science and Mathematics Education*. Dordrecht: Kluwer, 1997.

Stanford University. "How to Learn Math: For Teachers and Parents." [MOOC] (2014). http://online .stanford.edu/course/how-to-learn-math-for-teachers-and-parents-s14.

Stigler, James W., and James Hiebert. *The Teaching Gap*. New York: Free Press, 1999.

Takahashi, Akihiko, and Makoto Yoshida. "Ideas for Establishing Lesson-Study Communities." *Teaching Children Mathematics* 10, no. 9 (2004): 436–43.

PART II

Enhancing Mathematics Teaching within Schools and Districts

Introduction

Charlene Marchese, *Freehold Township Schools, New Jersey*
Robyn Silbey, *Robyn Silbey Professional Development, Gaithersburg, Maryland*

In this section of the volume, each chapter frames professional learning through site-based experiences. Providing teachers with job-embedded opportunities for professional learning is critical to improving the teaching and learning of mathematics. Effective professional development includes collaboration among teachers and a focus on teachers' communities of practice (Darling-Hammond and McLaughlin 2011). As stated in *Principles to Actions: Ensuring Mathematical Success for All* (National Council of Teachers of Mathematics [NCTM] 2014), an essential element of ensuring all students' success in mathematics is moving teachers from an isolated practice to an environment that cultivates and supports a culture of professional collaboration and continual improvement.

These six chapters each provide examples of collaboration among teachers and the subsequent effects on their professional experience. In addition to depicting teacher collaboration, a number of the chapters also highlight the importance of teachers' content and pedagogical knowledge. A recent position statement from the National Council of Supervisors of Mathematics (NCSM) entitled *It's Time: Themes and Imperatives for Mathematics Education: A Leadership Framework for Common Core Mathematics* (NCSM 2014) directly links teachers' mathematics, pedagogical, and mathematics curriculum knowledge to raising student achievement. Each chapter is described briefly in the paragraphs that follow.

In the first chapter in the section, **Learning *In* and *From* Practice with Others,** Rigelman describes ways in which the collaborative efforts of teachers, district specialists, and university specialists are responsive to teachers' identified learning needs while also fostering teacher self-assessment and growth. Teacher collaboration occurred through book studies and lesson studies, with the goal of designing and studying classroom practice and its impact on students' mathematical thinking and discourse. Tools and frameworks guided teachers' reflections on students' engagement in cognitively challenging mathematical work and thinking (e.g., Stein et al. 2009) and mathematical discourse (Smith and Stein 2011; Weaver, Dick and Rigelman 2005). The chapter features an example of teachers' collective analysis of a lesson where third graders decompose numbers in rectangular arrays as models of multiplication.

In **Fostering Professional Growth: A Three-Pronged Approach,** Marchese and Haimer describe a three-pronged framework (structural, practical, and philosophical components) that offers teachers multiple pathways and opportunities to gain content and pedagogical knowledge. The authors describe how each component contributes to teachers' professional growth within a school system: structural components such as common planning time and block scheduling; philosophical components of consistency and coherence in the vision of effective mathematics teaching and learning across the school system; and the practical components of coordinated and sustained professional development experiences. Furthermore, the interconnectedness of the components provides space for teachers to develop expertise to create quality mathematical learning experiences for all students and to enhance and improve communication and collaboration within the department.

In **Leveraging Coach-Facilitated Professional Development to Create Collaborative Teacher Networks for Enhancing Professional Practice,** Suh, Birkhead, Baker, Frank, and Seshaiyer note how the social network, developed through coach-facilitated lesson study, affects teachers' professional learning and how it promotes powerful learning by empowering mathematics teacher leaders and coaches within their districts and establishing collaborative teacher networks for enhancing their professional practice. Results from the analysis of teacher reflections, video analysis, and lesson-study debriefs reveal that the design of the coach-facilitated professional development and lesson study offer opportunities for coaches and teachers to mutually develop in their content and pedagogy while also deepening their understanding of middle school students' learning progressions in algebraic thinking. The authors ground the discussion in an example of teachers' and students' work and reflections on a patterning task lesson. The chapter also features a video-based coaching tool used to foster reflection and communication between teachers and coaches.

In the next chapter, **A Collaborative Approach to Strengthening K–2 Mathematical Practices with Technology,** Larsen, McCormick, Buffington, and Louie reveal how a team of co-investigators collectively design, test, reflect upon, and modify aspects of a co-developed intervention on an ongoing basis. The team consisted of mathematics teachers in a rural school system and STEM education researchers who came together to explore how to support students' learning of mathematics through the use of one-to-one mobile technology. The chapter describes the Design Based Implementation Research (DBIR) approach (Penuel et al. 2011) undertaken by the team to co-develop and investigate strategies for mathematics teaching and learning in the technology-supported environment.

In **Using Technology to Develop Shared Knowledge in and across Grade-Level Teams,** Webel and Lannin share their development of modules that engage school-based grade-level teams in generating topic-specific knowledge for teaching mathematics that can be shared across teacher networks. The authors share their efforts to develop and test a set of modules to engage teachers in sustained investigations of their students' thinking about fractions. Students' work and thinking are recorded using screencast technology, and this technology also allows for teachers' reflections and comments on students' screencasts using used an online annotation tool called Vialogues (https://vialogues.com). The chapter describes the affordances and constraints of the tools, including challenges the authors faced in creating a shared knowledge base that teachers would find useful for improving their own knowledge and practice and for learning from the experiences of other teachers.

In the last chapter of the section, **Improving the Teaching of Mathematics by Using Lesson Study and STEM-Based Activities,** Nabbout-Cheiban and Goldberg detail the collaborative process that participants experience as they collaborate to research and choose appropriate STEM activities to use in the classroom and to revise and strengthen those activities using the lesson study model. The chapter describes the work of mathematics and science teachers in developing and refining lessons through collaborative lesson study, using the "Math Flu" lesson as an example of a STEM lesson that models exponential growth and the spread of disease. The authors note how the lesson study process enabled teachers to strengthen students' engagement with the mathematics and science aspects of the lesson. They posit that professional learning experiences that support teachers to enact STEM lessons include bringing mathematics and science teachers together, providing content in both areas, and having professors from STEM and STEM education fields supporting teachers in planning, teaching, reflecting, and revising STEM lessons.

The chapters in this section provide concrete examples of job-embedded professional experiences. As you read them, consider the following questions:

- How does teacher collaboration positively affect teacher growth and student achievement?

- What strategies can administrators use to enhance productive teacher collaboration?

- How can the ideas presented in the chapter be applied to your own context and setting?

References

Darling-Hammond, Linda, and Millbrey W. McLaughlin. "Policies That Support Professional Development in an Era of Reform." *Phi Delta Kappan* 92, no. 6 (2011): 81–92.

National Council of Supervisors of Mathematics (NCSM). *It's Time: Themes and Imperatives for Mathematics Education: A Leadership Framework for Common Core Mathematics.* Bloomington, Ind.: Solution Tree Press, 2014.

National Council of Teachers of Mathematics (NCTM). *Principles to Actions: Ensuring Mathematical Success for All.* Reston, Va.: NCTM, 2014.

Penuel, William R., Barry J. Fishman, Britte Haugan Cheng, and Nora Sabelli. "Organizing Research and Development at the Intersection of Learning, Implementation, and Design." *Educational Researcher* 40, no. 7 (2011): 331–37.

Smith, Margaret Schwan, and Mary Kay Stein. *5 Practices for Orchestrating Productive Mathematics Discussions.* Reston, Va.: NCTM, 2011.

Stein, Mary Kay, Margaret Schwan Smith, Marjorie A. Henningsen, and Edward S. Silver. *Implementing Standards-Based Mathematics Instruction: A Casebook for Professional Development.* New York: Teachers College Press, 2009.

Weaver, Dave, Thomas Dick, and Nicole Miller Rigelman. "Assessing the Quality and Quantity of Student Discourse in Mathematics Classrooms." Paper presented at the *Mathematics and Science Partnership Evaluation Summit*, Minneapolis, Minn. (2005, September). http://pdxscholar.library.pdx.edu/cgi/viewcontent.cgi?article=1019&context=ci_fac.

CHAPTER 5

Learning *In* and *From* Practice with Others

Nicole Rigelman, *Portland State University, Portland, Oregon*

In a review of research-based characteristics of effective professional development (PD), Guskey (2003) found agreement about the need to attend to developing teacher content and pedagogical knowledge, as doing so positively influences student achievement. While features such as having sufficient time, resources, and opportunities for collaborative work are on some lists of effective PD characteristics, there is contradictory evidence regarding their effect on students. Yet what we know about mathematical knowledge for teaching and how that develops suggests the need for professional development (PD) designs that attend to these features. Table 5.1 summarizes the characteristics central to the PD model for the Developing Elementary Mathematics Instructional Leaders (DEMIL) project, in which district and university mathematics specialists collaborate with teacher leaders to develop a shared vision of effective mathematics teaching practices and skills for implementing such practice.

Table 5.1

Effective teacher professional development

Structural Features	<ul><li>Sustains teacher learning over time and involves a substantial number of hours.</li><li>Encourages purposeful collaboration among teachers guided by clear goals for improving student learning.</li><li>Develops beliefs and dispositions that foster continued learning.</li></ul>
Core Features	<ul><li>Helps teachers understand more deeply the content they teach and the ways students learn that content.</li><li>Develops skills with noticing, analyzing, and responding to students' thinking.</li><li>Engages teachers in active learning such as planning for classroom implementation, observing and being observed teaching, and reviewing student work.</li><li>Promotes coherence across teacher goals and experiences.</li></ul>

Adapted from Doerr, Goldsmith, and Lewis 2010; Garet et al. 2001; Guskey 2003.

For many years, there have been calls to reform teacher professional learning so that it is ongoing and supports teachers both in shifting their instructional practice and in engaging in learning *in* and *from* practice (Ball and Cohen 1999; Borko 2004; Smith 2001; Spillane 1999). Ball and Cohen (1999) argue that teacher PD rarely takes a curricular view; instead, teachers experience workshops that offer disconnected recommendations about teaching rather than ongoing, connected professional learning opportunities. In DEMIL, we have used the National Council of Teachers of Mathematics's (NCTM) *Principles to Actions* (2014) to support development of a shared vision for effective mathematics instruction, and we have designed teacher PD that supports teachers in taking on these ambitious teaching practices.

Elements of the PD include common professional learning focused on developing teachers' vision of effective mathematics teaching, learning and assessment. Supplementing these experiences are book studies, lesson studies, and, for a subset of teachers, teacher leader learning. This chapter focuses on lesson studies as a vehicle to support the systematic design and study of classroom practice and its influence on students' mathematical thinking and discourse. It includes descriptions of the ways in which the collaborative efforts respond to teachers' identified learning needs while fostering teacher self-assessment and growth.

■ Context

This project is a partnership between a local school district and Portland State University's Graduate School of Education, in which each partner shares the responsibility to contribute knowledge and ideas to support development of the mathematics knowledge needed for teaching (cf. Ball, Thames, and Phelps 2008). Ball and colleagues found that the mathematical and pedagogical knowledge and skills needed to reach each student are quite complex. To develop this knowledge, teachers continually need to learn and critically reflect on their practice, including how they use students' mathematical ideas. Therefore, the major goals of this collaboration are to—

- improve teachers' content and pedagogical knowledge and their ability to implement high-cognitive-demand tasks to deepen student engagement in mathematical reasoning, sense making, and discourse; and

- affect the culture of professional learning for teachers through the use of facilitated book studies and lesson studies.

The DEMIL project's hypothesis is that by successfully accomplishing these goals, the schools will see an increase in students' mathematical understanding and achievement as well as a deeper engagement with the habits of mind conveyed in the Common Core Standards for Mathematical Practice (National Governors Association Center for Best Practices and Council of Chief State School Officers [NGA Center and CCSSO] 2010).

DEMIL's PD structures, including membership in a cross-school professional learning community (PLC) and participation in multiple lesson-study cycles, help (1) develop teaching expertise both within and across schools and (2) influence teachers' visions of their collaborative work in schools. The project includes fifteen participating teachers and seven principals with team participation (two to four individuals) from seven schools. This design develops and leverages teacher-leader skills, which ensures the sustainability of the work once the grant has ended. One outcome of the DEMIL project is developing broad-based leadership capacity in the district's schools. In this way, the work is not dependent on any individual, but rather leadership is distributed to facilitate whole-school transformation (Crowther, Ferguson, and Hann 2002; Institute for Educational Leadership 2001) as these leaders lead both in and out of their classrooms (Katzenmeyer and Moller 2001).

■ Tools Supporting Collaborative Examination of Mathematics Instruction

The collaborative work in DEMIL is based on research-proven principles and tools supporting critical analysis of mathematics instructional practice. These tools include the Task Analysis Guide, the Mathematics Task Framework, and the 5 Practices for orchestrating productive mathematics discussion (Henningsen and Stein 1997; Smith and Stein 2011; Stein et al. 2009). They provide a lens for analyzing the cognitive demand of tasks, studying ways in which it is either maintained or diminished during implementation, and planning for productive mathematical discussions. In addition, given the important role of communication in learning mathematics, the teachers examine levels of student mathematical discourse using the Student Discourse Observation Tool (Weaver, Dick, and Rigelman 2005).

The DEMIL project supports teachers as they develop a "critical eye" for examining tasks and student discourse as well as engage in collaborative planning and examination of instructional practice. Within the lesson study cycles, the project leaders develop collaborative PLCs that (1) engage in reflective dialogue; (2) deprivatize practice and the study of other artifacts of practice (e.g., tasks, student work, video of students at work); (3) collectively focus on deepening student mathematical thinking and reasoning; (4) collaborate within and across schools; and (5) construct shared norms and values for mathematics teaching and learning.

Within these PLCs, participating teachers are supported in and accountable for implementing their new learning and developing shared vision and goals; essentially, they have a like-minded accountability team and are learning by doing. The structure and content of this experience addresses the consistent disconnect between what teachers learn in professional learning and what they actually implement in their classrooms (NCTM 2014; National Research Council 2000; Pitler 2008). Ultimately, DEMIL's leaders are interested in increasing student engagement in reasoning, sense making, and discourse through enhancing teaching practice with the assumption that this will positively influence student achievement and narrow achievement gaps.

■ Lesson Study as a Vehicle

A critical component of DEMIL's work is the lesson study cycle. This design feature is in response to the isolation reported by many teachers (Heider 2005; Horn 2008; National Council of Supervisors of Mathematics [NCSM] 2014; NCTM 2014; National Education Association 2000), as during these cycles, teachers collaboratively plan and examine the influence of instruction on student learning. The model differs from Japanese lesson study (Chokshi and Fernández 2004; Watanabe 2002), in which teachers carefully tune a lesson; in this case, the main focus is on having teachers tune their practice.

DEMIL's lesson pstudy cycles engage participating teachers in one of two PLCs with six to eight teachers. The PLCs examine mathematics teaching, learning, and student thinking. Simultaneously, teacher leaders examine the process and plan for ways to sustain and expand the work after the grant is over. The cycles provide opportunities to develop and sustain collaborative PLCs while all members engage in doing math; plan for student engagement in mathematical reasoning, sense making, and discourse; examine teaching and the impact on student learning; connect new learning to implications for individual practice; and implement new learning.

One teacher from each team serves as a lead teacher (LT), who opens her classroom as the focus classroom where participants observe the students' progress with reasoning, sense making, and discourse over the course of the year. The lesson study cycle has three major components: pre-planning, core learning, and between-cycle work. During the pre-planning component (usually a week in advance of the lesson), the LTs and facilitators select a task, analyze its cognitive demand, and modify it if necessary to assure it is high cognitive demand and relevant to the students. As the team explores the math, they note concepts, skills, and reasoning related to the task and anticipate student strategies and conceptions. They craft the learning targets to be shared with the students, and they plan for the lesson implementation in the LT's classroom.

During the core learning component, LTs, participating teachers (PTs), principals, and facilitators preview the lesson, gather data during the lesson, and debrief. During the preview, they (*a*) explore the math and the relative learning trajectory, (*b*) discuss the learning target and success criteria, and (*c*) further plan for implementation of the lesson. Participants use protocols and tools to gather data during implementation of the lesson. This is followed by debriefing the observation data and reflecting on participants' learning.

Finally, participants engage in the between-cycle work component, in which they implement new learning and use existing school structures to provide support, accountability, and motivation to follow through with implementation plans. The principal and district math specialist provide support by gathering student mathematical discourse data and providing supportive feedback related to each teacher's implementation plan. The observations and interactions during this component guide planning for the next cycle.

By design, the three components of the lesson study cycle work together to build teachers' capacity to engage students in mathematical reasoning, sense making, and discourse. The supportive yet rigorous structure allows teachers to make significant changes in their practice, as opposed to tinkering around the edges. Thompson and Zeuli (as cited in Smith 2001) describe this type of learning as *transformative* rather than *additive*. Highlighted in the next section is a specific example of the cycle in action.

■ Decomposing Numbers, Applying Properties, to Simplify Calculations

A grade 3 standard in the Common Core (3.OA.B.5; NGA Center and CCSSO 2010) calls for students to apply properties of operations as strategies to multiply and divide. In the EngageNY curriculum (https://www.engageny.org/resource/grade-3-mathematics), students are taught to break apart arrays to create two smaller arrays that help them find the product of the larger array. The teacher then demonstrates how this decomposition of arrays connects to the distributive property, and students practice this skill by labeling decomposed arrays and by decomposing arrays, given particular expressions. When LTs met with the facilitators (district and university math specialists), they determined that this task had the potential to align with the "Procedures *with* Connections" category of the Task Analysis Guide (Stein et al. 2009). Yet, if the task were implemented following the script provided in the lesson, the cognitive demand would be diminished and the discourse prompted would not be particularly rich or at a high level. The team developed a revised sequence of tasks because they hoped to prompt higher-level thinking and discourse. Note the parenthetical information regarding the tools made available to students. The plan was to engage students in the practice of choosing and using appropriate tools (MP.5; NGA Center and CCSSO 2010).

> **Part 1: Concept Development**—What are all the ways that I can decompose the given rectangle? Record number sentences that show your thinking. (Students are provided with repeated copies of 3×6 rectangles.)

> **Part 2: Application**—We have 28 desks arranged in 4 rows with 7 desks in each row. What are some different ways to create paths that cut from one side of the room to the other? (Students are provided with a choice of tools, including tiles, yarn, colored pencils, and repeated copies of 7×4 arrays mimicking the arrays used in EngageNY.)

> **Part 3: Extension/Challenge: Menu**—Imagine there are 28 students in each classroom in our school. Now consider seating for an assembly. Try 4, 6, or 12 classrooms. (Students are provided with a choice of tools, including base-ten pieces, yarn, colored pencils, and grid paper.)

The team explored the mathematics of the tasks and drafted potential questions to ask at various stages in the lesson to elicit mathematical thinking and prompt justification and connections.

During the Core Learning component, the lesson study PLC (which included one of the LTs, half of the PTs, the principals, and the facilitators) previewed the tasks in the lesson by doing the math. The strategies that emerged are shown in figure 5.1. The team first discussed connections to the distributive property. From there, they discussed ways that the LT could introduce recording strategies that invite connections to distributivity, if it did not come up naturally. The facilitators introduced the Student Discourse Observation Tool (Weaver, Dick, and Rigelman 2005) to the PLC along with the protocol for the observation. This provided a focus for participating teachers and had a twofold purpose. First, project leaders were interested in increasing teachers' abilities to attend to and respond to students' mathematical thinking. This procedure also turned attention away from what the teacher was doing, which often resulted in teachers feeling safer to open their practice to others, a critical component of effective PLCs.

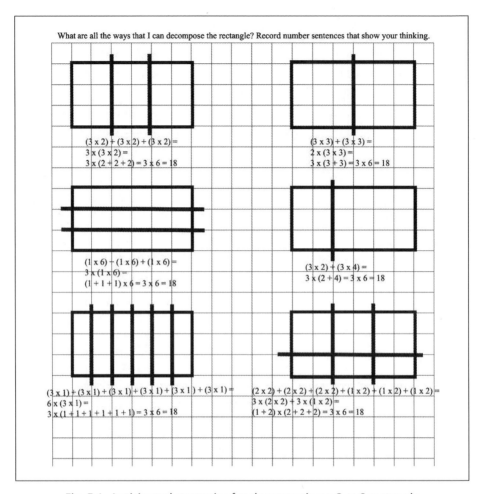

Fig. 5.1. Anticipated strategies for decomposing a 3 × 6 rectangle

When reconvening after the lesson, the LT spoke first about her impressions of the lesson and what she noticed about student thinking and reasoning. She stated that she was not surprised that she did not get as far along in the lesson as hoped; she knew that the choice of tools was new to students, and that this provided a challenge. She commented on being pleased that students were able to record equations to match their decompositions but was disappointed that she was unsure how to link what students shared to the distributive property.

In the next phase of the debrief, PTs note specific evidence of student mathematical discourse on sentence strips and categorize them based on discourse levels. Table 5.2 shows the initial results. This phase provided opportunities for clarification about the levels of discourse, given that similar statements were categorized as falling into three levels. For example, categorizing placed "I notice every equation makes 18" as Procedures and Facts (PF); "We made different number sentences but they equal 18" as Justification (J); and "Every equation equals 18" as Generalization (G).

After discussion, teachers realized that all these statements could be considered PF, as they were observations students were making about their results. A teacher could follow such statements by probing to raise the level of discourse. For example, she could ask "Why is that true?" to open further discussion about why all the equations equal 18. Students could then show arithmetic examples equal to 18 or argue that the area should be the same based on the fact that these are all rectangles of the same size.

Table 5.2

Excerpts of student mathematical discourse from lesson-study observation categorized by participating teachers

Procedures and Facts (PF)	Justification (J)	Generalization (G)
• You have to do it on the lines. • We were decomposing arrays. • Is it OK to make more than one path? • I notice every equation makes 18.	• We made different numbers sentences but they equal 18. • It makes it easier because you are working with smaller numbers. • Pretend that each is a box of candies that is always 18. Just different kinds of candies. • 2 + 2 + 2 + 2 + 2 + 2 + 2 + 2 + 2 . . . There are 9 groups and 2 in each group.	• Decomposing makes it easier. • It makes it easier because you are working with smaller numbers. • Every equation equals 18.

The next phase of the debrief provides the opportunity to hone in on specific students' thinking and consider next steps. Figure 5.2 is an image of one student's work. Teachers first describe what they think the work reveals about the student's understanding and then suggest specific teacher moves that could be made to either assess or advance the thinking. Teachers stated that they see evidence that leads them to believe that this student understands the commutative property and decomposing shapes, and they described how the reversal of color may show this. They brainstormed potential questions to ask this student:

• What are the number sentences you would use to label your picture?

• How can these smaller sections help you find the total?

• What connections do you see between the expression/equation from this model and another model?

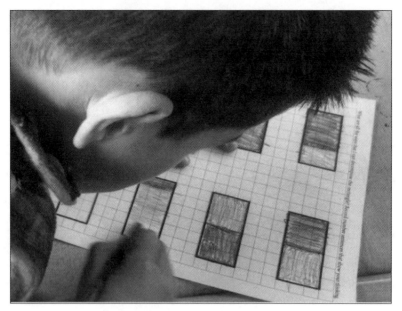

Fig. 5.2. Decomposition of the 3 × 6 rectangle
Photo Credit: Kellie Petrick

This process is repeated for other student work of interest. Finally, the group considered next steps. One suggestion was to connect a selected student's visual strategy to the distributive property by stating "I noticed you recorded your thinking as (3 × 4) + (3 × 2). I was thinking 3 × (4 + 2). Could we both be right?" This could be proposed to a single student or to the whole group and would then connect explicitly to the distributive property. The group then thought that students could revisit their work to see if they could find more evidence of the distributive property. This move would also provide the opportunity for students to engage in MP.7, making use of structure, and MP.3, critiquing the reasoning of others (NGA Center and CCSSO 2010).

Finally, the debrief ended with all participants reflecting on and articulating their learning, and making a commitment to what they will implement between cycles. Some ideas that emerged were the following:

- Provide time for students to engage in productive struggle ($n=4$)

- Provide choice of tools and give time to explore those tools ($n=3$)

- Model less, explore more ($n=3$)

- Consider cognitive demand of tasks and talk ($n=4$)

- Allow time for students to explore and make connections ($n=4$)

All of these takeaways are pedagogical, which suggests progress toward the goal of tuning instructional practice. Teachers focused on elements to improve their practice that were independent of the particulars of the lesson, as is illustrated through this statement: "Exit tickets are a great way to do a quick check on what my students got during the lesson!" While not all the student goals were accomplished within this one day, teachers engaged in a great discussion about how they might prompt students to make important connections between their strategies and the properties as the lesson continued.

■ Teacher Learning from Lesson Study

Based on exit surveys, teachers were extremely positive about their experiences with lesson study. The lesson study cycles provided opportunities for implementation of and reflection on ambitious mathematics practice. The vehicle supported teachers with recognizing needed shifts in their practice, as revealed in these statements:

- "I will be more prepared by planning what I will do/say if and when students begin to struggle—strategies that will get them moving in the right direction without tell[ing] them the answers."

- "Being mindful as a teacher about the kinds of questions I am posing to students so I am not leading them to a conjecture, but allowing them time to discover in a structured environment."

At the same time, teachers left the lesson study cycles empowered with tools to support self-assessment to support refinement of their practice.

- "It was helpful to analyze student discourse and categorize output into the Procedures/Facts, Justification, and Generalization."

- "Evaluator and Explainer protocol—this is what kids need to help them pose questions and dialogue/discuss with their peers. It is a useful tool to help foster dialogue."

- "Dissecting . . . lessons to make them more meaningful and engaging for the students. Identifying what the point of each lesson is and the big idea it is trying to get at to facilitate making that connection among the students."

Finally, teachers also wrote about the power of collaborative learning.

- "My biggest takeaway was the importance of 'doing the math' collaboratively prior to planning and instruction."

- "I want more time with this group of brilliant minds!"

- "More lesson studies!"

These statements reveal the potential of lesson study as a vehicle to support teachers' learning. Whether the teacher is just getting started with shifting practice or is a teacher leader continuing to refine practice, the lesson studies have been responsive to teachers' learning needs while fostering teacher self-assessment and growth. One commented, "The more we do these, the better our instruction and student learning will be."

■ Implications for Professional Development Design

Each phase of the cycle provided facilitators with information about teachers' learning needs that were used to guide further planning for the DEMIL professional learning. For example, the initial location of the sentence strips when categorizing discourse levels provided insights into what teachers understand about the levels of discourse. This led to a continued focus on discourse analysis through video cases and our lesson studies. Whenever there was a question about the level of discourse, we further inquired into what we would need to hear to categorize the discourse as Justification or Generalization.

Teachers also commented in their exit reflections about needing support with questioning to prompt higher-level discourse. In response, for our next book study session a Number Talk served as a vehicle to engage teachers in *doing math* while also illustrating questions that encourage reflection and justification. One facilitator led the Number Talk while the other collected question data that the teachers then sorted by using the question framework in *Principles to Actions* (NCTM 2014).

Feedback from between-cycle work and subsequent lesson studies revealed an interest in seeing the final, whole-group discussion of these problem-based lessons. That is, teachers were now increasingly comfortable with how to set up a lesson to assure productive inquiry; they were less sure about how to pull it all together with a whole-group discussion. Because we had been selecting rich tasks and using the 5 Practices (Smith and Stein 2011) for the lesson study, the lessons tended to be unfinished in just one math session. For the final lesson-study cycle, we engaged teachers in just that. The LTs agreed to implement the lesson a week in advance of the scheduled lesson study so that we had student work to analyze and plan for the whole-group discussion of the task.

■ Conclusion

This chapter describes ways that the DEMIL project's collaborative efforts are responsive to teachers' identified learning needs while fostering teacher self-assessment and growth. The lesson studies have also proven a useful vehicle for teacher leaders to support their colleagues' learning. When teacher leaders were asked to reflect on their role as leaders, one commented on the importance of trying new things in her own classroom before sharing with her colleagues. Similarly, another stated that there is more impact in showing colleagues through her own actions and student work than by telling them they should teach in particular ways. While the DEMIL grant pushes teachers into roles where they are not yet fully comfortable, a leader stated that "taking risks is worth it . . . pushing myself and leading by example is more powerful than I originally thought." Generally, DEMIL participants are more inclined to participate in other mathematics and/or leader professional development. Building principals and other administrators have commended the shifts they are seeing in their participating teachers' practice, and several school teams (teacher leader and principal) are working to find ways to use lesson studies within their own buildings, exploring ways to use existing structures to facilitate such learning for more teams of teachers.

Acknowledgments

This chapter was developed in part with support from the National Science Foundation, DUE 1540855. All opinions, findings, conclusions, and recommendations expressed herein are those of the author and do not necessarily reflect the views of the Foundation.

References

Ball, Deborah Lowenberg and David K. Cohen. "Developing Practice, Developing Practitioners: Toward a Practice-Based Theory of Professional Education." In *Teaching as the Learning Profession: Handbook of Policy and Practice,* edited by Gary Sykes and Linda Darling-Hammond, pp. 3–32. San Francisco: Jossey-Bass, 1999.

Ball, Deborah Lowenberg, Mark Hoover Thames, and Geoffrey Phelps. "Content Knowledge for Teaching: What Makes It Special?" *Journal of Teacher Education* 59, no. 5 (2008): 458–76.

Borko, Hilda. "Professional Development and Teacher Learning: Mapping the Terrain." *Educational Researcher* 33, no. 8 (2004): 3–15.

Chokshi, Sonal, and Clea Fernández. "Challenges to Importing Japanese Lesson Study: Concerns, Misconceptions, and Nuances." *Phi Delta Kappan* 85, no. 7 (2004): 520–25.

Crowther, Frank, Margaret Ferguson, and Leonne Hann. *Developing Teacher Leaders: How Teacher Leadership Enhances School Success.* 2nd ed. Thousand Oaks, Calif.: Corwin Press, 2009.

Doerr, Helen M., Lynn T. Goldsmith, and Catherine C. Lewis. "Goals of Professional Development." Reston, Va.: National Council of Teachers of Mathematics, Mathematics Professional Development Research Brief, 2010. http//www.nctm.org/Research-and-Advocacy/research-brief-and-clips/Goals-of-Professional-Development/.

Garet, Michael S., Andrew C. Porter, Laura Desimone, Beatrice F. Birman, and Kwang Suk Yoon. "What Makes Professional Development Effective? Results from a National Sample of Teachers." *American Educational Research Journal* 38, no. 4 (2001): 915–45.

Guskey, Thomas R. "What Makes Professional Development Effective?" *Phi Delta Kappan* 84, no. 10 (2003): 748–50.

Heider, Kelly L. "Teacher Isolation: How Mentoring Programs Can Help." *Current Issues in Education* 8, no. 14 (2005). http://cie.ed.asu.edu/volume8/number14/.

Henningsen, Marjorie, and Mary Kay Stein. "Mathematical Tasks and Student Cognition: Classroom-Based Factors That Support and Inhibit High-Level Mathematical Thinking and Reasoning. *Journal of Research in Mathematics Education* 28, no. 5 (1997): 524–49.

Horn, Ilana S. "The Significance of Teacher Community for Professional Learning." Presentation at the *Teachers Development Group Annual Leadership Seminar*, Portland, Oreg. (February 2008).

Institute for Educational Leadership. *Leadership for Student Learning: Redefining the Teacher as Leader.* Author, 2001. http://www.iel.org/programs/21st/reports/teachlearn.pdf.

Katzenmeyer, Marilyn, and Gayle Moller. *Awakening the Sleeping Giant: Helping Teachers Develop as Leaders.* 2nd ed. Thousand Oaks, Calif.: Corwin Press, 2001.

National Council of Supervisors of Mathematics (NCSM). *It's TIME: Themes and Imperatives for Mathematics Education.* Bloomington, Ind.: Solution Tree, 2014.

National Council of Teachers of Mathematics (NCTM). *Principles to Actions: Ensuring Mathematical Success for All.* Reston, Va.: NCTM, 2014.

National Education Association. "Rx for Teacher Isolation: The Professional Development School." *NEA Today* 18, no. 6 (2000): 10.

National Governors Association Center for Best Practices and Council of Chief State School Officers (NGA Center and CCSSO). *Common Core State Standards for Mathematics.* Washington, D.C.: NGA Center and CCSSO, 2010. http://www.corestandards.org.

National Research Council (NRC). *How People Learn: Brain, Mind, Experience, and School.* Expanded edition. Washington, D.C.: National Academies Press, 2000.

Pitler, Howard. "Classroom Walkthroughs: Learning to See the Trees and the Forest." *Changing Schools* 58, no. 4 (2008): 9–11.

Smith, Margaret Schwan. *Practice-Based Professional Development for Teachers of Mathematics.* Reston, Va.: NCTM, 2001.

Smith, Margaret Schwan, and Mary Kay Stein. *5 Practices for Orchestrating Productive Mathematics Discussions.* Reston, Va.: NCTM, 2011.

Spillane, James P. "External Reform Initiatives and Teachers' Efforts to Reconstruct Practice: The Mediating Role of Teachers' Zones of Enactment." *Journal of Curriculum Studies* 31, no. 2 (1999): 143–75.

Stein, Mary Kay, Margaret Schwan Smith, Marjorie A. Henningsen, and Edward A. Silver. *Implementing Standards-Based Mathematics Instruction: A Casebook for Professional Development.* 2nd ed. New York: Teachers College Press, 2009.

Watanabe, Tad. "Learning from Japanese Lesson Study." *Educational Leadership* 59, no. 6 (2002): 36–39.

Weaver, Dave, Thomas Dick, and Nicole Miller Rigelman. "Assessing the Quality and Quantity of Student Discourse in Mathematics Classrooms." Paper presented at the *Mathematics and Science Partnership Evaluation Summit*, Minneapolis, Minn. (September 2005). http://hub.mspnet.org/media/data /Weaver.pdf?media_000000006088.pdf.

CHAPTER 6

Fostering Professional Growth:
A Three-Pronged Approach

Charlene Marchese and Pamela Haimer,
Freehold Township Schools, Freehold, New Jersey

Regardless of their individual background and experience, all teachers can benefit from ongoing professional learning to refine their teaching practice and increase their own mathematical understanding. (Seeley 2016, p. 19)

In 2000, the National Council of Teachers of Mathematics (NCTM) challenged mathematics educators to "imagine a classroom, a school, or a school district where all students have access to high-quality, engaging mathematics instruction" (NCTM 2000, p. 3). The vision laid out by NCTM over the last twenty-five years, starting with the *Curriculum and Evaluation Standards for School Mathematics* (NCTM 1989) and restated most recently in *Principles to Actions* (NCTM 2014), provides a pathway for teachers, schools, and districts to improve the teaching and learning of mathematics. Rigorous state and national standards, such as the Common Core State Standards in Mathematics (CCSSM; National Governors Association for Best Practices and Council of Chief State School Officers [NGA Center and CCSSO] 2010), provide clear standards for mathematical content and practices, with the goal of preparing our students mathematically for college and careers. For the visions of NCTM and CCSSM to become a reality for all students, educators must study the art of teaching and learning mathematics through collaborative practice (NCTM 2014; National Council of Supervisors of Mathematics [NCSM] 2014). This article outlines a framework used by one school district to enhance the professional learning of mathematics teachers by focusing on the structural, practical, and philosophical components of the professional development (PD) experience. The authors will shed light on how the interconnectedness of this multipronged model fostered communication and collaboration within a middle school mathematics department, which in turn enhanced teachers' professional growth and their ownership of the professional learning initiatives.

■ Theoretical Framework: The Three-Pronged Approach

Communication and collaboration are considered to be important aspects of initiating and sustaining change in schools, (DuFour and Eaker 1998); National Association of Elementary School Principals 2001). Professional learning communities (PLCs), where teachers work in teams to engage in reflective inquiry with an emphasis on student learning (Blankstein, Houston, and Cole 2008), are an entity where communication and collaboration are essential. To maximize professional learning within PLC teams, teacher engagement, active participation, and trust must be present (Ning, Lee, and Lee 2015), as they are key ingredients for effective communication and collaboration. Authentic collegiality, defined in this study as "communication and collaboration," comprises and allows for evolutionary relationships consisting of openness, trust, and support among teachers, and it fosters an environment where they define and develop their own purposes as a community (Hargreaves and Dawe 1990). Further, the value of collaboration appears in Darling-Hammond's research, where she describes effective PD as engaging teachers in the concrete tasks of teaching, assessing, observing, and reflecting. These tasks illuminate the processes of learning and development and should be participant driven, collaborative, and sustained (Darling-Hammond and McLaughlin 1995).

Interestingly, while teacher collaboration is considered essential to school reform, it is not widespread. According to Darling-Hammond, "Overall, the kind of high-intensity, job-embedded collaborative learning that is most effective is not a common feature of professional development across most states, districts and schools in the United States" (Darling-Hammond et al. 2009, p. 4). Continuing professional learning activities after the initial implementation and/or funding of a PD program has ended is critical for long-term success and change in practice (Whitcomb, Borko, and Liston 2009). As PLCs require teachers' continuous collaborative efforts (DuFour 2004; cited in Ning, Lee, and Lee 2015), PLCs are a critical feature in implementing high-quality PD (Koellner, Jacobs, and Borko 2011). Therefore, establishing an educational environment where teacher collaboration and communication is fostered, developed, and sustained is a critical part of educational reform.

■ The Three-Pronged Framework

In our work, we strive to foster and sustain instructional change using a three-pronged framework that supports teacher collaboration and communication. Our framework consists of structural, practical, and philosophical components (see fig. 6.1).

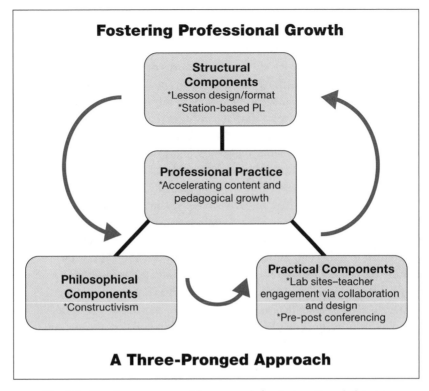

Fig. 6.1. The three-pronged framework for instructional change

First, the structural component pertains to the infrastructure of the school day for both teachers and students. For example, providing teachers with common planning time with their colleagues is an essential structural component that allows for content and grade-level teacher collaboration. Common planning time provides an opportunity for teachers to engage in collaborative practices by reflectively sharing their practice, revisiting beliefs on teaching and learning, and co-constructing knowledge (Musanti and Pence 2010). Whether teachers are collaborating in a PLC, planning lessons collaboratively, or discussing content and pedagogy, having common planning time scheduled within the school day is critical (Raywid 1993; Fullan and Miles 1992). While there are many models for providing teachers common planning time, an important element is to structurally embed the time within the school day to provide the opportunity for ongoing collaboration throughout the school year (Raywid 1993).

The students' schedules are also a structural component. Students' educational experiences are in part driven by their daily schedules. For example, incorporating a block schedule may allow students more continuous time to focus on an academic area in a given day. While research is inconclusive on whether block scheduling translates to higher student achievement (Education Partnerships, Inc. 2011), the extended time provides students the opportunity for sustained engagement with the discipline. The ultimate impact of a longer class period is dependent on the curriculum and instructional quality of the class (Baker et al. 2004), which illustrates the importance of teacher collaboration around instructional practices.

Second, the philosophical component refers to the overarching educational philosophy that drives the pedagogy and instruction of a school district. For consistency, the district's philosophy should align with the district's teacher evaluation tools. While teacher evaluation formats can vary from district to district, two widely used frameworks by Danielson (Danielson Group 2013) and Marzano (Marzano 2013) each require teachers to collaborate in a learning community (Battersby and Verdi 2015). A consistent philosophical message from all stakeholders (including administrators, coaches, and teachers) of what constitutes effective classroom practice should guide all formal and informal conversations around the teaching and learning of mathematics. This allows for diversity and teacher choice when making specific instructional decisions, while allowing for continuity and consistency within the district's instructional practice.

Third, the practical component consists of coordinated and sustained PD experiences, which provide teachers with the knowledge and skills to deliver quality instruction to students. These experiences are embedded in the work of teaching, such as lab sites (described later in the chapter) and book clubs, and they shift the PD from a curriculum-based approach to an approach that focuses on student thinking and learning (Whitcomb, Borko, and Liston 2009). It is critical that the PD feature the researched aspects of high-quality PD, such as fostering a professional learning community, developing teachers' mathematical knowledge (Ball and Forzani 2011), and adapting PD to support local goals and interests (Koellner, Jacobs, and Borko 2011). In addition, the practical component also includes providing PD that is sustained in duration and engages teachers through active learning (Desimone and Garet 2015). These experiences can be provided in a variety of formats, such as full-day workshop sessions, coaching meetings, pre-observation conferences, team/department meetings, faculty meetings, after-school minicourses, and classroom visitations.

While each of the components provides opportunities for teacher growth, the power of the framework is its interconnectedness. The interconnectedness of our framework enhances collaborative learning, as teachers are provided with time for learning with colleagues (structural component), engaging together in rich mathematical experiences (practical component), and collectively advocating a shared philosophy of education (philosophical component).

Darling-Hammond and McLaughlin (1995) state that PD must also be connected to other aspects of school change. In this framework, the philosophy anchors the structural and the practical components by providing a foundation for the vision of mathematics education. The practical experiences, grounded in the practices of teaching (Ball and Cohen 1999), can be designed, modeled, and implemented through a consistent philosophy. The structure of the school schedule provides teachers with time to engage in collaborative planning and students with time to engage in meaningful mathematics. While teachers may have different "styles of teaching," it is imperative that they follow the same philosophy (Munter, Stein, and Smith 2015). A consistent and clear vision and philosophy of mathematics education must be in place and be present in every interaction in order to empower teacher choice and foster collaborative team decision making. Promoting the alignment of the three prongs to support teachers in sustained implementation of the ideas learned in PD is the work and responsibility of all stakeholders—coaches, supervisors, vice principals, principals, and district administrators. In the next section, we describe the use of the framework model in our work.

■ The Three-Pronged Approach in Our Specific Context

The first author of this chapter serves as supervisor of mathematics and science, and the second author serves as assistant superintendent of curriculum and instruction in Freehold Township School District (FTS), a pre-K–8 suburban district located in western Monmouth County, New Jersey, consisting of one preschool, five elementary schools, and two middle schools. Freehold Township School District's enrollment of approximately 3,855 students consists of 76 percent white, 10 percent Hispanic, 8 percent Asian, 4 percent black, 2 percent multiracial, and less than 1 percent American Indian and Pacific Islander. Ten percent of the district's students are eligible for free or reduced-price lunch. FTS's two middle schools have twenty-four regular education teachers and thirteen special education teachers who teach resource room mathematics classes or teach in an inclusion mathematics class.

In FTS, the structural component of the framework consists of shifts in the structure of the school day for both teachers and students. First, students are provided with an eighty-minute block schedule in mathematics daily, allowing time for engaging in sophisticated mathematics. Second, within the block periods, teachers often use a station-based model in which groups of students rotate through various learning stations and engage in differentiated problem-based learning (e.g., tasks from Illustrative Mathematics [https://www.illustrativemathematics.org] or from Exemplars [http://www.exemplars.com]); digital math resources (e.g. LearnBop [https://www.learnbop.com] or TenMarks [https://www.tenmarks.com]); and small group instruction that provide dynamic interactions with peers and teachers. Hiebert and colleagues state, "Students build mathematical understandings by reflecting and communicating, so the tasks must allow and encourage these processes" (Hiebert et al. 1997, p. 18). Station-based instruction gives students the opportunity to discuss mathematics by solving large mathematical tasks while also receiving targeted instruction through the teacher and technology stations. Third, scheduling teachers for alternating days of forty-four minutes and eighty-eight minutes of common planning time provides opportunities for teachers to collaboratively discuss and craft lessons with grade-level colleagues.

In FTS, the practical component of the framework is represented by a variety of PD experiences to enhance teachers' understanding of the teaching and learning of mathematics. Over the last decade, these experiences have included lab sites, all-day professional development workshops, after-school mathematics department meetings, collaboration with universities, curriculum writing, and pre- and post-observation conferences. Lab sites (Houk 2010) were conducted over a full school day, where a team of teachers cowrote a lesson and the full grade level of mathematics teachers participated in a pre-lesson meeting, observation of a classroom mathematics lesson, and post-lesson meeting. Ten lab sites, including four that were affiliated with a university project, were conducted over a two-year period in 2014–2016. For example, two lab sites were conducted by teachers who attended Rutgers University Experience for Teachers in Engineering Program, where they created STEM lessons (sample materials provided on this book's page at NCTM's More4U website) for the mathematics classrooms, and two lab sites were conducted by a sixth-grade team of teachers who cowrote a unit of study with North Carolina State University. Each year, the topics of professional development workshops and bimonthly after-school department meetings were aligned with the district's mathematics goals. In addition to these experiences, teachers wrote the district's mathematics curriculum documents, incorporating content and pedagogical expectations; and they engaged in pre- and post-observation meetings focusing on the teaching and learning of mathematics. All the above formal experiences and informal teacher interactions make up the practical component.

For the philosophical component, the constructivist approach captures the essence of Freehold Township's Curriculum Departments beliefs about learning. It is a theory "about knowledge and learning, it describes both what 'knowing' is and how one comes to 'know'" (Fosnot 1996, p. ix). Fosnot describes constructivist teaching "as a model that emphasizes that learners need to be actively involved, to reflect on their learning and make inferences, and to experience cognitive conflict" (Fosnot 1996, p. 3). Freehold mathematics teachers applied the constructivist approach to their classrooms by embedding rich problem solving into their lessons, creating a safe culture for student collaboration, providing experiences that push student thinking, and questioning students on their mathematical understandings. The structure of the mathematics lessons moved toward a more child-centered approach, where whole-group instruction was minimized and replaced with a station-based format that provided a variety of quality mathematics activities that challenged students at various levels of content and targeted instruction and support for small groups of students. Station activities provided a variety of configurations such as group problem solving, individual work, and partner work, depending on the task and the mathematical goal.

The philosophy guided all interactions and conversations in and out of formal PD sessions. For example, teachers engaged in exploring mathematical tasks by completing the mathematics, discussing multiple solutions, identifying the critical mathematical concepts, and engaging in accountable talk. Pre- and post-observation conferences serve as another example. These conferences provided a space for coaching sessions where teachers and administrators discussed the plan of the observed lesson through the lens of a constructivist approach. These *in the moment* interactions translated the philosophy from theory to practice.

While educational trends are cyclical, this approach continues to support the CCSSM of today, as its mathematical practices expect students to engage in complex mathematical problem solving, communicate mathematical understandings with peers, and use mathematics as a vehicle to solve complex problems. Throughout the last decade of changes in state standards and state testing and the resulting political pressure to produce high standardized test scores, the philosophy of teaching and learning of mathematics stayed consistent within the FTS district. This is a result of the district's collective commitment to have teachers focus on teaching children mathematics with understanding.

■ Participant-Oriented Program Evaluation

To better understand the impact of the three-pronged approach to professional development in FTS, we utilized a participant-oriented program evaluation model, characterized in this study by (*a*) inquiry and inductive reasoning; (*b*) a flexible plan as the evaluation process evolved through conversations with participants, between the authors, and as data were collected and reviewed; and (*c*) the documentation of multiple perspectives as the authors captured participants' perspectives and interpreted them in order to reveal the central phenomenon and emergent themes (Fitzpatrick, Sanders, and Worthen 2004). The participants, consisting of FTS middle school math teachers and administrators, range in experience from two years to thirty years, with an average of ten years of education experience. Surveys, feedback forms, interviews, and evaluation documents from teachers and administrators, obtained via informal observations and informal conversations among teachers and the authors during daily interactions within the schools and district office, served as data. An initial survey was administered to the entire middle school math department. The survey utilized rank order to highlight the professional development sessions that were perceived by participants to have had the most influence in their professional careers in FTS. Twenty-eight teachers participated in the initial surveys, representing approximately 80 percent of the regular education mathematics teachers and 70 percent of the special education mathematics teachers.

The next phase of data collection included a survey consisting of a Likert scale and open-ended questions. Individual teachers from the math department were randomly surveyed, based on availability and willingness to participate. Finally, an interview protocol was used to gain further insight. We interviewed one team of sixth-grade teachers (four regular education teachers and one special education teacher) and each of the two middle school principals.

Results

In this section, we use results from the surveys and interviews of teachers and principals to identify what aspects of the PD were perceived as valuable and what changes in teachers' practice they attribute to PD experiences.

Collaboration and communication

Teachers reported that communication and collaboration positively progressed as a result of the PD experiences, as 83 percent of the online survey participants represented "improved communication skills among teachers in math department" as a 3 or 4, out of a 4-point scale, where a 4 is labeled substantial growth. The following quotes illustrate individual teacher's views on their collaboration with teammates:

> When I started working in Freehold the math department did not have a team approach. Over the years that has evolved and we now work as a cohesive team. . . . I feel that I support my colleagues as well as them supporting me. (Jill, grade 8 mathematics teacher, online survey)

> Working in a district that promotes teamwork and collaboration has strengthened my approach to collaboration with colleagues. I have always felt that having the support of your colleagues and working with them to plan lessons makes me a better teacher. (Betsy, grade 7 mathematics teacher, online survey)

In the interview with the sixth-grade team, one teacher shared this statement about her school-based mathematics team, "We created a math community . . . It is like our own PD . . . It made a world of difference."

Principals of the middle schools highlighted the collegiality of their mathematics teachers:

> This is something I think we have come a long way with . . . there is constant collaboration and working. . . . teachers are talking (about) their content area which is something that did not happen years ago and when you are talking (about) your content area, things happen. (John, middle school principal, interview)

> My math teachers work really well together, especially by grade level, each adds a strength to the team and a different breadth of experience. (Dianne, middle school principal, interview)

The professional and supportive teams described by the teachers and administrators were fostered in the PD sessions (practical component) and continued in the school setting on a daily basis through common planning time (structural component). Instructional planning with a common focus is enhanced when teachers are working with a common philosophy of education (philosophical component). Sustained conversations about the teaching and learning of mathematics served as the bridge between PD experiences and classroom practices. The goal is for the professional experiences to transition from being an event to being a culture, a way of thinking and interacting, that promotes inquiry and learning on the part of all.

Professional growth

In the online survey, teachers were asked to rate their overall professional growth, using a scale of 1 to 4, with 1 representing "no growth" and 4 representing "substantial growth." Approximately 96 percent of those surveyed gave themselves a growth rating of a 3 or 4. More specifically, 96 percent rated themselves a 3 or 4 in increased pedagogical knowledge and 93 percent rated themselves a 3 or 4 in increased content knowledge. Deborah Ball states, "Teachers must understand their subjects deeply and flexibly, and skillfully represent them in intellectually honest ways to a wide range of students" (Ball and Forzani 2011, p. 20). Increases in content and pedagogical knowledge and overall professional growth have the potential to positively affect teachers' practices and as a result, positively affect students' experiences in mathematics class. The focus of teachers engaging with mathematical content through a constructivist approach and the modeling of good pedagogy in PD sessions connected the philosophical and practical components of the frame. An extended eighty minutes of mathematics class (structural component) provided teachers the class time to give their students similar experiences in exploring mathematics that they experienced in PD sessions. The following quote from a sixth-grade mathematics teacher describes her growth in mathematical content knowledge through the practical and philosophical components:

> Having an exploration aspect to the workshops was what was mind-blowing to me. Being able to figure out the solution to a task and then having to get up and teach it to each other, we realized what mistakes we made and saw other ways to achieve the answer. Rather than just being told "Oh, this is the formula," we figured out where the formula came from. This was mind-blowing to me and was what made me go back to school to take extra math classes to get my certification to come to middle school. I thought how cool that people who aren't necessarily math inclined can explore and have big "aha" moments on their own. That was something that I had not gotten through my schooling, either college or growing up, and I wanted to bring that into the classroom where kids can explore to find the answer. (Liz, grade 6 mathematics teacher, interview)

Instructional approach and philosophy

Teachers' readiness (Wood, McQuarrie, and Thompson 1982), and their desire to learn and utilize new approaches based on a new schedule (structural) and previous PD (practical), made shifts in their instructional philosophy and approach possible. Understanding the essence of a philosophy is critical in creating an educational experience for students that reflects the philosophy. Almost 90 percent of the teachers surveyed rated their understanding of FTS's mathematics philosophy as a 4 or 5 on a 5-point scale. For example, one teacher describes a change in her "approach to instruction" that indicates an underlying change in her philosophy of teaching:

. . . my approach to instruction is extremely different. My students take ownership over their own learning and are encouraged to discover and discuss different strategies for solving problems. My instruction time is minimal giving students maximum time to work. Lessons are based on student needs using the standards as a guide. (Jill, grade 8 mathematics teacher, online survey)

Providing a mathematics environment where students are active participants includes strong communication among students in the classroom. In the online survey, 96 percent of the teachers surveyed answered with a 3 or 4 (substantial growth) to the questions of "Improved communication skills among students and student/teacher in classroom" and "Improved ability to establish a math community within your classroom." Lynn, a sixth-grade mathematics teacher, shares her thoughts on the changes in her classroom:

> . . . the differences that I have seen in the classroom really have been phenomenal . . . it is more on the students, having them decide the pacing when we work through stations . . . trying to have them pace themselves . . . they all don't have to be doing the same thing . . ., the (way the class) period is structured now, there is so much more math talk among students. (Lynn, grade 6 mathematics teacher, interview)

The structure of a mathematics class that provides student choice and empowers students to be leaders of their own learning is collaboratively developed.

Administration

School administrators provide an important lens on the day-to-day experience of the students in mathematics class. Over the last decade, school administrators have been engaged in conversations at both the district level and the school level on philosophy, best practice, and mathematical content and pedagogy. As a result, they support the work at the school level by providing consistency in teacher feedback, either informally or formally, through observation and evaluation.

> Over the last couple of years what I have observed is that students are engaged in our middle school classrooms, most classrooms, in a variety of tasks . . . there really is this exploratory piece . . . ultimately we want them to get to a point where they go "Aha" . . . What I am seeing is that students are deepening their understanding of the mathematics which is allowing them to go a little bit further in what they are learning. (Dianne, middle school principal, interview)

> In the 20 years I have been here, I have seen a definite change in how the math is taught in terms of the philosophy that is being lived by and taught by . . . when I go in [classrooms] . . . kids are working, they're talking, they like math, they are seeing real-life problems . . . and they are using math to do it, it is a whole different approach that we have taken. (John, middle school principal, interview)

Based on the data from teachers and principals, teacher collaboration and collegiality are embedded in the culture of the middle schools. It is valued by teachers as being an important part of their work with students, and it is observed and valued by principals. Through the interconnectedness of the three prongs—sustained professional development (practical component), consistent philosophy (philosophical component), and common planning time for collaboration (structural component)—teachers have developed and implemented their vision of instruction that supports students' learning of mathematics.

■ Promoting Teacher Leadership and Ownership through the Three-Pronged Approach

Having teachers take ownership of their craft (NCTM 2014) and become leaders in their schools is a critical part of school reform. As Dianne, the principal of a middle school, shares, "There is an energy and passion for mathematics that is really contagious. The teachers of math in my building really love math, they see themselves as mathematicians, they are excited to give the students opportunities to learn." It is this passion that has inspired teachers to lead their colleagues. From facilitating book studies, to seeking out connections with universities, to facilitating lab sites, teachers have taken a leadership role within the district. In the last year, with only some administrative help on logistics, teachers organized four lab sites for their colleagues. In addition to collaboratively crafting lessons, they collaborated with the teachers facilitating the lab site pre-meeting, taught the observed lesson, and were a critical part of the post-meeting. One teacher reflected after a lab site, "Now I see why this was more valuable than watching videos"; these experiences proved to affect the professional experience of the teachers.

■ Conclusion

The interconnectedness of the practical, philosophical, and structural components provides the frame to promote professional growth in a middle school mathematics department. The practical component gives teachers the opportunities to be engaged in the conversation of the teaching and learning of mathematics through professional learning experiences. The structural component provides the time for teachers to collaborate daily with their teams and for students to engage in meaningful mathematics. As the philosophical component, the constructivist approach guides all interactions and conversations, as it is embedded in the language, ideas, and tone of the conversations at the district level and spreads through all conversations at the school level. Educational trends will continue to cycle, making the need for a consistent and well-researched philosophy vital. Consistency in the face of pressure is possible when the philosophy guiding instructional decisions is well researched and focuses on teaching children mathematics.

According to teachers' and administrators' self-reports, it appears that the interconnectedness of the structural, practical, and philosophical components fostered collaboration and communication, changes in teacher instructional practices, and increased teacher leadership and ownership of their own learning. While this data is procured from FTS, the findings, as well as the model, bring value to the profession because they can be replicated in other departments and school districts by establishing this three-pronged framework: a common philosophy, providing professional learning that focuses teachers on content and pedagogical knowledge, and a structure for teacher planning and student learning.

References

Baker, David P., Rodrigo Fabrega, Claudia Galindo, and Jacob Mishook. "Instructional Time and National Achievement: Cross-National Evidence." *Prospects* 34, no. 3 (2004): 311–34.

Ball, Deborah Loewenberg, and David K. Cohen. "Developing Practitioners: Towards a Practice-Based Theory of Professional Education." *In Teaching as the Learning Profession: Handbook of Policy and Practice*, edited by Linda Darling-Hammond and Gary Sykes, pp. 3–32. San Francisco: Jossey-Bass, 1999.

Ball, Deborah Loewenberg, and Francesca M. Forzani. "Building a Common Core for Learning to Teach and Connecting Professional Learning to Practice." *American Educator* 35, no. 2 (2011): 17–21.

Battersby, Sharyn L., and Brian Verdi. "The Culture of Professional Learning Communities and Connections to Improve Teacher Efficacy and Support Student Learning." *Arts Education Policy Review* 116, no. 1 (2015): 22–29.

Blankstein, Alan M., Paul D. Houston, and Robert W. Cole. *Sustaining Professional Learning Communities.* Thousand Oaks, Calif.: Corwin Press, 2008.

Danielson Group. "The Framework" (2013). https://www.danielsongroup.org/framework/.

Darling-Hammond, Linda, and Milbrey W. McLaughlin. "Policies That Support Professional Development in an Era of Reform." *Phi Delta Kappan* 76, no. 8 (1995): 597–604.

Darling-Hammond, Linda, Stelios Orphanos, Nikole Richardson, Alethea Andree, and Ruth Chung Wei. *Professional Learning in the Learning Profession: A Status Report On Teacher Development in the United States and Abroad.* National Staff Development Council, 2009.

Desimone, Laura M., and Michael S. Garet. "Best Practices in Teachers' Professional Development in the United States." *Psychology, Society, and Education* 7, no. 3 (2015): 252–63.

DuFour, Richard. "What Is a Professional Learning Community?" *Educational Leadership* 61, no. 8 (May 2004): 6–11.

DuFour, Richard, and Robert E. Eaker. *Professional Learning Communities at Work: Best Practices for Enhancing Student Achievement.* Bloomington, Ind.: National Education Service, 1998.

Education Partnerships, Inc. "Research Brief: Length of Classes and Student Achievement" (2011). http://oregongearup.org/sites/oregongearup.org/files/research-briefs/lengthofclass.pdf.

Fitzpatrick, Jody L., James R. Sanders, and Blaine R. Worthen. *Program Evaluation: Alternative Approaches and Practical Guidelines.* 3rd ed. Boston, Mass.: Pearson Education, 2004.

Fosnot, Catherine Twomey. *Constructivism: Theory, Perspectives, and Practice.* New York: Teachers College Press, 1996.

Fullan, Michael M., and Matthew B. Miles. "Getting Reform Right: What Works and What Doesn't." *Phi Delta Kappan* 73, no. 10 (June 1992): 745–52.

Hargreaves, Andy, and Ruth Dawe. "Paths of Professional Development: Contrived Collegiality, Collaborative Culture, and the Case of Peer Coaching." *Teaching and Teacher Education* 6, no. 3 (1990): 227–41.

Hiebert, James, Thomas P. Carpenter, Elizabeth Fennema, Karen C. Fuson, Diana Wearne, Hanlie Murray, Alwyn Olivier, and Piet Human. *Making Sense: Teaching and Learning Mathematics with Understanding.* Portsmouth, N.H.: Heinemann, 1997.

Houk, Lisa M. "Demonstrating Teaching in a Lab Classroom" (June 2010). http://www.ascd.org/publications/educational-leadership/summer10/vol67/num09/Demonstrating-Teaching-in-a-Lab-Classroom.aspx.

Koellner, Karen, Jennifer Jacobs, and Hilda Borko. "Mathematics Professional Development: Critical Features for Developing Leadership Skills and Building Teachers' Capacity." *Mathematics Teacher Education and Development* 23, no. 1 (2011): 207–12.

Marzano, Robert J. "Scales and Evidences for the Marzano Teacher Evaluation Model" (2013). http://www.marzanocenter.com/files/Marzano_AST_Domain1234_20130107.pdf.

Munter, Charles, Mary Kay Stein, and Margaret S. Smith. "Is There a Common Pedagogical Core? Examining Instructional Practices of Competing Models of Mathematics Teaching." *NCSM Journal of Mathematics Education Leadership* 16, no. 2 (Fall 2015): 3–13.

Musanti, Sandra, and Lucretia Pence. "Collaboration and Teacher Development: Unpacking Resistance, Constructing Knowledge, and Navigating Identities." *Teacher Education Quarterly* 37, no. 1 (2010): 73–89.

National Association of Elementary School Principals (NAESP). *Leading Learning Communities: Standards for What Principals Should Know and Be Able to Do*. Alexandria, Va.: NAESP, 2001.

National Council of Supervisors of Mathematics (NCSM). *It's Time: Themes and Imperatives for Mathematics Education: A Leadership Framework for Common Core Mathematics*. Bloomington, Ind.: Solution Tree Press, 2014.

National Council of Teachers of Mathematics (NCTM). *Curriculum and Evaluation Standards for School Mathematics*. Reston, Va.: NCTM, 1989.

———. *Principles and Standards for School Mathematics*. Reston, Va.: NCTM, 2000.

———. *Principles to Actions: Ensuring Mathematical Success for All*. Reston, Va.: NCTM, 2014.

National Governors Association Center for Best Practices and Council of Chief State School Officers (NGA Center and CCSSO). *Common Core State Standards for Mathematics*. Washington, D.C.: NGA Center and CCSSO, 2010.

Ning, Hoi Kwan, Daphnee Lee, and Wing On Lee. "Relationships between Teacher Value Orientations, Collegiality, and Collaboration in School Professional Learning Communities." *Social Psychology of Education* 18, no. 2 (2015): 337–54.

Raywid, Mary Anne. "Finding Time for Collaboration." *Educational Leadership*, September 1993: 30–34.

Seeley, Cathy L. *Building a Math-Positive Culture: How to Support Great Math Teaching in Your School*. Alexandria, Va.: ASCD; Aurora, Colo.: NCSM; Reston, Va.: NCTM, 2016.

Whitcomb, Jennie, Hilda Borko, and Dan Liston. "Growing Talent: Promising Professional Development Models and Practices." *Journal of Teacher Education* 60, no. 3 (2009): 207–12. doi:10.1177/0022487109337280.

Wood, Fred H., Frank O. McQuarrie, Jr., and Steven R. Thompson. "Practitioners and Professors Agree on Effective Staff Development Practices." *Educational Leadership* 40, no. 1 (1982): 28–31.

CHAPTER 7

Leveraging Coach-Facilitated Professional Development to Create Collaborative Teacher Networks for Enhancing Professional Practice

Jennifer M. Suh, Sara Birkhead, Courtney Baker, Toya Frank,
and Padmanabhan Seshaiyer, *George Mason University, Fairfax, Virginia*

Job-embedded professional development (PD) models like lesson study (LS) provide opportunities for teachers to observe how students respond to a mathematics task and develop collective professional learning (Suh and Seshaiyer 2014). Additionally, effective mathematics PD should be related and responsive to school and teaching contexts, connected to content and standards, enhance pedagogical practices and content knowledge to further student learning, include extended time and significant contact hours with focus on classroom implementation; including ongoing support of peers and experts to create and support communities of practice (Garet et al. 2001; Stein, Smith, and Silver 1999). Research indicates that teachers change their underlying beliefs about teaching approaches only after they see their students succeed (Guskey 2002). More specifically, Guskey's model of teacher change describes a sequence of outcomes resulting from professional development that begins with changes in teachers' classroom practices, such as, implementing new instructional approaches or using new curricular materials. When teachers employ a new instructional strategy or curriculum and succeed in helping students learn, teachers' attitudes and beliefs change with the evidence of improvements in student learning. In addition, professional development of teachers is "an experientially based learning process for teachers" (Guskey, 2002, p. 387) where teachers need to receive regular feedback on the effects of their efforts so that they can sustain their new practices and receive continued support.

Successful implementation of instructional reform is challenged by critical issues in schools, such as building capacity, making time, developing leadership, ensuring equity, building a professional culture, garnering support and scaling up (Loucks-Horsley et al. 2003). Promising studies point to the nature and quality of teachers' professional relations as a key contributor to sustaining instructional reform (Gersten, Chard, and Baker 2000). Professional learning is sustained when teachers' interactions provide the type of knowledge, feedback, and social support that enables teachers to deepen their knowledge and practice. A longitudinal study (Coburn et al. 2012) examined how teacher social networks affected the ability to sustain new instructional strategies within district reform after the mathematics initiative supports were removed. Findings indicated that teacher social networks combined with strong ties, high-depth interaction, and high expertise enabled teachers to maintain the pedagogical approach.

Our study explores how a coach-facilitated LS PD model promoted the development of teacher social networks by providing access to knowledge, feedback, and social supports that deepened coaches' and teachers' understanding and enactment of ambitious teaching reform-oriented practices. The following research questions guided our study: (1) How did specific mathematics coaching practices and professional activities provide unique opportunities for teachers to enact important instructional practices and deepen their content knowledge? and (2) How did the coach-facilitated LS model appear to support the development of teacher social networks?

■ The Method for Our Study

Participants and Procedures

This study included seventy-seven elementary and middle grades mathematics teachers (grades 5–9) and twelve mathematics coaches (K–8) recruited from four suburban and two rural school districts, all within one hour of a major eastern city. The suburban districts have diverse student populations that are predominantly students of color, and one of the two rural districts has a majority of students who qualify for free or reduced lunch. Some of our participants were recruited as a team of teachers with a school-based coach or district math leader. University-based facilitators, including faculty and members of the PD design and facilitation team, also attended the LS host lessons to support the coaches and to further the groups' thinking about content and pedagogy.

Teachers and coaches met for the algebraic thinking and problem-solving summer institute and then conducted LS during the academic year. As PD designers and implementers of the PD institute, we felt the need to adapt the follow-up LS model (Lewis 2002) to meet the needs of teachers and overcome constraints within districts, while staying true to the implementation portion of immersing teachers in collaborative planning, teaching, observing, debriefing, and reflecting both individually and collectively. We referred to our modified version as a "coach-facilitated" LS structure, which had two optional structures for the second iteration of the research lesson. In the first option (see fig. 7.1, option 5a), the coach was able to observe and provide feedback to each teacher during the "re-teach," and the coaches and teachers then came together as a whole group to present their professional learning at the LS symposium. In the second option (see fig. 7.1, option 5b), during the "re-teach" the participating teachers taught and videotaped the second iteration of the lesson and reflected collectively using Edthena, an online, video-based coaching tool that allowed teachers and coaches to view and mark episodes and to reflect on lessons by making comments and asking questions. We created these optional structures in the second iteration of the lesson because we encountered challenges in scheduling additional professional days (released time) for our participating coaches. Although we recognized that there were some trade-offs, we noticed very quickly that the coach-facilitated LS structure provided differentiated PD for our coaches and a chance to build relationships among participants who served as coaches and who served as peer coaches in addition to LS participants.

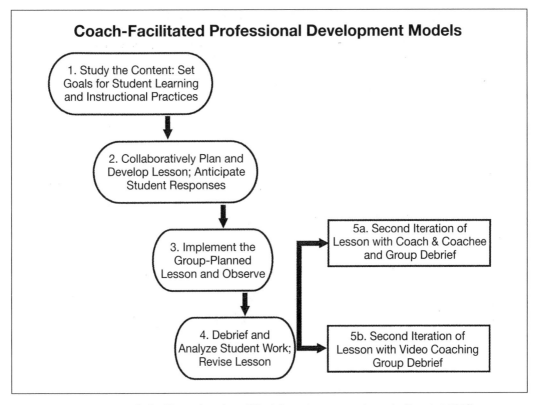

Fig. 7.1. Coach-facilitated LS (modified from lesson study cycle [Lewis 2002])

Data Sources and Analysis

The data sources included video clips from the research lessons, including teaching and lesson debriefs, student work, teacher reflections, and researchers' memos. In addition, we captured the coaches' and teachers' exchanges for the second lesson iteration through Edthena. Finally, we administered a survey to the participants inquiring about the nature of the coach-facilitated LS PD experience. We systematically analyzed the data using Dedoose, a web-based application for developing initial codes and used the method of axial coding to find categories that drew emerging themes (Miles and Huberman 1994). Each of these data sources contributed to compiling a comprehensive picture of teachers' and coaches' learning experiences.

■ Results

For the first research question, we analyzed the specific coaching practices and professional activities implemented in the PD (such as the coach-facilitated LS and the use of Edthena video coaching) to assess the impact of these practices on teacher professional growth, as evidenced by the professional artifacts such as collaborative lesson plan, reflections, observations of teaching, and collective debrief.

Differentiating PD for Coaches and Teachers to Support Professional Growth

Through differentiated PD for coaches during the content-focused institute, we wanted coaches to concentrate more on their role as facilitators who could support teachers while they implemented problem-based learning and examined student thinking during the follow-up LS. During the institute, we brought the coaches together each day to work on mathematics problems prior to the teacher groups' experience with them so that we could anticipate the strategies and misconceptions we wanted to address with the school-based teacher teams. During these coaching sessions, we used the Five Practices (Smith and Stein 2011) to help teachers anticipate how students might approach the problem and determine what struggles students might have. The conversations were vertical in nature, as the grade band experience of the coaches was K–12. Providing coaches with this time to think collaboratively appeared to develop their content and leadership skills in facilitating teachers' engagement with the mathematics and teachers' practices in implementing the tasks in their own classrooms. This preparation provided an opportunity that allowed the coaches to assume the role of the experts and be seen as knowledgeable others.

The Coach as the "Knowledgeable Other"

As we moved into the follow-up LS, the coaches served not only as facilitators but also as knowledgeable others who pushed the mathematics forward to help teachers think more critically and deeply about the content. In this section, we share a case study of four teachers and their mathematics coach engaged in a modified coach-facilitated LS that took place as part of a larger PD project. Of the four teachers, Julie was a veteran teacher of twenty years while the others were in their first three years of teaching: Val was a seventh-grade mathematics teacher with three years of experience, Dylan was a first-year sixth-grade mathematics teacher career-switcher, and Sloan was a fifth-grade multi-subject teacher with two years of experience. This team was facilitated by Nancy, the district coach who also participated in the PD project. The team selected the lesson titled "Tiling the Garden" (fig. 7.2; Driscoll 1999) and collaborated to create their lesson plan.

TILING THE GARDEN

The Manassas Park Garden Club is collecting handmade tiles from different art
classes to put around their school garden. They will not start planting until all tiles
have been collected. While they wait, the garden club is trying to predict what the
garden will look like. The size of their garden will depend on how many tiles they
receive.

Here are three sizes of gardens framed with a single row of tiles. The white squares represent
the tiles and the dark squares represent the possible garden:

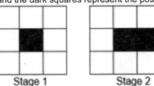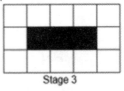

| Stage 1 | Stage 2 | Stage 3 |

Answer the following questions using pictures, words, tables, graphs, and/or symbols.

1. Draw Stage 4. How many white tiles are there?
2. How many white tiles at Stage 10? Stage 50?
3. How would you find the number of white tiles for any stage?

Fig. 7.2. The Tiling problem (Driscoll 1999)

The PD organizers provided a lesson plan template modeled after *5 Practices for Orchestrating Productive Mathematics Discussions* by Smith and Stein (2011). Teachers spent their time working through and analyzing the problem to try to anticipate all possible strategies that their students might use (e.g., guess and check, drawing, making a chart, writing an algebraic expression) as well as crafting questions that they felt would guide students without reducing the cognitive demand of the task (e.g., Are you following the pattern? Can you test your rule against any stage? What remains the same in each stage?). Once the lesson was complete (see this book's page at NCTM's More4U site for the complete lesson plan for Tiling the Garden), the teachers (including the host), the coach, and the university facilitator met to debrief the lesson. Using a coach-facilitated PD model was intended to provide a knowledgeable other to press teachers' content knowledge and pedagogy throughout the entire cycle.

When the host teacher implemented the Tiling the Garden lesson, his sixth-grade students were able to successfully extend the pattern by using the illustrations on the problem sheet and drawing subsequent stages if needed. Some of the student groups were able to describe the pattern in terms of a rule, whereas others struggled to generalize their observations. The host teacher and observing teachers used the questions from the lesson plan to guide students forward. The host teacher then had groups share different descriptions of the rule, written in algebraic form, and he simplified the expressions to show students that all the rules were equivalent.

During the post-lesson debrief discussion, Sloan, the fifth-grade teacher, wondered about the connections her students would make from finding a pattern in a table to writing the algebraic equation. She stated, "I'm kind of worried that [my lesson is] going to go more like that one table that was having more trouble. . . . They were like so close . . . but they weren't able to transfer that into their equation." Later she elaborated, "I'm just worried that my kids will not be able to see what's changing." Val, the seventh-grade teacher, had a similar concern, "I'm scared because I don't think my kids are going to write equations." In responding to these concerns, Nancy helped reassure the teachers that the vertical progression of algebraic standards moves from extending and recognizing patterns, to expressing patterns though verbal descriptions, and finally to symbolic representations using variables (National Governors Association Center for Best Practices and Council of Chief State School Officers [NGA Center and CCSSO] 2010). To support their students through this progression from different starting points, Nancy guided the teachers to create a collection of "pocket questions" (e. g., What pattern emerges when you analyze the numbers? Can you write a sentence that describes the relationship you found? Can you write a formula that uses your sentence?) as a way to advance student thinking.

Fig. 7.3. Students' use of manipulatives to represent the tiling pattern

Later in the debrief, Nancy and university facilitators led the teachers to discuss the use of manipulatives. This discussion helped Val consider deeply the idea of using manipulatives, after seeing how the use of colored tiles supported students to verbalize and make sense of their different ways of seeing the growing pattern. Val had not previously used manipulatives with her middle school students. The coach shared in the post-interview that Val was encouraged to use manipulatives in her second iteration of the lesson because of the experience of observing the success of Dylan's students in using the concrete tool to explain and connect to their abstract and symbolic representations.

In summary, as the groups debriefed about the host teacher's lesson and their own implementation, the coach (Nancy) was able to push teachers toward the goals of thinking about learning progression with respect to algebra (e.g., moving from verbal descriptions to algebraic expressions) as well as pedagogical practices around facilitation of tasks (e.g., creating "pocket questions" and providing manipulatives).

Focusing on Teachers' Instructional Practice via a Video Coaching Tool

In most of our coach-facilitated LS groups, the first rendition of the lesson taught by the host teacher was observed by the entire team; however, it was not always possible for the second iteration of the lesson (taught in the other members' classrooms) to be observed by the team members and the coach. To enrich their collaborative professional practices, we asked each member of the LS team to videotape their second iteration of the lesson. The team then watched one another's lessons by using Edthena and marked areas in the video clip that they considered strengths in each lesson (as described in the coach-facilitated LS model; see fig. 7.1, step 5b).

We examined one of the team's video coaching exchanges and found that the coach and the teachers had meaningful dialogue about the teaching episode. Because of their collective experience with the original lesson, they were very invested in providing feedback on the reteaching of the lesson. In the following video coaching excerpt from Edthena, the teacher and coach reflected on how her students' thinking is enriched through the teacher's intervention and how students took ownership of mathematics instruction and persevered through the task:

> *00:36 – Coach:* Great way to get them started [with individual work-time]—it makes sure all kids are engaged and thinking for themselves instead of relying on group members!
>
> *01:43 – Teacher:* I was impressed with this [group]. They worked backwards pretty fast. I then challenged them to show me another way of getting the solution, and they were the first to start to work with the manipulatives.
>
> *Coach:* That is awesome—great way to get them to think about it differently!
>
> *02:52 – Coach:* This group had a student who was unable to get the right answer at first. Instead of just telling her the answer . . . they sat down and walked through the process. It was amazing to see the explanations and the moment the student understood the process and answer.

In the teacher's comments, it is clear that she values the first group's willingness to try something new to extend their thinking. The coach's comments highlight the importance of student agency and perseverance, encouraging the teacher to be aware of these opportunities. In her own reflection, the coach noted a change in teacher behavior through questioning and wait-time to encourage and support students to reach answers on their own. In addition, she noted a change in students' motivation as a result of this support: "students who have struggled and failed over and over were . . . engaged in the lesson and excited about figuring it out." The video coaching forum provided some time for teachers to revisit one another's lessons, and the group experience led to a collective ownership of teaching practices. This excerpt shows teachers conversation about a peer's lesson:

> *00:59 – Teacher:* The time allowed for group presentations needed to be expanded; not enough time to allow all groups to better explain thought process used to solve.
>
> *02:08 – Peer Teacher 1:* The questions that were asked engaged the students' thought process and did not guide the students.
>
> *02:11 – Peer Teacher 2:* Students comparing pictures and discussing their different approaches is a great way for them to see the problem slightly different and learn a new way of looking at something.

10:54 – Peer Teacher 3: Going around and checking all students' work, giving them a chance to explain, guiding them without telling them [was a] great way to keep them going. I agree that time is always not enough but watching the videos has given me a broader insight of how students process information and also the use of oral [academic] language.

The shared experience of the lesson study and the exchange of feedback through the debrief and the video coaching appeared to contribute to the teachers' collective knowledge.

Coach-Facilitated LS Supported the Development of Teacher Social Networks

For the second research question regarding how the coach-facilitated LS model supported the development of teacher social networks, we identified several affordances of using the coach-facilitated PD model in the school-based PD design. In one of the survey questions, we asked, "How did working in a small school-based LS team help implement content and new strategies in teaching this lesson? Do you have a teacher or a coach from your own school in this course; if so, how did having a colleague enhance your learning?" Through participants' responses, we found that teachers and specialists had developed different collaborative networks through the coach-facilitated school-based LS. The analysis of teachers' responses to this question yielded four distinct types of teacher networks (see table 7.1). The first type of collaborative network mentioned as support was (1) the coach and teacher networks, identified in thirteen out of forty-nine responses, which was expected since the coach facilitation was built into the fabric of the PD design. However, we were very pleased to see that there emerged other social networks: (2) multidistrict teacher networks with cross-grade "vertical" teacher networks and the same grade "horizontal" teacher networks mentioned in seventeen of forty-nine responses; (3) school-based professional learning community (PLC) teacher networks mentioned in sixteen of forty-nine responses, and (4) resource specialists networks mentioned in six of forty-nine responses. Two responses were coded for both supporting school-based PLC networks and developing the coaching network, and another two responses were coded for supporting both a multidistrict teacher network and a coaching network.

Table 7.1

Development of collaborative teacher networks

Type of Teacher Network	Participants
Coach and teacher network	Teachers and coach within a school or district
Resource specialists network	Classroom and resource teachers within a school
Multidistrict teacher network	Content teachers from multiple districts
School-based PLC teacher network	Teachers teams at same content and grade level

The Coach and Teacher Network: Trusting the Coach as the "Insider"

The coaches working with the university facilitator showed the collaborative nature of our efforts, and teachers saw their coaches endorsing our PD. With the prior relationships established with these teachers, the coach seemed to garner immediate trust, or "buy in" to our PD efforts. The coaches from eight districts participating in our project had a forum to discuss their own challenges as mathematics specialists and coaches in their districts. Inviting district leaders and administrators to attend the LS also validated the work the teachers were doing. In fact, one elementary teacher who did not have a school team formed a team with the teachers in her feeder middle school and her district math supervisor, and she shared how she felt supported in her professional learning.

> The small school-based team was a very personal and effective way to enhance my teaching. Although I did not have a teacher or coach from my school, I was able to meet with the teachers and coach at our middle school as well as with the director of our division's math department. All of the connections made me feel less isolated and more like I was part of a powerful teaching community.

Resource Specialists Network: Support for Teaching Diverse Student Populations

We formed LS teams as communities of practice where teams of general educators worked with teachers of English language learners (ELL) and special education teachers. In this way, we also saw what we called "collaborative coaching," where different participants shared their specialized professional expertise. The special education and ELL specialists shared their expertise on how the task would need modification to provide access for all students, and they helped generalists anticipate how learners might need extra support to navigate through the problem task. One teacher commented, "Having the ability to plan with an ELL teacher provides opportunities to discuss and understand some of the issues and misconceptions students deal with on a regular basis." This exchange among professionals became one of the notable ways teachers recognized that all learners are capable of problem solving, as noted by this educator:

> Prior to this PD, I was a teacher who focused on basic fact memorization and simple computation. I've always taught the inclusion class and I felt that the students I taught couldn't handle or weren't ready for real-life problem-solving activities. I have found this not to be true at all.

This collaborative mentoring through the community of practice allowed for teachers to go beyond "your kids" vs. "my kids" and rethink their beliefs about who can and cannot do mathematics.

Multidistrict Teacher Network Formed from Vertical and Grade-Level Teachers

The work with learning trajectories supported *vertical teaming* by teachers, for it allowed a "chance for teachers to discuss and plan their instruction based on how student learning progresses. An added strength of a learning trajectories approach is that it emphasizes why each teacher, at each grade level along the way, has a critical role to play in each student's mathematical development" (Confrey 2012, p. 3). Some of our LS teams were vertical teams and others were grade-level teams from across districts. In this quotation, teachers voice appreciation for new ideas they gained from teachers across multiple grade levels.

> Working in a cross-grade level team enabled us to plan for success of students of all abilities. We were looking at extensions and remediation opportunities to provide all students an access point. It was very helpful to hear new strategies/ideas and see where students need to take the knowledge [for future grades].

School-Based PLC Networks Sustained Professional Learning with a "Carry-Over Effect"

The effect of the PD appeared to extend beyond the time and scope of our initiative. One coach noted a carry-over effect on her teachers' interactions and focus on learning trajectories in their weekly PLC meetings.

> The majority of their time [was] spent writing lesson plans together. . . . Now . . . the focus of their weekly meetings has shifted to evaluating student work [and] . . . revis[ing] the assignments given to students so that questions require higher order thinking which require students to engage in algebraic habits of mind.

Just as teachers appeared to begin to change their practice after seeing their students engaged in the mathematics learning, the coaches had a parallel experience watching their teachers take on the instructional practices that promoted student thinking through questioning during a problem-based lesson:

> I've noticed a change in the teachers as well—instead of "is that right or wrong," they are looking for more than just a correct answer. . . . Just like the students are learning that . . . there are many ways to get to the same conclusion, the teachers are as well.

Coaches saw this willingness by their teachers to cross the boundary to reform-based teaching practices as an opportunity to support change for positive student outcomes aligned with new district initiatives:

> Teachers not used to teaching using groups and more open-ended tasks saw the difference in how students reacted. If teachers can transfer this knowledge into building lessons from the current curriculum rather than thinking of the lessons they did as "special" we will be on the right track. I see many opportunities to be able to link the lesson study experiences with other site-based efforts.

For novice teachers, this also provided the teachers a jump-start in getting to know their support network. One new teacher commented on how she was able to build a resource base with a coach from her school and other colleagues:

> I think having a small school-based team was a big help regarding planning and talking about the lessons. You could get instant feedback and compare results from classes with similar characteristics. Having colleagues and a coach all in that same school was a great support for checking in on progress.

In all, we found that the coach-facilitated PD model allowed for meaningful growth in the participating teachers' content and pedagogical approach. Further, through well-planned and supported interactions, teachers were able to build helpful networks across grade levels, with their coaches, and across the learning needs of their students.

■ Conclusion

The opportunity for in-service teachers at multiple grade levels to collaboratively plan a learning task and to observe students respond to the task is not a common professional activity. Through our coach-facilitated lesson-study PD model, we were able to leverage this professional learning opportunity to build collaborative teacher networks that empowered teachers, coaches, and specialists.

> Having colleagues to participate with in this class enhanced our learning. We were able to share ideas and collaborate with ease, not just about assignments for this class, but also to support each other with other lessons as we each began to implement algebra rich tasks into our classrooms more frequently. We were also able to present at a school-based PD, and begin to show other teachers this teaching approach.

The coach-facilitated LS appeared to support the development of different teacher collaborative networks. Teachers with various expertise mutually contributed to and benefited from the vertical articulation of algebraic concepts and professional dialogue and in essence provided a collaborative coaching environment. One of the most important takeaways for our PD design team is learning more deeply about how our coach-facilitated PD can provide the continued social support that is needed to sustain and support teachers' intellectual growth in content knowledge and the instructional shifts in their practice as they work to enhance student learning. We are encouraged by the outcomes from the coach-facilitated PD and LS model that helped develop social networks and supported teachers as they implemented the high leverage practices.

References

Coburn, Cynthia, Jennifer Russell, Julia Kaufman, and Mary Kay Stein. "Supporting Sustainability: Teachers' Advice Networks and Ambitious Instructional Reform." *American Journal of Education* 119, no. 1 (2012): 137–82.

Confrey, Jere. "Articulating a Learning Science Foundation for Learning Trajectories in the CCSS-M." In *Proceedings of the 34th Annual Meeting of the North American Chapter of the International Group for the Psychology of Mathematics Education*, edited by Laura R. Van Zoerst, Jane-Jane Lo, and James L. Kratky, pp. 2–20. Kalamazoo: Western Michigan University, 2012.

Driscoll, Mark. *Fostering Algebraic Habits of Mind*. Portsmouth, N.H.: Heinemann, 1999.

Garet, Michael S., Andrew C. Porter, Laura Desimone, Beatrice F. Birman, and Kwang Suk Yoon. "What Makes Professional Development Effective? Results from a National Sample of Teachers." *American Educational Research Journal* 38 (2001): 915–45.

Gersten, Russell, David Chard, and Scott Baker. "Factors Enhancing Sustained Use of Research-Based Instructional Practices." *Journal of Learning Disabilities* 33, no. 5 (2000): 445–56.

Guskey, Thomas R. "Professional Development and Teacher Change. Teachers and Teaching." *Theory and Practice* 8, no. 3 (2002): 381–91.

Lewis, Catherine. *Lesson Study: A Handbook of Teacher-Led Instructional Change*. Philadelphia: Research for Better Schools, 2002.

Loucks-Horsley, Susan, Katherine E. Stiles, Susan Mundry, Nancy Love, and Peter Hewson. *Designing Professional Development for Teachers of Science and Mathematics*. Thousand Oaks, Calif.: Corwin Press, 2003.

Miles, Matthew, and A. Michael Huberman. *Qualitative Data Analysis*. Thousand Oaks, Calif.: Sage, 1994.

National Governors Association Center for Best Practices and Council of Chief State School Officers (NGA Center and CCSSO). *Common Core State Standards for Mathematics.* Washington, D.C.: NGA Center and CCSSO, 2010. http://www.corestandards.org.

Smith, Margaret S., and Mary Kay Stein. *5 Practices for Orchestrating Productive Mathematics Discussions.* Reston, Va.: National Council of Teachers of Mathematics, 2011.

Stein, Mary Kay, Margaret S. Smith, and Edward A. Silver. "The Development of Professional Developers: Learning to Assist Teachers in New Settings in New Ways." *Harvard Educational Review* 69, no. 3 (1999): 237–69.

Suh, Jennifer, and Padmanabhan Seshaiyer. "Examining Teachers' Understanding of the Mathematical Learning Progression through Vertical Articulation during Lesson Study." *Journal of Mathematics Teacher Education* 18, no. 3 (2014): 1–23.

CHAPTER 8

A Collaborative Approach to Strengthening K–2 Mathematical Practices with Technology

Shannon Larsen, *University of Maine at Farmington*
Kelly McCormick, *University of Southern Maine, Portland*
Pamela Buffington, *Education Development Center, Waltham, Massachusetts*
Josephine Louie, *Education Development Center, Waltham, Massachusetts*

In this chapter, we tell the story of a research-practice collaboration between the Education Development Center (EDC), the University of Maine at Farmington, the University of Southern Maine, and the Auburn School District (ASD), Maine. We highlight the steps we took to establish and maintain an equitable partnership, and we explain key features of the design-based iterative methodology that served to support the collaborative nature of our research. We describe our experiences and ongoing observations and present our preliminary analysis of data that supports an emerging theory about how one-to-one mobile technology can support student learning in mathematics. (A number of examples of our research data, observations, and project materials can be found at this book's page on NCTM's More4U website.) Our findings suggest that the strategic use of digital tools, explored by teachers in collaboration with researchers, and offered to students for representing and expressing their mathematical thinking, has helped increase student engagement in mathematical discourse, perseverance in problem-solving tasks, and participation in peer and self-assessment. Our partnership also appears to have helped teachers align their pedagogical practices more closely with those described in *Principles to Actions: Ensuring Mathematical Success for All* (National Council of Teachers of Mathematics [NCTM] 2014). We discuss these findings and how our close collaboration among researchers and practitioners may have contributed to the observed student and teacher outcomes of our study.

■ The Collaborative Research Process

Auburn is a city with a population of 3,600 students, a high percentage of whom live in poverty. Consistently, its students in the early grades have scored low on achievement tests in mathematics. In an effort to increase student achievement, the district launched a one-to-one mobile technology initiative in 2011 as a way to improve instruction in both mathematics and literacy in early elementary classrooms. Although literacy scores improved, students' mathematics scores did not.

EDC came to this setting as a member of the Research + Practice Collaboratory, a project funded by the National Science Foundation to study promising ways of bridging the gap between research and practice in STEM. The project posits that if researchers and educational practitioners work together closely to exchange knowledge and to collaborate in the design and development of educational interventions, then researchers are more likely to integrate practitioner knowledge into their research, and educators are more likely to use evidence-based practices in their instruction. More sustainable and scalable efforts to improve educational outcomes are likely to emerge.

The collaboration began with a series of meetings between EDC and the ASD. We formed a project design team and signed a memorandum of understanding to make explicit mutual roles and responsibilities. These partners then invited two mathematics educators from local universities to join the collaboration. In March 2014, we convened a meeting with almost thirty school leaders, teachers, and education specialists from the district's six elementary schools to elicit their views on the primary persistent problems that underlie low mathematics achievement in the district. Auburn educators identified two core issues: students displayed weak numeracy skills, and teachers did not have a clear view of effective mathematics learning and teaching either with or without tablets in the classroom.

EDC spent the next several months analyzing Auburn data to develop a deeper understanding of the needs and opportunities that Auburn educators identified. They interviewed district and school leaders, observed mathematics instruction and mobile tablet use in early elementary classrooms, and examined district trends in student mathematics achievement scores. Drawing on this information and in consultation with district administrators, we designed and facilitated a thirty-hour series of professional learning in summer 2014 for a cohort of seventeen Auburn educators, which included principals and teachers from the district's three lowest-performing elementary schools. In the second year of our work together, the group grew to include additional teachers from these initial partner schools and other schools in the district.

Each month throughout the subsequent two school years, project researchers worked with cohort participants in a monthly two-hour professional learning community (PLC). We began in fall 2014 with a "toe-in-the-water" phase, when teachers explored mathematics learning strategies and mobile technology tools with their students. Our efforts to shape shared insights into hypotheses and to identify possible research questions for group exploration continued until January 2015, when the group decided on a strategy to co-investigate together. Specifically, teachers observed high levels of engagement and mathematical discourse among students when they used screencasting apps during mathematics lessons, and they hypothesized that students' communication and learning would improve if they asked students to record, explain, and review their thinking when solving mathematics problems at least twice a month. We agreed to co-investigate this strategy, including how teachers implemented it, how students responded to it, and for whom and under what conditions this strategy might generate improved mathematics learning outcomes.

■ Establishing Spaces for Joint Learning

We discovered that the teachers needed some initial structured professional learning opportunities to become familiar with existing research and recommended strategies on supporting early numeracy. To address this need, we engaged in a book study of Fosnot and Dolk's (2001) *Young Mathematicians at Work* to examine strategies that children might use when solving problems, and we discussed research that identified learning trajectories for the development of numeracy skills

(Clements and Sarama 2004). We also examined how digital technology tools might aid in the goal of improving student learning in mathematics. EDC provided participants with a summary of research related to technology use in elementary mathematics classrooms, which highlighted that developmentally appropriate technological tools can help support student learning (Lewis Presser 2014). This research brief outlined best practices for use of technology in schools, and it suggested that student use of technology should provide students with opportunities to engage deeply with mathematics and that the work students do with technology should be used as a method for ongoing assessment of students' mathematical learning (Lewis Presser 2014).

The university faculty partners, knowledgeable about mathematics education research but less familiar with the literature on technology in education, benefited from these regular PLC meetings as well. Collectively, during these meetings, we strengthened our knowledge of relevant research, uncovered through discussions of student work the limitations and challenges of implementing recommended research strategies, and deepened our understandings of the contexts and working conditions of our school partners. Through our work together, the boundaries between group professional learning activities and site-based research began to blur.

■ Nonlinear Path

We initially thought that by the end of the first summer we might arrive at a single tablet-based intervention or set of strategies to explore in the classroom. Instead, we found that teachers needed the entire fall to try different mobile apps and mathematics learning approaches with their students. Along the way, teachers raised many questions, such as "What strategies promote students' mathematical discourse? What do rich mathematical tasks look like? What is productive versus unproductive struggle?" These questions often spurred the group to examine new research, which helped everyone understand how we might better meet students' mathematics learning needs in such a technology-rich setting. In our early meetings, we studied the use of math congress (Fosnot and Dolk 2001). Teachers then became curious about the types of tasks that might engage their students in effective discourse practices, and researchers shared information focused on implementing rich tasks and open questions (Stein et al. 2000; Small 2012).

■ Methodology

The partners adopted a design-based implementation research (DBIR) approach to co-develop and investigate technology-supported strategies that have the potential to improve mathematics learning and teaching at scale in Auburn and beyond. Penuel and colleagues (2011) indicate there are four key elements to this type of research: (1) a focus on persistent problems of practice from multiple stakeholders' perspectives; (2) a commitment to iterative, collaborative design; (3) a concern with developing theory related to both classroom learning and implementation through systematic inquiry; and (4) a concern with developing capacity for sustaining change in systems (p. 332).

In the first year of our study, eight teachers and nine building and central office administrators participated in the collaborative work. In the second year, five teachers and four building administrators from the first cohort continued the work, and nine new teachers and one new administrator joined. Each month a researcher visited the classrooms of participating teachers. Prior to the visit, teachers completed a strategy planning form. After each video-recorded observation, teachers and researchers collaboratively debriefed the lesson and implementation of the technology strategy and then completed logs about the use of the strategy. At each PLC, teachers shared their use of the screencasting strategy from the preceding iterative cycle. All members of the collaborative used a sharing protocol to discuss the implementation and reflect on the outcomes. During this time, teachers shared the screencasts made by their students as evidence of their work. EDC staff conducted a total of seventeen interviews with targeted members of the collaborative (all considered as *key informants*), which included administrators, teachers, math coaches, and researchers. When coding the data, researchers generated a list of themes that they presented to the collaborative. Teachers and administrators then reviewed the list, provided feedback, and identified new themes.

■ A Snapshot of Three Second-Grade Classrooms' Use of Screencasting Apps

As teachers started sharing their approaches to using the screencasting apps, it became apparent that their methods of implementing this technology varied. For example, Mrs. S., a second-grade teacher, integrated the mobile technology into her morning meeting. Students entered the classroom to find a problem like the following written on the board: "I bought a package of cardstock last night. There are fifty sheets of paper in a package. The paper comes in red, green, blue, and yellow. How many sheets of each color were in the pack?" Each student took a photo of the problem, imported it into his or her screencasting app, and began to work on the problem individually, in partners, or in small groups. These groupings ebbed and flowed as students entered into and exited from discussions. After about fifteen minutes, Mrs. S. would ask two or three students to share their still incomplete videos with the class. Following a short discussion of what they had seen, Mrs. S sent the students back to continue working on the problem. Once Mrs. S felt most students had completed their videos, they met again as a whole group to watch and discuss two or three final products.

Mrs. H's second-grade class used the screencasting tools as a part of the math block. Some days Mrs. H shared videos with her students at the beginning of class. The students began to identify the features of a strong screencast and, with Mrs. H, co-constructed a checklist of indicators for a strong video (e.g., "I can hear my explanation; I can see a picture that helps explain my thinking; My picture and writing are clear and easy to read; I say what problem I am solving; My explanation is easy to understand; I explained the math words when needed; My math is correct"). They used this tool to assess their own and their partner's videos after solving a math problem. Students were not required to re-record their screencast, but many chose to do so after using the checklist to assess the work. For example, when Brian solved the problem, "You bought something at the store for 63 cents. You paid $1.00. How much change did you receive?" he used a number line in his video and made 7 jumps of one from 63 to 70, followed by a "really big hop" of 30 to 100. He miscounted the jumps of one and recorded 38 cents as his solution to the problem. After working with his partner to observe their videos and use the checklist, he created a new recording. His second video shows a more efficient strategy as he made a jump of 7 and a jump of 30 to reach 100. He also recorded the correct answer, 37 cents, in his new video.

Mrs. M., a second-grade teacher, continually adapted the strategy she implemented to encourage communication and peer feedback. Her approach began by introducing an open problem to the whole class (i.e., "Mrs. Davies is teaching a new game to first and second graders. She needs 91 balls. How many could be small, how many could be medium, and how many could be large?") and then providing students with individual time to "think first" and reflect on the problem without technology. Next, she paired students in groups of two to three to create their videos using a screencasting app. After everyone created and shared their videos with their partners, they joined a new group of three to four students for critical feedback. To support her students' communication, Ms. M always provided sentence starters for the videos (e.g., "I know my work is correct because . . ."). During the feedback time, she encouraged compliments and questions and often provided prompts to support this as well (e.g., "I noticed . . ." "I liked . . ."), which her students regularly used. For example, after viewing another group member's work on the previously mentioned problem, a student, Daniela, commented, "Grace, so I like that you had friendly numbers [referring to the fact that Grace used one small ball and nine large balls]. . . . My question is why is eighty-one the biggest number in all of them?" referring to the fact that Grace chose to make eighty-one of the balls medium. During the week following this process, the whole class would review the videos using the co-constructed checklist of indicators that contribute to a strong video, which Mrs. H's class had created and shared with Mrs. M's class. Throughout the entire process, Mrs. M encouraged students to strengthen their videos by adding to or re-recording them. She also encouraged students to solve and represent their problems in multiple ways.

■ Findings

Our collaboration appears to have supported teachers' use of the following four effective teaching principles outlined in NCTM's *Principles to Actions: Ensuring Mathematical Success for All* (2014): use and connect mathematical representations, facilitate meaningful discourse, pose purposeful questions, and support productive struggle in learning mathematics. We also noticed students' increased engagement in four of the Common Core State Standards for Mathematics (CCSSM) mathematical practices: MP.1: Make sense of problems and persevere in solving them, MP.3: Construct viable arguments and critique the reasoning of others, MP.4: Model with mathematics, and MP.5: Use appropriate tools strategically (National Governors Association Center for Best Practices and Council of Chief State School Officers [NGA Center and CCSSO] 2010).

Changing Teachers' Practices and Beliefs

For some teachers, the opportunity to hear all of their students' mathematical thinking increased their expectations for their students. Mrs. S reported, "I watched children from other schools explain their thinking and assumed they were just 'smarter' than the kids I work with. Now my students are those 'smart' kids because they can explain and show their thinking!" (e-mail message to author, May 20, 2015). The technology provided teachers with the ability to hear and see students' thinking and methods of solving problems much more than traditional paper-and-pencil work, and this helped teachers see the importance of supporting their students' discourse. Mrs. C, a math coach, indicated in her log (January 23, 2016) that when students engage in mathematical communication they make connections for themselves and their peers. Mrs. M echoed this in her log (January 23, 2016). Mrs. G, a kindergarten teacher, admitted, "In the past, I'd never really thought about how important it is to have [students] explain what they're doing, what they're thinking. So it has been huge for me; it's really been an eye-opener, and a changer, in how I teach my kids" (interview, February 25, 2016).

The opportunity to hear their students' thinking not only helped increase the value that multiple teachers placed on mathematical communication, but it helped them realize the value of productive struggle and wait time. In an anonymous end of year survey, one teacher reported, "Students have taken risks to record their thinking and will go back to add or fix their work. Something about the recording seems to motivate students to complete given tasks" (June 3, 2015).

The teachers also discovered that they couldn't stop a students' prerecorded solution to prompt student thinking as they would during an in-time explanation and that students often self-corrected in the middle of the video.

Data also suggest that participating in the collaborative promoted changes in instruction. Some teachers reported that this project spurred them to restructure their pedagogy by focusing more of their lessons around hearing, sharing, and discussing students' strategies and ways of thinking. Teachers conveyed that observing students' screencasts helped them plan instruction to better meet their students' needs. Mrs. M stated, "The opportunity to observe students self-correct their thinking as they talk out a problem with a peer gives us lots of information. It gives us a window into their thinking and helps us plan next steps for instruction and explorations for students" (e-mail message to author, April 11, 2015). To provide their students with better opportunities to share their reasoning, participating teachers implemented more high-level, open tasks that allowed for multiple entry points, strategies, and solutions. These types of problems promoted richer mathematical explanations that students then captured on their screencasting apps. The focus of lessons appeared to change from simply "getting through" the districtwide curriculum toward engaging students' thinking and on solving and discussing tasks that promote reasoning and sense making.

Teachers also made more strategic use of the technology in their planning. To support their students' communication with the screencasting apps, the teachers identified, created, and shared a variety of tools with one another. These include the use of sentence starters, sentence frames, co-constructed checklists of indicators that contribute to a strong video, classroom norms for productive discussions, and anchor charts about quality explanations. In addition, teachers provided their students with more autonomy over which tools to use to solve problems and represent their thinking (e.g., representing their thinking on a virtual number line or ten frame, using manipulatives, or just drawing symbols or a picture).

Changing Students' Practices and Beliefs

The strategic use of screencasting apps may support improvement in mathematical reasoning and discourse by empowering students' mathematical voices and encouraging students to become aware of their own and others' mathematical thinking. Survey data indicate that the teachers believe that this increased communication provided their students with more ownership over their learning. One second-grade teacher, Mrs. K, reported in an interview (February 2, 2016) that using the screencasting app promoted mathematical conversations among her students with and without technology. Observations showed students engaging more productively in rich tasks, strengthening their discourse, and participating in more self and peer assessment. Before the project began, students in the district used mobile devices as an interactive version of a worksheet. They often sat in silence, with headphones on, tapping at their screens. After two years in the project, students use the mobile technology to help communicate, share, and represent their thinking.

We believe that the most powerful findings of the collaborative are the increased opportunity for *all* students to communicate and share their thinking, as well as the more equitable access to the rich student data that the screencasting tool provides teachers. In a typical classroom, a few students may present their ideas daily, but in classrooms using screencasting apps, all students can explain their thinking. The teachers reported that using technology in this way "forces everyone to engage in that problem and everyone to talk" (interview, Mrs. K, second-grade teacher, February 2, 2016) and that "creating the videos requires ALL students to think" (log, Mrs. K, second-grade teacher, January 23, 2016). Observations confirm the strategic use of screencasting apps as a move to support equity in the classroom. Researchers witnessed students on the autism spectrum and those who are selectively mute record their voices by using the screencasting tool. A second-grade teacher, Mrs. B, reported in an interview (January 26, 2016), "With my English language learners, sometimes they don't have the language and the ability to write down what they're thinking. But if they can use this recording tool and an app, they can show it and can talk about what they've done a little bit more easily than if it was pencil/paper."

■ Changing Higher Education Faculty Practices

The project empowered university faculty to better connect the use of technology to meaningful and purposeful learning for their preservice teachers. They asked their students, preservice teachers, to solve problems and share their solutions by using a screencasting app in a method similar to that used by K–2 students in the project. The preservice teachers then shared their work with classmates and discussed both the approach to the mathematics and the use of the technological tool. Preservice teachers also watched and discussed videos created by students in ASD. These discussions enabled preservice teachers and faculty members to engage in conversations about student thinking, representations, discourse, and the affordances of the technology. This powerful experience allowed the preservice teachers to view work from real students in contexts similar to those in which they would soon be teaching.

■ Discussion

Many of the results of the collaborative parallel the results in K–2 classrooms. While the co-investigative nature promoted the teachers' agency over their professional learning, the work of the collaborative increased the K–2 students' agency over their mathematics learning. Similarly, the collaborative nature of the project strengthened participants' teaching. One of the ways that it did this is by encouraging the teachers to create a more collaborative learning environment in the K–2 classrooms. Teachers integrated more peer work, sharing, and formative assessment into math lessons as a result of this project. The nature of screencasting apps enabled the teachers to share their students' thinking with one another, which made their practices more visible to one another. This regular sharing in the monthly meetings helped create and support a community of collaborative learning and helped the teachers build on one another's work, just as it did in the K–2 classrooms. Higher-education faculty partners brought the K–2 students' videos into their classes for elementary school preservice teachers to observe and discuss and implemented strategies for using screencasting apps learned from the K–2 classroom teachers.

Our findings also suggest changes in teachers' beliefs and pedagogical approaches, including increased use of the math practices outlined in CCSSM (NGA Center and CCSSO 2010) and more facility with the high-leverage teaching principles defined in *Principles to Actions* (NCTM 2014) as well as a change in student learning and engagement in mathematics. The inclusion of teachers and administrators in the research team throughout the entire process has been critically important to our work. School practitioners often identify ideas that remain unseen to outside researchers, and education researchers often highlight key features of the work invisible to practitioners. Our collaborative approach allowed us to create a shared vision for our work as well as shared responsibility and ownership for implementing strategies and analyzing the findings.

The work done through the collaborative also facilitated the growth of teacher-leaders who have shared their work with nonparticipating teachers in their schools and at local and state conferences. Teachers have created resources and tools that support the implementation of screencasting strategies in K–2 classrooms and will be published and shared with other educators. In addition, Mrs. C, a participating first-grade teacher, became her school's math coach during the second year of the study. When reflecting on the new role, she indicated, "The co-investigative model was so valuable. Thinking, wow, we could do this with all teachers. . . . I definitely would not have even considered going into a math coaching role had it not been for the work that I did with EDC" (interview, January 27, 2016).

One key to the success of a research-practice partnership is the readiness of the district, at all levels, to actively participate in the collaborative. At the same time, researchers must also pay attention and be responsive to other district initiatives. As researchers, we often found ourselves challenged to align our work with such initiatives. Ultimately, with support and active participation by district leaders, an open, honest, flexible approach to the process by all participants, and a focus on the importance of equitable voices and the experiences of all members of the team, we have found the research-practice collaborative experience to be productive and valuable for everyone involved.

Acknowledgments

This chapter was developed with support from the National Science Foundation (grant DRL–1238253. The opinions expressed in this chapter are those of the contributors and do not necessarily reflect those of the Foundation.

References

Clements Douglas H., and Julie Sarama. "Learning Trajectories in Mathematics Education." *Mathematical Thinking and Learning* 6, no. 2 (2004): 81–89.

Fosnot, Catherine Twomey, and Maarten Dolk. *Young Mathematicians at Work: Constructing Number Sense, Addition, and Subtraction*. Portsmouth, N.H.: Heinemann, 2001.

Lewis Presser, Ashley. "Using Technology to Promote Mathematics Learning in the Early Grades." *EDC Research Summary*, 2014. *http://interactivestem.org/wp-content/uploads/2015/04/Technology-Math-Brief-4.10.15.pdf*.

National Council of Teachers of Mathematics (NCTM). *Principles to Actions: Ensuring Mathematical Success for All*. Reston, Va.: NCTM, 2014.

National Governors Association Center for Best Practices and Council of Chief State School Officers (NGA Center and CCSSO). *Common Core State Standards for Mathematics*. Washington, D.C.: NGA Center and CCSSO, 2010. http://www.corestandards.org.

Penuel, William, R., Barry J. Fishman, Britte Haugan Cheng, and Nora Sabelli. "Organizing Research and Development at the Intersection of Learning, Implementation, and Design." *Educational Researcher* 40, no. 7 (2011): 331–37.

Small, Marian. *Good Questions: Great Ways to Differentiate Math Instruction*. 2nd ed. New York: Teachers College Press, 2012.

Stein, Mary Kay, Margaret Schwan Smith, Marjorie A. Henningsen, and Edward S. Silver. *Implementing Standards Based Mathematics Instruction: A Casebook for Professional Development*. New York: Teachers College Press, 2000.

CHAPTER 9

Using Technology to Develop Shared Knowledge in and across Grade-Level Teams

Corey Webel, *University of Missouri, Columbia*

John K. Lannin, *University of Missouri, Columbia*

Although research knowledge about effective mathematics teaching has increased dramatically in the last thirty years, mathematics teaching in the United States has not been significantly affected by this knowledge (Hiebert 2013; Jacobs et al. 2006). We see two fundamental reasons for this limited impact on classroom instruction. First, much of the knowledge needed for effective mathematics teaching is topic-specific (Jacobs and Empson 2016; Sztajn et al. 2012) and requires significant time and resources to develop adequately (Koellner, Jacobs, and Borko 2011). Second, because few practical means exist for preserving and sharing knowledge generated beyond the immediate participants in any particular school community, it remains localized and unavailable to other teachers (Hiebert, Gallimore, and Stigler 2002). Given the lack of supporting infrastructure for teachers to share their practice-based knowledge, it is unlikely that knowledge developed through typical professional development (PD) will spread widely on its own, even if the PD is highly effective.

One possible solution is to create a dynamic knowledge base where topic or task-specific knowledge can be stored, accessed, tested, and improved over time (Hiebert, Gallimore, and Stigler 2002). The knowledge referenced here is not knowledge residing in the minds of individuals, but knowledge as represented in "conceptual artifacts" produced by a community of practitioners (Bereiter 2002). For example, such an artifact could be a lesson plan, a task, or an annotated representation of student thinking. Morris and Hiebert (2011) describe these as "shared instructional products"—sharable, testable, and revisable artifacts that preserve topic-specific knowledge for teaching. Teachers learn not only by accessing and using these artifacts but also by refining and improving them through testing in their own classrooms. In this way, teachers advance knowledge in a broader sense—not just appropriating knowledge for themselves, but contributing to the knowledge of a community in a process of continual improvement (Hiebert, Gallimore, and Stigler 2002; Bereiter 2002).

■ Developing Shared Knowledge in Grade-Level Teams

One potential vehicle for structuring the development and refininement of knowledge for teaching is the professional learning community (PLC). A PLC is a school-level structure that supports collaborative teams of teachers, usually in the same grade level, who work on a variety of school-related tasks (DuFour 2004). Although such grade-level teams (GLTs) are present in many schools, their focus is often not on problems of instructional practice (Vescio, Ross, and Adams 2008). And because GLTs are embedded within the immediate school context, any improvements to instruction are likely to stay within the school, limiting the impact of the learning that occurs within the GLT.

We see the PLC structure as a relatively untapped vehicle for engaging teachers in developing topic-specific knowledge for teaching mathematics. The GLT's position as a school-based, teacher-led group means that activities can be situated within the work of teaching and structured around the challenges that are specific to the school and team. If connected to a larger network that encourages collaboration between GLTs across multiple schools and districts, potential exists for sharing knowledge developed in GLTs beyond the local context.

In this chapter, we share our initial efforts to develop and test a set of modules for four third-grade GLTs in a school district in a midsized Midwestern town. The modules were designed to engage teachers in sustained investigations of their students' thinking about fractions through the use of rich tasks, recorded by using screencast technology. The seventeen teachers in the project gave the same tasks to their students and then used an online annotation tool called Vialogues (https://vialogues.com) to collectively comment on selected students' screencasts. These tools served two purposes: (*a*) to elicit teachers' ideas about student thinking and engage them in comparing and contrasting one anothers' ideas in a virtual space that provided time to consider others' insights and (*b*) to record and preserve teachers' developing ideas about student thinking, so that these insights could be shared beyond the local school context. In the following sections, we describe a single student screencast, characterize the online annotations made by the teachers when they viewed the screencast individually, and share excerpts from the face-to-face discussions we had with the teachers following the annotation period. Our goals in this chapter are to help the reader see both the affordances and constraints of the tools and strategies we used, including the challenges that we faced in establishing and creating structure for a knowledge base that teachers might find useful both for sharing their improving knowledge and for learning from the experiences of others.

■ Screencast Recordings

All teachers gave the following task to their third-grade students:

> *How can 4 kids share 7 pancakes fairly? (Don't let any pancakes go to waste!) Draw a picture of the pancakes to show your thinking.*

Such equal sharing tasks provide students with opportunities to develop the concept of a fraction as a multiplicative structure through coordinating two different quantities (e.g., aligning a number of objects with a number of sharers equally and exhaustively) and then describing the resulting state (how much each sharer gets) in relation to a single object (Empson et al. 2006). The students solved the task on their tablet devices using a screencasting app called Educreations (http://www.educreations.com), which provided a simple "whiteboard" interface for drawing with different colors and recording audio. Students solved the task individually, and they then paired and took turns redrawing and explaining their solutions while using the app to record their explanations and drawings. Later, teachers viewed their students' screencasts and chose two or three screencasts to share with their GLT, posting it to a private page on the Vialogues website.

Ty's Recording

One example that became a focus of attention in one GLT was a solution constructed by Ty (a pseudonym). Ty's screencast can be viewed at this book's More4U page at the NCTM website. Like many students, Ty drew seven pancakes (the seven circles at the top of the screen) and four "kids" (the four bottom circles) (see fig. 9.1). Instead of distributing whole pancakes, Ty split each pancake in half, declaring, "Now we have fourteen half-pancakes." Note that in the upper-right-hand portion of the screen, he wrote "14" and "$^1/_2$" in that order from right to left.

Fig. 9.1. Ty's depiction shows fourteen half-pancakes and four children

He continued, "So let's split 'em up again and see how much we have." He drew two 7s, then crossed these out, and underneath, wrote a 3, a 4, and another 3 and 4 (see fig. 9.2). He explained that he was attempting to share the fourteen pieces evenly with the four children. "So let's say I want to give three to one kid, four to another, three to another, and four to another. That would NOT work."

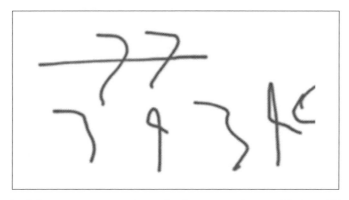

Fig. 9.2. Ty attempts to share the fourteen pieces with four kids

Ty adjusted his sharing, assigning three half-pancakes to each child (see fig. 9.3a), noting that there were two left over: ". . . but then we have two up here in the corner. Now let's cut that two in half. And when we do that, instead of one half, instead of halves, we have [*pause*] fourths. Okay?" During this explanation, Ty wrote four 3s, and drew a small 2 next to the original 14 to indicate that two of those fourteen pieces hadn't yet been distributed. He then crossed out the 2, and wrote ¼, as he explained that "instead of halves, we have [*pause*] fourths" (see figs. 9.3a and 9.3b).

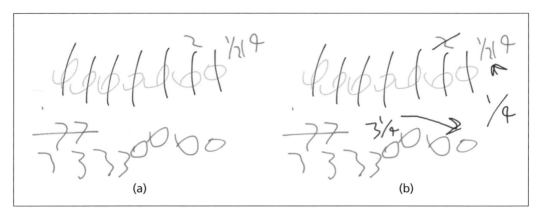

(a)   (b)

Figs. 9.3a and 9.3b. Ty completes his depiction

Ty concluded, "So, every kid gets three and a ha– . . . three and a fourth. So that goes to every kid." He wrote 3¼, and drew an arrow (see fig. 9.3b).

We saw Ty's solution as a particularly rich example of student thinking. Some important features included the following:

- His initial strategy to divide the pancakes in half (this was notable but not uncommon).

- His use of whole-number symbols to illustrate the shares (using 14, 7, and 3), and his operation on symbols as quantities (cutting the 7s and the 2).

- His recognition that one half of one half was one fourth.

- The switching of units for referencing pancakes and half-pancakes when he noted that each child would receive $3^{1}/_{4}$. We wanted to investigate whether teachers recognized that the "3" referred to half-pancakes and the "$^{1}/_{4}$" referred to whole pancakes, and whether they focused on the underlying meaning of *his* symbolic representation rather than the standard meanings for formal mathematical fraction symbols.

- His generally accurate use of symbols for unit fractions ("$^{1}/_{2}$," "$^{1}/_{4}$").

Teachers' Shared Annotations of Ty's Recording

Ty's screencast was posted on the Vialogues site by Ty's teacher, where other third-grade teachers in her school could watch and add time-stamped comments at points in the recording, as well as respond to the comments of others (see fig. 9.4). This provided an opportunity for teachers to share what they noticed and thought was interesting or important about the solution, as well as learning what their colleagues noticed. The Vialogues tool preserved a record of their noticing, an annotated screencast that we treated as an artifact of knowledge that could be saved and shared. (We later did share these artifacts by creating a larger group within Vialogues consisting of all seventeen teachers in the project and posting annotated screencasts from each GLT.) The teachers were given approximately two weeks to add and respond to comments.

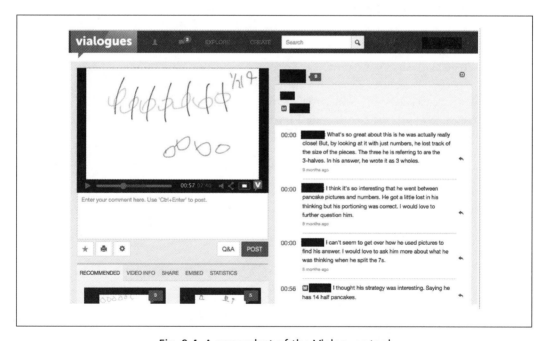

Fig. 9.4. A screenshot of the Vialogues tool

In viewing Ty's screencast, the teachers recognized the treatment of numerals as quantities, but they interpreted Ty's symbolic representations in different ways. One teacher commented, "This is so interesting! He seems to be more comfortable crunching numbers than looking at a problem with a visual perspective." This teacher contrasted the visual and the numeric representations, viewing

Ty's solution as an indication of his preference for symbols rather than recognizing the connections between the two ways of representing quantities. Another teacher commented, "I think it's so interesting that he went between pancake pictures and numbers," hinting at these connections but lacking detail about what the teacher thought was significant about Ty's work.

In some comments, teachers expressed appreciation for Ty's thinking and his partitioning strategy, such as, "He has great number sense" and "His portioning was correct." One teacher was more detailed, noting that "He recognizes that there are 14 pieces, and he's trying to figure out a way to split 14 equally amongst four students. He split it in half to get 7 and 7. And then, I think he struggled, because you can't split seven into two equal whole numbers." Other teachers also expressed doubts about Ty's solution, especially in the latter half of his solution. One commented, "He would have lost me when he split the sevens"; another posted a comment at the point where Ty split the sevens, saying "This is where he started to lose me. . . . I wasn't sure where this was going." Another teacher's comment indicated that she thought Ty himself was struggling in his solution, stating, "He got a little lost in his thinking."

Although Ty's screencast elicited various responses from teachers, in general the teachers' annotations lacked detail and insight into student thinking. Only one teacher commented that the 3 and $\frac{1}{4}$ in Ty's solution referred to different wholes, and no teacher responded to this comment. They struggled to interpret his use of whole numbers to represent half-pancakes, and in at least one case concluded that Ty was confused ("a little lost in his thinking").

Discussing Ty's Screencast

At our next face-to-face GLT meeting, we viewed Ty's solution and engaged in a discussion about his understanding. One goal of this discussion was to allow teachers to elaborate on their points of confusion and together move toward a clearer understanding of Ty's thinking. Based on the Vialogues posts, this required unpacking the part of the screencast in which Ty crossed out the 7s and wrote the 3s and 4s (fig. 9.2). After eliciting teachers' perspectives on Ty's work so far in the screencast, including the fact that the 14 represented 14 half-pancakes, a facilitator asked the teachers to explain the 3 and the 4.

T1:	Yeah, so he took the 14 and split the 7s and then he split . . . I thought when I first watched it, I was hoping he would say 3 and a half and 3 and a half.
. . .	
F1:	Oh, so he's splitting the 14 of these into . . .
T2:	7 and 7. Into 3 and 4.
F1:	7 and 7.
T2:	And is eventually he's trying to make 4 groups for 4 people.
F1:	So he's got 7 half-pancakes and 7 half-pancakes. But he needs 4 groups so then he goes, a group of 3, a group of 4, a group of 3, and a group of 4.
T3:	3 pancakes and 4 groups . . . Oh my god [*as a revelation*].
Several teachers:	Yeah, uh-huh.
F1:	So this is 3 half-pancakes, 4 half-pancakes, 3 half-pancakes, 4 half-pancakes.
Several teachers:	Yes.

This discussion enabled teachers to clarify what Ty meant when he "split the 7s," a point of difficulty that teachers had encountered when they watched the screencast individually.

Our second goal was to promote consideration of ideas that the teachers did not address in their annotations of Ty's video. In particular, we encouraged further discussion about whether Ty intended for the "3" in his solution to represent three half-pancakes. We viewed the rest of the screencast, and then asked about the "2" Ty wrote after changing the 4s to 3s. A teacher claimed, "He did know they were still halves because he made 'em into fourths." However, teachers continued to debate whether Ty understood that the three pieces in each share (in his final answer of $3\frac{1}{4}$) were halves, focusing on his notation: "But when he took the 3 up, instead of doing the 3 halves, it should have been one and a half." At one point, a facilitator (F2) pressed for evidence, asking, "Why are you saying he forgot they were halves?"

T1:	Well, in my mind all of a sudden, those 3s have become . . .
Several teachers:	Wholes.
T1:	'Cause he said each kid gets 3 pancakes and a fourth, didn't he?
Several teachers:	Mm-hmm.
T1:	So I think that he forgot that those were 3 halves.
F2:	Did he say 3 whole pancakes?
T1:	I thought . . . maybe I misheard.
T2:	He just said 3 and a fourth.
F1:	I think he just said 3 and a fourth.
T3:	So that'd be a question I'd want to ask him.
T1:	Yeah . . . are these 3 halves here or 3 wholes?
F1:	So the 3 stands for what?
T4:	3 halves.
F1:	3 halves and the fourths?
T4:	Um . . . stands for a fourth.
F1:	In terms of fourths of . . . ?
T5:	A pancake.
T4:	'Cause 3 halves would be one and a half, adding that quarter would mean that's the answer.
T3:	So he's switching his whole, though. 'Cause then one-fourth would come from one whole pancake. But then the 3 you're saying comes from the . . . halves.

Throughout this discussion, the teachers tried to interpret Ty's answer of $3\frac{1}{4}$, pondering what Ty intended the 3 to represent. At one point they indicated a need for evidence, wondering whether he had said "3 pancakes and a fourth" for his final answer, one teacher saying "that'd be a question I'd want to ask him" (about the meaning of the 3). Multiple teachers focused on the "correct" answer of $1^3/_4$, with T4 eventually articulating that if Ty understood that the 3 stood for halves, his answer could be correct. This discussion reveals how these teachers struggled to separate their own meanings for symbolic notation (3 must represent three whole pancakes, or three halves should be written as $1^1/_2$) from the meanings that Ty intended for these symbols.

■ Implications and Challenges

One overarching goal of our work with these teachers was to help them appreciate the depth and ingenuity of children's thinking, not by explaining research findings on informal knowledge of fractions (e.g., Empson et al. 2006) but instead by drawing on their own students' work to generate their own knowledge. We wanted to support them in moving beyond vague descriptions like "Ty got lost" or "Ty's answer is incorrect" to recognizing that Ty drew on his existing knowledge and the context of the task to construct a sophisticated solution to the Pancake Task, even though his class had not yet received formal instruction in fractions. The excerpts provided here demonstrate that analyzing Ty's screencast, particularly in the face-to face meetings, led to increased attention to the mathematical details of his solution and a greater appreciation of his informal thinking. This work is intricate and challenging, but our project shows the small and important steps that teachers can make as they work collaboratively to make sense of their students' recorded screencasts.

We believe that the Vialogues tool played an important role in setting up the face-to-face conversations, by helping us, as facilitators, to understand what teachers were noticing and to create a plan for the discussion. It also may have helped teachers engage more deeply, since they had already watched and annotated the screencast on their own prior to the face-to-face meeting. However, we came to recognize various challenges in using Vialogues for generating and sharing knowledge across teacher teams. Within the online discussions, teacher comments did not reflect the deeper insights that eventually surfaced in the face-to-face discussions; and when we posted Vialogues from each GLT for all participants to view, it was not clear that teachers found this resource valuable. Perhaps their lack of experience annotating children's mathematical solutions limited what they thought to include in their comments. Perhaps they struggled to see how documenting specific ways that students solved the Pancake Task could help them or others reconsider fraction instruction more generally. Or they may have they lacked awareness of the other GLTs involved in the project, so they failed to see sharing their learning with other teacher teams as a worthwhile purpose of the Vialogues annotations.

In future iterations of the modules, we hope to improve teacher engagement in the online discussions by tweaking the modules to test conjectures such as those raised above. For instance, we wonder whether providing examples of possible annotations might help teachers consider the types of annotations that might be helpful to them and others. Would including lesson plans or instructional strategies within the modules help teachers connect examples of student thinking to more general implications for fraction instruction? Might the completion of more tasks help teachers see similarities in students' ways of thinking across different tasks, and would documenting and sharing these patterns then become more valuable? Could an initial meeting with all participants help teachers have a better sense of the community with whom they will be sharing their ideas? These questions will frame our future work.

Despite the challenges we encountered in our work, we are encouraged about the potential of screencast and annotation technologies for empowering teachers to generate topic-specific knowledge within grade level teams and enabling them to share this knowledge more widely. Our future work will continue to explore how such tools and structures might enable a collaborative team of teachers to generate artifacts of knowledge for teaching mathematics that are seen as useful and sharable by members of their own and other communities of teachers.

References

Bereiter, Carl. *Education and Mind in the Knowledge Age*. Mahwah, N.J.: Lawrence Erlbaum, 2002.

DuFour, Richard. "What Is a 'Professional Learning Community'?" *Educational Leadership* 61, no. 8 (2004): 6–11.

Empson, Susan B., Debra Junk, Higinio Dominguez, and Erin Turner. "Fractions as the Coordination of Multiplicatively Related Quantities: A Cross-Sectional Study of Children's Thinking." *Educational Studies in Mathematics* 63, no. 1 (2006): 1–28.

Hiebert, James. "The Constantly Underestimated Challenge of Improving Mathematics Instruction." In *Vital Directions for Mathematics Education Research*, edited by Keith R. Leatham, pp. 45–56. New York: Springer, 2013.

Hiebert, James, Ronald Gallimore, and James W. Stigler. "A Knowledge Base for the Teaching Profession: What Would It Look Like and How Could We Get One?" *Educational Researcher* 31, no. 5 (2002): 3–15.

Jacobs, Jennifer K., James Hiebert, Karen Bogard Givvin, Hilary Hollingsworth, Helen Garnier, and Diana Wearne. "Does Eighth-Grade Mathematics Teaching in the United States Align with the NCTM Standards? Results from the TIMSS 1995 and 1999 Video Studies." *Journal for Research in Mathematics Education* 37, no. 1 (2006): 5–32.

Jacobs, Victoria R., and Susan B. Empson. "Responding to Children's Mathematical Thinking in the Moment: An Emerging Framework of Teaching Moves." *ZDM* 48, no. 1–2 (2016): 185–97.

Koellner, Karen, Jennifer Jacobs, and Hilda Borko. "Mathematics Professional Development: Critical Features for Developing Leadership Skills and Building Teachers' Capacity." *Mathematics Teacher Education and Development* 13, no. 1 (2011): 115–36.

Morris, Anne K., and James Hiebert. "Creating Shared Instructional Products: An Alternative Approach to Improving Teaching." *Educational Researcher* 40, no. 1 (2011): 5–14.

Sztajn, Paola, Jere Confrey, P. Holt Wilson, and Cynthia Edgington. "Learning Trajectory Based Instruction: Toward a Theory of Teaching." *Educational Researcher* 41, no. 5 (2012): 147–56.

Vescio, Vicki, Dorene Ross, and Alyson Adams. "A Review of Research on the Impact of Professional Learning Communities on Teaching Practice and Student Learning." *Teaching and Teacher Education* 24, no. 1 (2008): 80–91.

CHAPTER 10

Improving the Teaching of Mathematics by Using Lesson Study and STEM-Based Activities

Marie Nabbout-Cheiban and Adam Goldberg,
Southern Connecticut State University, New Haven

Educators generally agree about the importance of using STEM activities (Science, Technology, Engineering, Mathematics) as they expose students to real-world applications. This emphasis is a hallmark of the Common Core State Standards (National Governors Association Center for Best Practices and Council of Chief State School Officers [NGA Center and CCSSO] 2010), the National Council of Teachers of Mathematics (NCTM) *Principles and Standards* (NCTM 2000), and the newly released Next Generation Science Standards (NGSS Lead States 2013). However, there is still a major disconnect between the S, T, E, and M in the classroom. Although we know that mathematics and science are intimately related, we aren't doing enough to use this knowledge to enhance education. Mathematics teachers, as well as the creators of textbooks and other curricular materials, are often satisfied to simply include a science context in their mathematics problems. This, though, is far from creating a true integration of mathematics and science in a meaningful STEM activity. When science is used only as a "decoration" for problem solving in mathematics, it lessens the real-world value. Similarly, without true integration, students do not see mathematics as a powerful tool to solve scientific problems.

This chapter is a showcase of how professional development trainings based on the lesson-study model can positively affect teachers' practices in choosing and implementing real-life STEM activities and, at the same time, improve teachers' and consequently students' understanding of mathematics. To that end, we present an activity that was developed during project CCSS-STEM, a grant-funded project that took place in New Haven, Connecticut, with the participation of five school districts. The goal of the project was to empower teachers with the needed skills to select, design, and implement STEM activities that foster the Common Core Standards for Mathematical Practice (SMPs; NGA Center and CCSSO 2010) in their classroom with truly integrated lessons. To accomplish this goal, it was essential to allow the teachers to work collaboratively; that is, to have mathematics and science teachers working together with experts in the field, as research suggests (Honey, Pearson, and Schweingruber 2014).

■ Theoretical Framework

The work in the project was based on the lesson study model (Takahashi and Yoshida 2004). The concept of lesson study originated in Japan, where it is viewed as the most important method for professional development (Takahashi and Yoshida 2004; Fernandez et al. 2001). The process of lesson study allows a group of colleagues (teachers, coaches, administrators, etc.) to determine an area of focus and then research and develop a lesson. This lesson is taught by one member of the group while the others observe. After the lesson, the group convenes for a reflection. The group discussion is driven by the data and information collected during observation. The core of this discussion is to reflect on the lesson and its effectiveness and to evaluate whether the goals of the activity were achieved. Modifications and revisions are then proposed. After the revision, the lesson is retaught by another group member to a different class and again observed by team members. The lesson study group then reconvenes, and final revisions are made. By the end of the process, a truly effective lesson usually emerges.

The goal of lesson study is not limited to improving the quality of lesson or unit plans. When done right, it helps to increase teachers' knowledge of subject matter, improve their pedagogical skills, foster their ability to observe student behavior and performance, and promote a sense of efficacy. It also encourages fidelity of implementation, because the teachers feel a sense of ownership in the materials (cf. Takahashi and Yoshida 2004). The beauty of the lesson study model is that it can work with different teaching techniques. Since the goal of this project was to focus on the Standards for Mathematical Practice (SMPs) and on conceptual understanding, we promoted teaching techniques consistent with inquiry-based pedagogy. The lesson study model provided the vehicle to reach this goal, because lesson study supports teachers while they home in on what students are thinking and doing throughout the research lessons.

The summer institute focused on the lesson study model and on designing *effective* STEM activities, rather than merely *interesting* ones. That is, the goal was to improve teachers' ability to create STEM activities that promote conceptual understanding and that students were intrinsically motivated to solve. We consider these to be effective activities. This is in stark contrast to interesting activities, which might stimulate the attention of students for a short period of time but do not lead to long-term understanding. Such activities may be procedural in nature, or the stimulation may not be enough to lead to internal cognitive interest. We tried to lessen the teachers' dependence on these.

■ Context of the Project

This grant project brought together twenty-two middle- and high-school mathematics and science teachers (from twelve different schools and five different districts) with coaches and six university mathematics and science faculty from medium-size public universities and community colleges. The twenty-two teachers and coaches consisted of thirteen women and nine men (seventeen Caucasian, three African American, one Latino/a, and one Native American), and their average number of years teaching was 4.6 years. Participants attended ten sessions, six during the summer institute and four throughout the school year. The focus of these sessions was to enable teachers to become familiar with technology-based activities, use data from scientific experiments to model mathematically, and work with dynamic statistical software to improve their statistical knowledge.

At many of the grant workshops, participants were given the chance to assume the role of students and experience the integrated activities as their own students would, which is a rich development practice (Wei et al. 2009). Later, teachers worked in teams to research and create their model lessons. The teams were composed of three to six teachers and were supervised by two specialized college professors (one in mathematics or mathematics education and one in a science or science education field), who were called *mentors*. In most cases, the teachers and coaches on each team were from different schools and sometimes were from different districts, which was valuable because the districts were quite different demographically (for example, a mix of urban and suburban, and percentages of students eligible for free/reduced lunch ranged from 5.5 to 66 percent). Based on the model described previously, each of the teams went through the full lesson-study cycle. The activities were first field-tested with teachers, observed by the different teams, and revised based on feedback before trying them with real students. In the early stages, the role of the mentors was to guide their teams, answer specific content questions, and suggest questions to elicit deep understanding. During the reflection session following the first round of teaching, the mentors assessed the teaching with their team, evaluated what had worked and what had not, and helped their team propose a modification of the activity.

■ The Math Flu Activity

At the outset of the project, teachers were enthusiastic about using STEM activities in their classrooms. However, they were unsure how STEM lessons would benefit their students other than by providing interesting problems. Teachers admitted to choosing real-world problems or contexts without knowing ahead of time how to explore them in a mathematics class. Working with a task or context to determine ways to use it in the classroom enabled teachers to deepen their mathematical knowledge and understanding. It also provided the opportunity to think about what makes an effective task (e.g., targeting the conceptual understanding rather than procedural skills; and focusing on students' explaining, knowing the why and how, and supporting one's opinion). As an illustration, we present one activity that was developed in the project: the Math Flu activity.

The Ebola outbreak spent a lot of time in the headlines in 2014, because people around the world were genuinely concerned and felt threatened by it. One team of teachers decided to simulate the spread of a disease with middle school students. This allowed them to explore exponential functions while also raising awareness of epidemics. A plethora of equally engaging phenomena involving both mathematics and science concepts could also have been considered (e.g., studying the algae growth in Lake Erie or drought issues in California).

Step 1: Planning and Peer Teaching

By using some of the activities that are available online, science teachers proposed and designed the activity. (For examples of online activities, see Marc Stephenson's webpage at http://www .csun.edu/~ms4288/646/ or the activity featured at http://www2.nau.edu/lrm22/lessons/disease /disease_lab.html.) They named the virus "Math Flu," and the activity is based on the chemical reaction between sodium bicarbonate (i.e., baking soda) and a phenolphthalein solution, which is easy to obtain at online sellers of science education supplies. In the initial stages of planning, the team proposed to use the following sequence: (1) begin by asking students to estimate how many students would be infected after three trials; (2) have students complete three rounds of exchanges by filling two pipettes of liquid from their cups and putting them in the cup of a random classmate and vice versa; (3) use the phenolphthalein solution to check the number of "infected" cups; (4) have students compare their original answers to the actual number of "infections"; and (5) through class discussion, compare linear and exponential functions.

As part of the professional development summer institute, the team tried out their activity in front of other participants, to simulate the experiment. The team members decided to follow this plan, but they seemed to be more focused on the mechanics of the experiment itself, particularly when they added the phenolphthalein solution and did not get eight "infections." They soon realized that the directions on how to make the exchanges needed to be more clear to end up with eight cases after three trials; that is, they needed to direct students to do each of the exchanges at the same time, write down the name of the partners after each exchange, and avoid exchanging liquids in the second or third round with the same people or with people who had common partners in previous rounds. The simulation in front of the group was restricted to the operational side of the experiment, which was the new challenge for math teachers.

The group wrote up the detailed lesson plan for an algebra 1 class, addressing the CCSS standard 8.F.5 (Use functions to model relationships between quantities) and SMPs 2 and 7 (NGA Center and CCSSO 2010), and then decided who would be teaching it first.

The software that was used in the teaching was GeoGebra (Hohenwarter 2002). While other statistical analysis tools (e.g., TI-84, Excel) could be used, we chose GeoGebra because it is freely downloadable and has been designed explicitly for use in school classrooms.

Step 2: Teaching the Lesson to Students

The lesson started with a talk about the Ebola virus and epidemics. The teacher explained the experiment that simulated the virus spread, forgetting to ask students to make their conjecture, as planned, about the number of students who would be infected at the end of the experiment. All students except one were given paper cups filled with water. The other student, "patient zero," had sodium bicarbonate. Students filled a pipette from their cups and exchanged it with two other students; this simulated shaking hands. After three rounds of exchanges, two drops of phenolphthalein solution were added to all cups. The ones containing the flu turned dark, as shown in figure 10.1.

Fig. 10.1. After the last round of "exchanges," cups with the Math Flu turn purple

The teacher drew a table on the board to track the "infected" students, as shown in figure 10.2. In a class discussion, the group noted that there are two names that appear in the three rounds and thus tracked the start of the infection with Adam and Lucy without being able to find the patient zero. Using that information, they tagged the other names who made exchanges with Adam and Lucy. (In the table, Adam and Lucy appear in rounds 1–3 and marked with the lightest shade; Nathalie and Melissa, who appear in rounds 2 and 3, are marked with a darker shade; and Tom, Todd, Tim, and Marie, who appear only in round 3, are marked with the darkest shade). The teacher then used the pattern of infected people (1 – 2 – 4 – 8) to introduce exponential functions $(2^0, 2^1, 2^2, 2^3)$.

Round 0	Round 1	Round 2	Round 3
Melissa	Alex	Adam	Tom
Marie	April	Rob	Nathalie
Lucy	Adam	Nathalie	Todd
Adam	Lucy	Melissa	Tim
Nathalie	Rita	Lucy	Marie
Tom	Troy	Matthew	Melissa
Tim	Crystle	Allison	Adam
Todd	Brian	Ella	Lucy

Fig. 10.2. Tracking the students "infected" with the math flu

The activity was fun and interesting, but far from effective, as the focus of the lesson was on finding the original pair from which the disease started spreading, rather than the selected mathematical goal. What was missing were the opportunities to make the lesson minds-on as planned, where students are given the chances to compare exponential functions with linear functions, and more important are able to understand and use the model that they find for extrapolation.

Issues with the effectiveness of the first teaching of the lesson to students were not unexpected, and this is an anticipated part of the lesson-study process. Teachers are used to selecting activities for mathematical content that they are familiar with and know well. Using inquiry-based activities to teach mathematics was not their typical practice, even though they were starting to use it as a teaching strategy with their new algebra curricula. For this STEM activity, teachers were asked to work outside their comfort zone, to think and teach differently by asking questions and using materials and experiments different from the typical nature of their mathematics classes.

Step 3: Reflection and Feedback

In the reflection session that followed the first round of teaching, teachers evaluated the teaching and started to question the purpose of using such activities in a math class. While science teachers were pleased with the success of the experiment, math teachers questioned its usefulness. One remarked, "It is motivating for students, but is it worth the time that we spent in class?"; another asked, "Did we succeed in this activity, [and] did students really learn more about math? Was the lesson effective?" These questions were of particularly great importance because they were asked *by* the teachers, and they led to the modification of the activity. The teachers' focus shifted from modeling a problem with a mathematical function to the main purpose of mathematical modeling (cf. Bleiler-Baxter, Barlow, and Stephens 2016; Cirillo et al. 2016), which is "What does the modeling with the exponential function help us do?" In this activity, the mathematical model helps with extrapolating data; and later on, when returning to the context of the problem, it helps with understanding the severity of the spread of the disease. The revision of the task consisted of reworking the problem and adding analysis questions to broaden the discourse and thinking. For example, in the original lesson, before the experiment, students were asked simply to predict how many people would be affected after three exchanges. In the revised lesson, a new question was added: "Write a prediction about how many exchanges it will take for the entire class to be infected. Consider what mathematical model would represent these exchanges." Also, the following set of new questions was added to the end of the activity:

> Assuming one exchange represents the spread of infection in one day, predict [and] then find the number of days it would it take to infect: a. the town of Branford, CT? (population of 28,000); b. the state of Connecticut? (population of 3,600,000); c. the entire USA? (population of 316,000,000).

The revision of the activity focused on understanding the importance of using mathematical modeling to make decisions and solve problems. Mathematical modeling is essential for using applied mathematics to understand, evaluate, or predict something relative to the world outside mathematics (Pollak 2003; Cirillo et al. 2016), and it thus should be focused on effective learning instead of interesting learning. The real-world application of this problem was to raise awareness of the danger of epidemics and the need to act fast to protect the community. Teachers also discussed possible misconceptions, such as using 2×3 instead of 2^3; and they planned on discussing this misconception, using visuals, even if students do not give such an answer as a way to check students' understanding.

It is important to note that the activity was planned for an algebra 1 class where inverse functions are beyond the scope of instruction. However, at the group discussion, one teacher suggested using this moment to talk about inverse functions as a new tool to solve this problem without the need to guess and check. Her choice was based on the ease of using inverse functions in GeoGebra, which enables users to "switch" the variables and accordingly calculate the inverse function (see fig. 10.3b). The mentors, as well as the other team members, thought this was an excellent extension and truly signified the power of the lesson study approach.

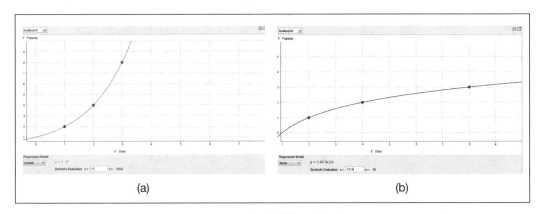

(a)   (b)

Fig. 10.3. Graph of f(x) and its inverse

Step 4: Reteaching

In the re-teaching of the lesson, the experiment took a smaller amount of class time than the first teaching of the lesson did, which enabled teachers to focus more on the mathematics.

Two main misconceptions occurred in this class: The first was modeling the problem with a linear function, where students made their conjecture based on their analysis of the task prior to the experiment, but only took into consideration two exchanges: "For the first round, there will be two students infected, and them each of them will get one student infected . . . that is a total of 4. Oh, I see the pattern each new round we add two." The second misconception is predicting that the whole class would get the flu since every student is involved in exchanging their solutions and since the flu is an epidemic. This second misconception differs from the first in that students did not make any conjecture based on their model. These examples gave the teacher the opportunity to lead a class discussion about modeling the problem and later comparing the two functions $y = 2x$ and $y = 2^x$. Technology played two important roles in this activity: first as a tool to explore the function $f(x) = 2^x$ and compare it with $g(x) = 2x$ (see fig. 10.4), and second as a means of computation to determine the results. First, by using the data collected from the experiment, students quickly realized that the spread of the math flu could not be modeled with a linear function. The graphs were studied graphically, and that helped students compare them. While zooming in, students realized that the rate of change in the exponential function $y = 2^x$ is larger than the linear function $y = 2x$. Students also realized the importance of the model by using its graphs to make two decisions: (1) predicting the number of patients given the number of days and (2) estimating the number of days given the population (see fig. 10.4).

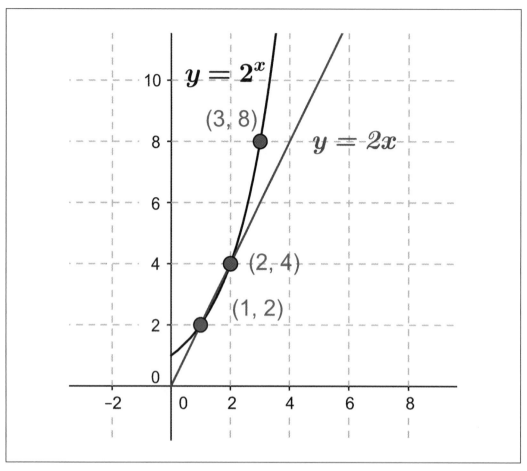

Fig. 10.4. Comparing $f(x) = 2^x$ and $g(x) = 2x$

To estimate the number of days it took for the whole town to become infected, students considered the question to be impossible since the number of days is the independent variable: "We cannot find the number of days; we can find the number of patients if we know the number of days." However, and after some clarifications from the teacher, they guessed and checked to arrive at the answer. The mathematics learned in this activity went far beyond simply comparing an exponential function and a linear function. Students grappled with questions where the relationship between the two variables x (time) and y (number of patients) was not the typical one-way relationship of the independent variable predicting the dependent variable. Rather, it was also possible to predict the time if we knew the number of patients and the model of the function.

Discussion

In our field observations, we noticed an evolution in teachers' disposition toward STEM activities that evolved over two stages. In stage 1, which was illustrated by the first round of planning and teaching, teachers looked for real-world problems that modeled the math concepts they needed to teach in their classes. Their main question was "Where can we use this math concept in real life?" This also worked in reverse. That is, they tried to find math concepts that could be explored by certain real-world problems. At this stage, teachers were satisfied just to have found a science example or a real-life example that could be modeled by using math and where technology was used as an investigation tool; they chose examples without considering what to do next. Even though the aim of the project was teaching mathematics with understanding, the focus of the teachers at this stage was simply to find problems that modeled mathematical functions. It was more of a procedural approach. The activities that were selected at this stage were interesting activities rather than effective activities.

In stage 2, illustrated by the revised planning and reteaching, teachers started to attend to the benefits of using real-life examples to enhance the mathematical learning of students. They also thought about how to spend class time efficiently on these activities. At this stage, teachers' goals evolved from selecting interesting STEM tasks to finding effective STEM tasks that used good questions that make the tasks richer. It is important to highlight that the collaboration between teachers led to these results. While observing a colleague teaching the activity, the other teachers were able to reflect on the learning of the math concept that they aimed for as a team (e.g., "What can the model help students do, other than guessing where the flu started? Can we introduce the concept of inverse function so that they find the number of days it takes the whole town to be infected?") It is much harder for teachers to do this reflection while teaching.

Moreover, we noticed a change in the attitude of the teachers. At first, they were comfortable simply choosing application problems for the mathematical notions that they taught (e.g., using an experiment as "decoration" for discussing exponential growth). As the project went on, they made the shift from interesting activities to effective ones. We also noticed that they were open to using activities that led students to discover and work with new math content that makes sense in the context of the task even if it is not part of the curriculum. We see in this an important dispositional adjustment to problem solving. That is, instead of the application just being the vehicle to practice a concept or skill, it now serves as an opportunity to examine new mathematical content (e.g., using the experiment to compare linear vs. exponential functions and as a way to introduce inverse functions).

As illustrated by the lesson study process with the Math Flu activity, the lesson study contributed to the growth of teachers, with respect to collaborating with colleagues to prepare, plan, reflect, and rethink their activities. More important, this process helped teachers pay attention to students' misconceptions in the classroom and plan ways for addressing them.

■ Conclusion

The type of professional development and the ensuing collaboration between mathematics and science teachers within the CCSS-STEM Project exemplifies what is needed to enhance STEM teaching and learning in schools. Based on formal and informal evaluations and data, essential components of this professional development plan include bringing math and science teachers together, providing content in both areas, and having professors from STEM and STEM education fields available to support teachers every step of the way—from research, to lesson planning and design, to revising and reteaching. This project also served to model positive cooperative practices among the different STEM fields, as we noticed the teachers becoming more confident while the project progressed in seeking answers to the content questions they might have. While the science teachers were very familiar with inquiry-based teaching practices, many of the mathematics teachers were not. This partnership gave those mathematics teachers the opportunity to experience inquiry-based practices in the classroom while they learned from their peers. After going through the summer institute and ensuing lesson-study cycle, the participating teachers expressed confidence in being able to create STEM lessons on their own.

While the activity described in this chapter related to a particular event, the spread of the Ebola virus, the concept is universal. That is, there are a multitude of similar real-world events for students to explore, such as the melting of the polar ice cap and the worldwide issues concerning a lack of clean water, just to name two. Hence, this work in using lesson study as a vehicle for creating and refining STEM activities can be generalized and scaled up. The most essential components are time for teachers to collaborate and an understanding that it is okay not to know everything at first. What teachers gained from this exercise was an understanding that the collaboration led to the ownership of the activity by everyone involved. And thus, the success of a lesson depends on *all* the group members. That is what transforms a group of teachers into a true professional learning community.

Acknowledgments

The authors wish to acknowledge the late Betsy Carter, Jeff Webb, Loel Tronsky, Doreen Mantilia, Natalie Branowski, Jennifer Iovanne, and the teachers and mentors who participated in the CCSS-STEM project. Project CCSS-STEM was a Connecticut Teacher Quality Partnership Grant issued by the Connecticut Office of Higher Education, grant number 130HE1186AA. The funding source was the U.S. Department of Education as authorized by PL 107-110, the No Child Left Behind Act of 2001, Title II, Part A, Subpart 3, Improving Teacher Quality State Grant funds.

References

Bleiler-Baxter, Sarah K., Angela T. Barlow, and D. Christopher Stephens. "Moving beyond Context: Challenges in Modeling Instruction." In *Annual Perspectives in Mathematical Modeling (APME) 2016: Mathematical Modeling and Modeling Mathematics*, edited by Christian R. Hirsch, pp. 53–64. Reston, Va.: National Council of Teachers of Mathematics, 2016.

Cirillo Michelle, John A. Pelesko, Mathew D. Felton-Koestler, and Laurie Rubel. "Perspectives on Modeling in School Mathematics." In *Annual Perspectives in Mathematical Modeling (APME) 2016: Mathematical Modeling and Modeling Mathematics*, edited by Christian R. Hirsch, pp. 3–16. Reston, Va.: National Council of Teachers of Mathematics, 2016.

Fernandez, C., S. Chokshi, J. Cannon, and M. Yoshida. "Learning about Lesson Study in the United States." In *New and Old Voices on Japanese Education*, edited by Edward Beauchamp. Armonk, N.Y., 2001.

Gann, Cheryl, Tamar Avineri, Julie Graves, Marìa Hernandez, and Daniel Teague. "Moving Students from Remembering to Thinking: The Power of Mathematical Modeling." In *Annual Perspectives in Mathematical Modeling (APME) 2016: Mathematical Modeling and Modeling Mathematics*, edited by Christian R. Hirsch, pp. 97–106. Reston, Va.: National Council of Teachers of Mathematics, 2016.

Hohenwarter, M. GeoGebra, 2002. http://www.geogebra.org.

Honey, Margaret, Greg Pearson, and Heidi Schweingruber, eds.. *STEM Integration in K–12 Education: Status, Prospects, and an Agenda for Research*. Washington, D.C.: National Academies Press, 2014.

National Council of Teachers of Mathematics (NCTM). *Principles and Standards for School Mathematics*. Reston, Va.: NCTM, 2000.

———. *Principles to Actions: Ensuring Mathematical Success for All*. Reston, Va.: NCTM, 2014.

National Governors Association Center for Best Practices and Council of Chief State School Officers (NGA Center and CCSSO). *Common Core State Standards for Mathematics.* Washington, D.C.: NGA Center and CCSSO, 2010. http://www.corestandards.org.

NGSS Lead States. *Next Generation Science Standards: For States, By States.* Washington, D.C.: The National Academies Press, 2013.

Pollak, Henry O. "A History of the Teaching of Modeling." In *A History of School Mathematics*, edited by George M. A. Stanic and Jeremy Kilpatrick, pp. 647–71. Reston, Va.: National Council of Teachers of Mathematics, 2003.

Takahashi, Akihiko, and Makoto Yoshida. "Ideas for Establishing Lesson-Study Communities." *Teaching Children Mathematics* 11 (2004): 165–71.

Wei, Ruth Chung, Linda Darling-Hammond, Alethea Andree, Nikole Richardson, and Stelios Orphanos. *Professional Learning in the Learning Profession: A Status Report on Teacher Development in the U.S. and Abroad.* Dallas, Tex.: National Staff Development Council, 2009.

Models and Frameworks for Enhancing Mathematics Teaching

Introduction

Thomasenia Lott Adams, *University of Florida, Gainesville*

The chapters in this section provide a variety of professional learning models and frameworks for mathematics professional development. Key to these models and frameworks are opportunities for teachers' collaboration and empowerment in their own professional learning and instructional change. The aim of each effort is to improve the teaching of mathematics and, subsequently, to improve students' learning of mathematics. The authors use a variety of contexts for facilitating professional development. Video clubs, lesson study, exploration of mathematical practices, and formative assessment are just a few of the effective angles presented across these chapters. Preparing and supporting teachers to teach mathematics effectively and to become agents in their own professional growth is the primary thrust of this section, and each chapter gives a strong response to options for mathematics professional development.

In the first chapter of the section, **Organizing to Learn Practice: Classroom-Focused Professional Development**, Garcia and Shaughnessy provide insight on the Elementary Mathematics Laboratory (EML), which engages teachers in designing detailed lesson plans, facilitating the plans in a "live" classroom, observing the lessons, assessing students' work, and debriefing the teaching and learning experience. Solving and discussing the mathematical problems used in the lesson plans are also important aspects of the professional development experience. Through the EML, teachers work to improve their practice of teaching and their mathematical knowledge for teaching, as illustrated in an example of a lesson focusing on fractional parts and improper fractions. The common context provided by the live classroom used for the EML is a valuable aspect of the professional development and provides opportunities for teachers to collaboratively investigate issues of mathematics teaching and learning.

In the next chapter, **Teacher Empowerment and Leadership of the Standards for Mathematical Practice**, Hofacker, Ernie, and Serros draw attention to the Standards for Mathematical Practice (SMPs) of the Common Core State Standards for Mathematics (National Governors Association Center for Best Practices and Council of Chief State School Officers [NGA Center and CCSSO] 2010). The reasoning for this effort is the noticing of teachers not having a strong awareness of the SMPs and how they can undergird instruction. The authors facilitated a one-year professional development program to support teachers' understanding and to observe teachers' application of the SMPs. Hofacker and colleagues utilized a collection of rich mathematics tasks as a framework for exploring the SMPs with teachers. Frameworks for enhancing mathematics teaching in the chapter include a continuum of teachers' learning of Standards for Mathematical Practice and an Empowerment Model that positions teams of mathematics teachers as facilitators of their own professional learning experiences.

Making inferences about student thinking is an important activity in the course of teaching. In **Developing Teachers' Professional Knowledge when Combining Video Clubs with Lesson Study,** Deal and González use a professional development model of combining video clubs and lesson study to engage teachers in focusing on student thinking during mathematics lessons. The project occurred over a two-year period and included opportunities for teachers to reflect on their own practice. As illustrated in an example featuring a lesson on perpendicular bisectors, self-assessments of teaching supported teachers to contribute to and sustain the team effort and process of lesson study (e.g., how to discuss and revise their own and others' lessons captured via video). The authors contend that mathematics teachers' change and professional growth can be enhanced when teachers are supported to self-reflect and share their knowledge about student thinking.

Formative mathematics assessment is built upon understanding the learning goal and subsequently collecting evidence of students learning as they interact with the task, activity, or lesson that is aligned with the learning goal. In **The Development and Use of Student-Learning Data Tools as Formative Mathematics Assessments,** Slavit, Deuel, and Nelson discuss a professional development experience where teachers learn how to collect, analyze, and use student-learning data (SLD) to improve the teaching and learning of mathematics. The authors suggest that SLD include any data that provide information about how students might be progressing toward a mathematics learning goal or engaged in thinking related to a learning goal. Using the model of teacher teams, the outcome of the authors' research is a collection of collaborative practices that support teachers to think clearly and deeply about SLD. The chapter features protocols for classroom observations and facilitation of "collaborative inquiry meetings" that can be used by teachers or teacher leaders to improve practice.

In **Using Formative Evaluation to Support Teachers in Increasing Student Reasoning,** Melhuish and Thanhieser introduce the Mathematically Productive Habits and Routines (MPHR) classroom observation tool. This tool is designed to provide effective feedback to classroom teachers that relates to the teachers' professional development experiences and to student learning. Describing the relationship between teacher practices and student learning is not easy, particularly because there are so many facets to student learning and so many factors that affect student learning. The authors, however, use the tool to hone in on *what students do* and *what teachers do* in the context of the mathematics classroom. Melhuish and Thanhieser provide two descriptions of the use of the tool in research settings, examining teacher's and students' actions during two different lessons on dividing fractions and making sense of the remainder. The authors' rich narratives of using the MPHR for classroom observations can benefit conversations of formative evaluation between mathematics teachers and school leaders.

It is commonly known that the largest part of an iceberg is not what is seen above water; it is the part below the surface. In the last chapter of this section, **The Iceberg Model: Rethinking Mathematics Instruction from a Student Perspective,** Webb suggests that the tip of the iceberg can be said to represent the goal of instruction. The remainder of the iceberg, the part below the surface, represents a myriad of other considerations, such as the opportunity for students to engage with multiple representations of mathematical concepts and to reason about mathematics. It is also in this space that students apply their mathematical knowledge in different contexts. Webb provides examples for what engagement in mathematics looks like across the span of the iceberg's shape. He suggests that a valuable professional development exercise for teachers is to reflect about mathematics (content and instruction) and create "mathematics icebergs." Doing so, he posits, helps teachers to think about instructional pathways that might present themselves in a lesson as ways to optimize student learning. Specific mathematics icebergs for systems of equations and graphing polynomials are shared in the chapter. The author also describes the broader use of the Iceberg Model as a basis for teachers' collaborative activity around planning, instruction, and assessment.

As you read these chapters or reflect on them afterward, consider the following questions:

- How do variables such as grade band or content matter when designing professional development for teachers of mathematics?

- What is the role of school and district leaders in the facilitation of professional development to teachers of mathematics?

- How can we determine which professional development framework is a best fit for a group of teachers?

References

National Governors Association Center for Best Practices and Council of Chief State School Officers (NGA Center and CCSSO). *Common Core State Standards for Mathematics.* Washington, D.C.: NGA Center and CCSSO, 2010. http://www.corestandards.org.

CHAPTER 11

Organizing to Learn Practice:
Classroom-Focused Professional Development

Nicole Garcia and Meghan Shaughnessy, *University of Michigan, Ann Arbor*

Teachers profit from well-designed opportunities to develop new visions for practice, learn more about students' thinking, or work on specific mathematical topics or tasks, but such opportunities are often insufficient to support teachers with the complexity of classroom teaching. These kinds of professional opportunities do focus on critical resources for instruction, but not on the details of practice itself. Numerous studies have demonstrated that too often many common approaches to professional development do not adequately support increases in teachers' capabilities (e.g., Cohen and Hill 2008; Garet et al. 2001). In response to critiques that professional development in the United States is ineffective for systematically improving practice, there has been increasing momentum toward developing new and different forms of professional development. "Video clubs" have been designed to increase capabilities at noticing student thinking (van Es and Sherin 2008). Lesson study has been adopted as a means for teachers to learn from teaching and to develop and share knowledge (Perry and Lewis 2009). Other efforts have focused on developing teachers' mathematical knowledge for teaching by engaging teachers in the work of the student curriculum and the work at the disciplinary horizon (DeBellis and Rosenstein 2007). Overall, there has been increasing interest in designing professional development that is likely to positively affect teacher practice.

Our project is another effort to develop and improve practice through collaborative processes focused on instructional practices linked to increases in student learning. We support the learning of practice by designing and studying an approach to professional development situated in a common "live" case of elementary mathematics instruction. The approach uses this classroom as a "common text" for working on practice, where participants not only are watching and discussing but also are engaged in developing and learning practice. Teachers' engagement in the classroom approximates a form of "legitimate peripheral participation" (Lave and Wenger 1991) through structured conversations about the lesson plans, close observation, mathematical analysis of student tasks, and examination of records of teaching and learning practice. In this chapter, we describe how our professional development program provides opportunities for teachers to legitimately participate in "live instruction" and the learning opportunities such professional development provides. We then turn to considering what it would take to develop this type of peripheral participation in live instruction as a form of professional development within and across school districts, and we share our early work in this area.

■ The Professional Development Approach

Mathematics teaching is something that people do; it is not merely something to know. Teachers must use knowledge flexibly and fluently as they interact in specific contexts with students, with the aim of helping those students become proficient with mathematics. Conceptualizing the work of teaching as the building of individual and collective knowledge through interactions among teachers, students, and content in particular environments (Cohen, Raudenbush, and Ball 2003) has important implications for the design of professional development. This means that simply knowing a lot of math is not enough to be able to help students learn mathematics. Teachers must understand mathematics content and practices in specialized ways that are attuned to their learners. Simultaneously, teachers must be able to engage in practices that enable them to interact with subject matter and students in multiple organizational formats, as well as to support students' interactions with the mathematics being studied. Furthermore, the complex nature of mathematics teaching and the ever changing nature of the environments in which teaching happens also require a commitment to, and means of, professional learning in, from, and for practice. Thus, teaching requires the integrated use of specific knowledge and skills in particular contexts of instruction. This emphasis on knowledge use, responsiveness to learners, and context sets a challenge for professional development to support teachers' actual practice.

Since 2007, colleagues and we have conducted a summer mathematics program for rising fifth graders that serves as setting for professional development. With the assistance of a partner school district, the program enrolls approximately thirty students each summer. The district receives districtwide Title I funding, and mathematics achievement is a broad concern in the district, as indicated by students' scores on the state assessment program. Students are randomly selected for participation in the program to reflect district demographics. The class comprises primarily black children. Most of the students say that they have not enjoyed or felt confident with school mathematics, and, in more than a few cases, they have been told by teachers or parents that they need "to work on getting better at math." Still, we do not make the assumption that these students are weak at math, and the program is not designed or advertised as a remedial program. Instead, it seeks to surface and leverage students' strengths, fill gaps, and support them to do challenging and complex mathematical work.

The students work on mathematics with an experienced elementary teacher for two and one-half hours each day for ten days across two weeks. The mathematical content of the instruction is core to the elementary and middle school curriculum, including work on fractions and equations. The students encounter and are supported to solve complex mathematics problems. Mathematical practices include explaining, representing, proving, presenting in public, and listening to others' ideas attentively, respectfully, and critically. Work with these students serves as a "common text" for the development and study of mathematics teaching and learning.

■ How Is the Live Instruction Used to Support Teacher Learning?

Each summer approximately eighty kindergarten through grade 8 teachers participate in the Elementary Mathematics Laboratory (EML). Detailed lesson plans are prepared that include (1) design or enactment problems that have been identified and instructional experiments that have been designed to address the problem and (2) detailed lesson plan segments including timing, goals, details, and commentary, including anticipations. Figure 11.1 contains a segment of a detailed lesson plan. The instruction is documented both to support real-time and subsequent study. Each day is structured in the following way to support participant learning: (1) read lesson plan and solve mathematics problems, (2) pre-briefing, (3) observation of the class, (4) review of the children's work, and (5) debriefing of the class. We next turn to illustrating how these structures are used in conjunction with live instruction to support teacher learning using examples from a single lesson incorporating the instructional segment outlined in figure 11.1.

Learning goal(s)	Detail	Commentary: notes and anticipations
Students will begin to understand and use the concepts of "the whole" and "equal parts."	Problem on chart; ask students to paste it into their notebooks and write what they think: What fraction of the rectangle below is shaded gray? What fraction of the rectangle below is shaded gray? As students work independently on the problem, note the responses that are being recorded.	The purpose of this problem is to learn about what students know about fractions as shaded parts of area. Use this problem to articulate what is required to explain fractions: identification of the whole, equal partitioning. Begin with an equally partitioned rectangle and use this to contrast and support reasoning about the unequally partitioned rectangle.
Students will begin to use elements of a definition of a fraction to name parts of areas.	Launch discussion by asking for a volunteer to share his/her answer for the equally partitioned rectangle. Elicit other answers, as needed, based on the responses that students produced independently. Support the class in coming to a consensus that 1/3 of the rectangle is shaded because there are three (equal) parts and one part is shaded.	Students might think that a square is not a rectangle. Will need to discuss/clarify this if it comes up. The language of rectangle is deliberately being used to address this common misconception. The task is drawn with the area of the gray squares in both questions being equal. This allows a discussion of how the fraction of the rectangle is determined by the size of the shaded part in relation to the size of the whole.
Students will begin to use the language of the whole and equal parts.	Move to the second problem. Consider commenting that there were several different answers that students recorded (e.g., 1/3, 1/4, 1½) and that today and tomorrow we will be working on coming to a consensus on this problem. Encourage students to listen carefully to others' ideas and to try to understand how classmates named the gray part and why. Ask for a volunteer to share his/her response and reasoning. Ask another student to restate the explanation in his/her own words. Elicit several different responses for the task. • If 1/3 and 1/4 are not shared by students spontaneously, consider asking a student to explain how one might have come up with each of these answers. • If students want to partition the shape, use a removable sticky line. • Listen for and draw out reference to needing to make parts that are equal in size. Conclude the discussion by noting what the class has learned so far about the different ways to name the rectangle and indicate that the discussion will be continued.	The focus here will be on learning to give oral explanations so students will not be writing a written explanation. Students might think that 1/4 of the rectangle is shaded gray when there is a line drawn, but go back to thinking that that same area is 1/3 of the rectangle when you take the line away. Will need to be attentive to this in students' talk.

Fig. 11.1. Sample of a detailed lesson plan

- *Read lesson plan and solve mathematics problems (30 minutes).* Particular parts of the detailed lesson plan for the day are studied. For example, participants solved the fractions task shown in figure 11.1 and considered potential misconceptions.

- *Pre-briefing (1 hour).* The lesson plan is discussed with the teacher, including design and enactment problems and questions that are surfaced by the teacher or participants. Focus questions are provided to guide their viewing of the laboratory class (e.g., choose a focal student and consider evidence of that student's learning in verbal and written interactions).

- *Observation of the class (2.5 hours).* Live observation of the class. In the lesson from the excerpt, one student offered an explanation of why she believes the second representation shows ¹/₃. Then, another student offered this explanation for why he believes it shows ¹/₄:

  > S: I think this is an improper fraction because see how this one [*points to the top half of the unequally partitioned rectangle*] is bigger than both of these two [*points to bottom half of rectangle*]. There's no possible way that this would be correct (¹/₃) because see how all three of these are the same size [*points to equally partitioned rectangle*]? That's a proper fraction, this is an improper fraction cuz this one is bigger than both of the little ones.

  > T: Okay, so you're, what you're saying is it can't be ¹/₃, it can't be a fraction at all?

  > S: Well, it can, you just have to add a line right here [*points to the middle of the larger partition*] to make it one fourth.

- *Review of the children's work (30 minutes).* The children's classwork is read and analyzed by participants. An excerpt from one student's end-of-class check shows his thinking on a similar problem after hearing the explanation shared above. In this sample of student work (fig. 11.2), it is evident that the student has correctly named the fraction and that he appears to have adopted the language of "improper fraction" to refer to the way that the parts are not equal.

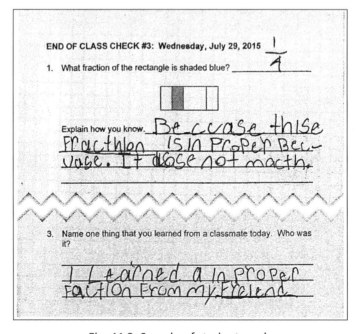

Fig. 11.2. Sample of student work

- *Debriefing of the class (1 hour).* Structured debriefing is organized around particular foci, some of which are predetermined and others determined based on the work that unfolds during the lesson. On this day, one participant raised a question for the group regarding precision of mathematical language around students' use of the term *improper fractions.* A short excerpt from the discussion follows.

    P: So, I'm wondering what people are thinking about, um, when . . . there would be any stepping in about the use of the word *proper* and *improper*? . . . We looked over at Davion, and Davion has the last one incorrect, ¹/₄, and in his explanation he uses the language, . . . "I learned about improper fractions from Michio," which is interesting, but he gets it incorrect and says ¹/₄ . . . [*reading from notebook*] "because this fraction is improper because it does not match." So now they're adopting what I think is poor language that we call fractions greater than 1 improper to begin with. What should we be doing about that as teachers?

    T: I have a very complicated thought about that, which is that *proper* and *improper* are not mathematical terms, they're school terms, and they're not really very helpful because they tend to help kids not really understand fractions as numbers. . . . I think for school survival, they'll have to know those terms but I think he's using *proper* and *improper* in the vernacular also, . . . but I feel differently about this than I would, like, *equation*, which is actually a mathematical term. So I do think that I should probably need to do some clarifying but it makes me inside just sort of worry about the number of vocabulary, the vocabulary that you have to learn sort of to manage school as opposed to know math.

Through this discussion, the group engaged in work that is central to teaching, including hearing students even when their language is inaccurate and considering the role of vocabulary.

Importantly, our participants are not preparing to teach the lesson themselves nor are they necessarily preparing to teach the same content. We use the live observation to work on the practice of teaching mathematics rather than on the teaching of particular content. Participants are legitimate peripheral participants in the practice of teaching. The learning is happening within the practice of teaching, and participants take on particular aspects of the work, such as modifying tasks, anticipating students' responses, analyzing student work, and considering ways to manage the classroom learning environment.

■ Learning Opportunities in Legitimate Peripheral Participation in Live Instruction

The laboratory intertwines the development of practice with the development of the professionals who participate in the laboratory (Ball and Cohen 1999), and, in doing so, it provides opportunities to learn in, from, and for practice, an essential feature of effective teacher education (Ball and Cohen 1999; Ghousseini and Sleep 2011). The laboratory creates a context in which there is a need to develop shared language for talking about teaching practice and student learning. The improvement of teaching has long been hampered by the lack of technical language to talk about the work of teaching in professionally nuanced detail (Jackson 1968; Lortie 1975). This lack of shared language constrains both the detail with which teachers can talk with their colleagues about their practice and what they are able to take from such conversations. In the laboratory, developing shared language is an imperative because teaching practices are discussed in the pre-briefing, teachers have opportunities to notice the enactment of those practices, and then there are opportunities to discuss them in the debriefing. This building of common language has been powerful for the participants, with one noting, "What was most powerful for me was the opportunity to be a part of a collective that was intentionally watching teaching and learning and then talking about it together."

A different sort of learning is exemplified by the work that goes on related to studying the work of teaching practices, such as leading a whole-class discussion. Our teacher participants frequently report that they are told they should be doing this work in their own classes, but the work is often not unpacked in a way that makes it accessible. Arming teachers with a small set of questions they might ask students to promote discourse and showing them short vignettes of discussions is not enough to either convince teachers that engaging students in discussions produces enough student learning to be worth the time investment nor to support them in actually engaging in the practice. Through participation in the laboratory, teachers are able to consider together when discussion is a productive practice, what students have learned through discussion, and how to deal with common issues that occur during discussions, such as how to conclude a discussion when there is not yet consensus. The same is true with respect to other teaching practices.

Third, the context is one in which teachers are invested in but not solely responsible for—that is, student learning that affords opportunities to further develop skill in close observation of students, including analyzing evidence of students' understandings and skills. Such skill in close observation is crucial to supporting students' success (Carpenter et al. 1989). In the laboratory, teachers have rich access to students' thinking and representations through writing, drawing, talking, and other forms of discourse, which affords learning to focus on what students can do and understand. Teachers are therefore guided to move beyond noticing lacks and errors to describe what students are doing and saying and to look for evidence to support hypotheses about students' learning and engagement in the class. In the words of a participant, "I noticed that my own mind-set shifted from seeing student work as having 'deficits' to seeing student work, and the students themselves, as having assets on which to build. Because of EML, my understanding of what student growth and achievement looks like expanded as well."

In a different vein, the laboratory offers a rich environment for the development of mathematical knowledge for teaching (MKT). MKT comprises the specialized ways of knowing mathematics entailed by the core tasks of teaching, such as explaining and representing ideas, interpreting students' thinking, and appraising the quality of tasks (Ball, Thames, and Phelps 2008). Opportunities for developing MKT arise as teachers study and engage in the selection of instructional examples as well as consider different definitions and explanations that could be used with students, focusing on their accessibility and mathematical integrity. Thus, the legitimate peripheral participation in "live practice" in the laboratory affords multiple learning opportunities for teachers, including shared language for talking about children, specific teaching practices, skill with close observation of children, and development of MKT.

■ What Would It Mean to Provide These Opportunities for Teachers at Scale?

While the professional development described above provides a rich set of learning experiences for the teachers in attendance, this is necessarily a group of fewer than 100 educators because of the time and the travel costs associated with attending such a professional development and the space constraints. We began to consider structures that would allow this type of learning opportunity to be more broadly available. One such possibility was to build local versions of the laboratory setting that took up many of structures and opportunities of the "live" laboratory within a particular school district or consortium of school districts. This model was appealing in that it could be designed to allow for teachers to focus on issues of instruction tied to their own students, teachers, and curriculum. In the following sections, we describe the components of such an opportunity that were developed in one local laboratory and the challenges and benefits that we are finding as we begin partnering with districts around this work.

In transitioning the model to a local setting, we want to ensure that the learning opportunities remain as similar as possible across settings. The EML offers teachers opportunities to examine a common text of teaching, build common language around teaching and learning, develop understanding of and skill with particular teaching practices, closely observe students and analyze evidence of their understanding and skills, and build mathematical knowledge for teaching. We seek to ensure that these same opportunities are available for teachers participating in local mathematics laboratory (LML) settings. Below we consider each of these learning opportunities, the structures that we are designing to make them available for participants, and the supports that are necessary to facilitate this work. In the context of the LMLs, we are partnering with a large school district in the southeastern United States to enact and test the model in the context of school-based professional development. In this context, mathematics coaches serve as the "teacher" and "facilitator" and classroom teachers serve as the participants.

Common Text for Teaching

A laboratory setting can provide a common text for examining teaching. This requires having a teacher who is skilled at making teaching and thinking visible for participants; lesson plans that highlight and make visible the decision-making process and considerations of the teacher and the particular teaching practices, mathematical content, norms, and routines employed; and space and structures for observation. To provide this common text for teaching, we are designing and providing professional development focused on "public teaching." Laboratory teachers are provided with strategies to make their decision making and the work of teaching visible to teacher participants both during instruction and in the planning process. Focal public teaching methods include real-time strategies such as posting mathematical work in the public space, annotating instructional choices (e.g., "I'm going to wait two more minutes because we're still working on writing about our thinking"), and annotating teaching observations (e.g., "I see that there are many different strategies being used to solve this problem"). Additionally, we are supporting the development of lesson plans that make explicit the mathematical knowledge for teaching necessary to enact the plan, the metacognitive processes behind instructional choices, and the unpacking of particular instructional practices such that observers could see and consider the decomposition of the practices.

Because public teaching is not natural, we recommend that laboratory teachers have the opportunity to enact public teaching practices in settings that allow for them to receive actionable feedback prior to working with participants. This opportunity was provided at our pilot LML through a study group of laboratory teachers who opened their practice to one another and rehearsed pre-brief and debrief conversations with our support. This setting allowed not only for enactment of and feedback on public teaching but also for enactment of and feedback on the facilitation of adult learning. Participants reported that these opportunities made them feel more prepared to lead their local laboratory classrooms.

Common Language about Teaching and Learning

It is particularly critical at a school district level to develop common language about teaching and learning as teachers are working across grade levels and content areas to study the practice of teaching. Additionally, many districts across the United States are involved in a large number of initiatives, all of which used varying language to talk about the work of teaching. The LML can serve as a site in which the multiple ways of talking about practices can be coordinated and a strengths-based approach to talking about student progress can be reinforced. To do this work, we designed a process to map out the current initiatives present in a district and employed this process at our pilot site. For each initiative we identified the associated instructional strategies/practices, the language used to describe teaching practice, and the particular requirements of teachers in the district for participation. We then came to consensus on the language to be reinforced during the LML and the connections to be made between this agreed upon language and the current language in the district and other existing initiatives. This language was then incorporated into lesson plans, pre-briefing, and debriefing.

Teaching Practices and Mathematical Knowledge for Teaching

Working with a small set of teaching practices focuses the work that laboratory teachers need to do to make their teaching visible, particularly in the lesson planning. Second, using this small set can help to support teachers in connecting this work with district initiatives. To choose an appropriate focus, we recommend using the map of initiatives described above to determine which teaching practices are both high leverage and present across multiple initiatives. We also recommend identifying key mathematical topics for the work using district curriculum maps and/or state standards. At our pilot site, the laboratory focused on three practices. This focus resulted in the transfer of practice to the classrooms of the participating teachers. One coach reported that the observing teachers all incorporated teaching strategies from the observed lessons into their own teaching.

Close Observation of Children

In order to support others in their observation of and attentiveness to the learning of children, we designed supports for learning how to facilitate focused pre-briefs and debriefs. Key parts of this work include making the laboratory teacher and all teacher participants comfortable in the conversation, keeping the conversation focused on the focal teaching strategies, and shifting participants' language about teaching and children. This work is challenging, so we designed highly detailed protocols that included both norms and routines for the sessions and suggested language for enacting the work with participants. One laboratory teacher attributed the success of the laboratory to the opportunities to engage in pre-briefing activities, observation of the lesson, and debriefing of the observation, all of which focused on close observation of children and a focus on teaching practices.

■ Next Steps

We have finished a pilot year, and our partner district, including those directly participating, sees the LML as a successful program that involves teachers in collaboratively investigating issues of mathematics instruction. However, much work remains to ensure that this work is scalable and sustainable. We are continuing to pursue the development of both the LMLs and the EMLs. In the context of the EML, we are engaging in an NSF-funded study of the impact of the experience on participants' teaching practice, including their skill at leading discussions, noticing students, and talking about teaching. To do this, we are gathering data both before and following participation in the professional development. Such studies will better enable us to understand the impact of the professional development and lead to improvements in the design. Our future work will also involve more clearly articulating and refining the supports necessary for the implementation of an LML.

Acknowledgments

This chapter was made possible by support from the National Science Foundation through DRK-12 Award No. 1621104. Any opinions, findings, and conclusions or recommendations expressed in this material are those of the authors and do not necessarily reflect the views of the funding agency. The authors gratefully acknowledge the contributions of the following individuals to the design of the Elementary Mathematics Laboratory: Deborah Loewenberg Ball, Hyman Bass, Laurie Sleep, and Kara Suzuka.

References

Ball, Deborah, and David Cohen. "Developing Practice, Developing Practitioners." In *Teaching as the Learning Profession: Handbook of Policy and Practice,* edited by Linda Darling-Hammond and Gary Sykes, pp. 3–32. San Francisco: Jossey-Bass, 1999.

Ball, Deborah L., Mark Hoover Thames, and Geoffrey Phelps. "Content Knowledge for Teaching: What Makes It Special?" *Journal of Teacher Education* 59, no. 5 (2008): 389–407.

Carpenter, Thomas P., Elizabeth Fennema, Penelope L. Peterson, Chi-Pang Chiang, and Megan Loef. "Using Knowledge of Children's Mathematics Thinking in Classroom Teaching: An Experimental Study." *American Educational Research Journal* 26, no. 4 (1989): 499–531.

Cohen, David K., and Heather C. Hill. *Learning Policy: When State Education Reform Works*. New Haven, Conn.: Yale University Press, 2008.

Cohen, David K., Stephen W. Raudenbush, and Deborah Loewenberg Ball. "Resources, Instruction, and Research." *Educational Evaluation and Policy Analysis* 25, no. 2 (2003): 119–42.

DeBellis, Valerie A., and Joseph G. Rosenstein. "Creating an Equitable Learning Environment for Teachers of Grades K–8 Mathematics." In *The Learning of Mathematics,* 2007 Yearbook of the National Council of Teachers of Mathematics (NCTM), edited by W. Gary Martin and Marilyn Strutchens, pp. 271–88. Reston, Va.: NCTM, 2007.

Garet, Michael S., Andrew C. Porter, Laura Desimone, Beatrice F. Birman, and Kwang Suk Yoon. "What Makes Professional Development Effective? Results from a National Sample of Teachers." *American Educational Research Journal* 38, no. 4 (2001): 915–45.

Ghousseini, Hala, and Laurie Sleep. "Making Practice Studyable." *ZDM* 43, no. 1 (2011): 147–60.

Jackson, Philip Wesley. *Life in Classrooms*. New York: Holt, Rinehart and Winston, 1968.

Lave, Jean, and Etienne Wenger. *Situated Learning: Legitimate Peripheral Participation*. New York: Cambridge University Press, 1991.

Lortie, Dan Clement. *Schoolteacher: A Sociological Study*. Chicago: University of Chicago Press, 1975.

Perry, Rebecca R., and Catherine C. Lewis. "What Is Successful Adaptation of Lesson Study in the US?" *Journal of Educational Change* 10, no. 4 (2009): 365–91.

Van Es, Elizabeth A., and Miriam Gamoran Sherin. "Mathematics Teachers' 'Learning to Notice' in the Context of a Video Club." *Teaching and Teacher Education* 24, no. 2 (2008): 244–76.

CHAPTER 12

Teacher Empowerment and Leadership of the Standards for Mathematical Practice

Erick B. Hofacker, *University of Wisconsin–River Falls*
Kathryn T. Ernie, *University of Wisconsin–River Falls*
Sherrie J. Serros, *Mount Mary University, Milwaukee, Wisconsin*

The Standards for Mathematical Practice (SMPs) are a vital part of the Common Core State Standards for Mathematics (National Governors Association Center for Best Practices and Council of Chief State School Officers [NGA Center and CCSSO] 2010). These habits of mind are critical to developing procedural fluency, conceptual understanding, and mathematical reasoning. We have found that professional experiences related to the SMPs have been minimal in schools in our region and therefore are often ignored or misunderstood. Based on previous work (Ernie et al. 2015), we have learned that teachers need more time to develop an awareness of the eight Standards for Mathematical Practice (fig. 12.1) and an understanding of how to encourage student development of these practices as habits of mind while learning mathematics content. Additionally, teachers are looking for continued guidance on the type of tasks they can implement to engage students in the SMPs, as many new textbooks designated as "Common Core Aligned" have only a superficial alignment with the standards (Heitin 2015).

1. Make sense of problems and persevere in solving them.
2. Reason abstractly and quantitatively.
3. Construct viable arguments and critique the reasoning of others.
4. Model with mathematics.
5. Use appropriate tools strategically.
6. Attend to precision.
7. Look for and make use of structure.
8. Look for and express regularity in repeated reasoning.

Fig. 12.1. Standards for Mathematical Practice (NGA Center and CCSSO 2010)

In this chapter, we describe a one-year professional development (PD) program that addresses content through the reflective study of tasks of high cognitive demand (Stein and Smith 1998) with an emphasis on the mathematical habits of mind identified in the Common Core SMPs. Our project included thirty-seven K–grade 12 mathematics teachers from eight rural Wisconsin school districts and seven of our university teacher candidates, who served as apprentices. Eighty-five hours of PD were provided throughout the school year and summer through four different types of events: eight Just-In-Time (JIT) seminars on Wednesday nights, three Core Mathematics in Progress (CMIP) sessions on Saturdays, Classroom Showcase Events where we observed the teachers demonstrating mathematics lessons in their own classroom, and a weeklong Core Content (CC) workshop in the summer.

In one year, we observed teacher knowledge and facility in the use of the SMPs grow from minimal knowledge to incorporating and reflecting about the use of SMPs in the classroom by their students. We provide evidence of teachers' growth and a continuum for describing this growth, and we also illustrate sample tasks promoting this growth in our professional learning community. We begin our illustrations with our first task on the Magic Triangle (Trotter 1972).

■ Digging into Our First Task

On a Saturday in early September, we launched our first session with a focus on the Standards for Mathematical Practice by working together on low-floor, high-ceiling tasks (Boaler 2016). The first task shared was the Magic Triangle task in figure 12.2.

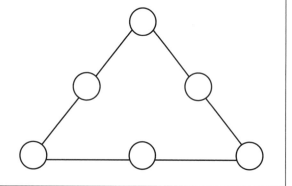

Place the numerals 1 through 6 in the circles of the triangle so that the sum of the three numerals on each side is the same as the sum of the other sides. Use each number only once. Use only one number per circle.

Fig. 12.2. Magic Triangle task

Teachers engaged in the task individually at first, recording their work on whiteboards, and they quickly became engaged with sharing what they learned with other teachers at their tables. Early approaches might be best described as guess and check, as teachers became familiar with the problem. This activity reinforced the contribution of the corner values as compared to the mid-side values. A common first solution was placing the smallest three numbers at the corners of the triangle or the largest three numbers at the corners. Sample teachers' work is shown in figure 12.3. Teachers talked about balancing the numbers placed on the sides so that if the two lowest numbers were placed in the corners, the largest number would need to be added to them.

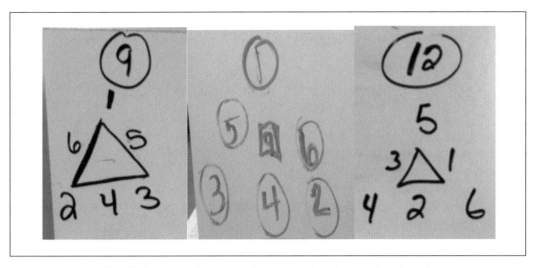

Fig. 12.3. Sample teacher solutions to the Magic Triangle task

Having 9 for the sums of sides of a triangle and also a sum of 12 for another resulted in more questions asked by the teachers. Do we have all the different solutions? When is a solution different? What other possible sums might we find? How do we know when we have found all the solutions? What are the boundaries for the possible sums? Is there a different way to separate the numbers into two groups other than largest numbers and smallest numbers? The teachers observed early that we as facilitators did not provide the answers. Teachers were so engaged that they collectively found all the solutions for the task, argued how they knew they had found them all, and discussed SMPs they were starting to use, particularly SMP1, SMP3, and SMP7. More on this task with variations may be found at this book's page on NCTM's More4U website.

■ Launching Our Professional Development

After a welcome at our first session, teachers completed surveys about their confidence and experience with the SMPs. On a scale of 1 (strongly disagree) to 4 (strongly agree), participants responded to the prompt "The Common Core Mathematics Practice Standards are evident in my students' interactions" with an average of 2.9 and a standard deviation of 0.6. Despite this self-reported agreement about evidence of the SMPs, when asked to list the SMPs and provide examples of what the implementation of each would look like in their classroom, few were able to fully identify the practices, as shown in figure 12.4. Discussion following the survey revealed that many teachers relied on their curricular resources to embed the SMPs in their lessons. At least one teacher thought that "MP7" appearing in her curricular resource stood for "more practice, problem 7."

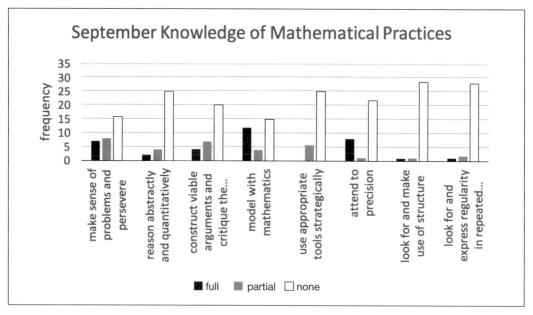

Fig. 12.4. Data collected on the SMPs at the beginning of the project

After the surveys, teachers worked in small groups to combine their working knowledge of the SMPs, sharing experiences that they had had incorporating them into their student learning activities. Teachers shared whiteboard posters of this information and by this process identified SMPs they had difficulty understanding or SMPs they had a challenge to exemplify. Collectively, teachers shared that they had trouble understanding SMP2, SMP7, and SMP8. Even with a team of teachers working together there were holes in the descriptors for the SMPs, particularly omitting "make sense of problems" in SMP1, the "strategically" part of "use appropriate tools strategically" in SMP5, and "construct viable arguments" in SMP3. Instead of the correct "look for and make use of structure," SMP7 appeared as "organize your work."

A hallmark of our project was the continuity of meeting with our teachers on a regular basis throughout the school year. The JIT and CMIP events provided our teachers opportunities to work on mathematical tasks that emphasized the SMPs. These sessions engaged teachers in the development of strategies and meaningful tasks that they could bring back to the classroom and use with students (Loucks-Horsley et al. 2010). Since we met so often, teachers were able to report back to their colleagues in a timely manner on how they saw the SMPs being incorporated into their classrooms by both them and their students.

Early in the project, it was evident to us that many of the teachers struggled with SMP7, "Look for and make use of structure." Figure 12.5 shows a task we used to support teachers' learning about SMP7 without prior direction mentioning this SMP.

Find the sum of 4.32 + 4.32 + 8.64 + 6.8 + 4.32 + 4.32 + 4.32 + 4.32 + 8.64

Fig. 12.5. The Sum task

We asked teachers to show their individual work on personal whiteboards and not use calculators. Disequilibrium took place when teachers realized some of their peers were able to solve this problem mentally or with little written down. They observed some teachers drawing diagrams and others accomplishing this task quickly. It was instrumental to learn from colleagues to start by carefully looking for structure and then using this structure to solve the task, rather than immediately using a procedure. Teachers using SMP7 often saw 4.32 as a unit that was repeated ten times in the task (since each 8.64 is built from twice the unit of 4.32). Others focused on 8.64 as a unit and determined that there were five copies of 8.64 by combining doubles of the 4.32 into a single copy of 8.64. In each case, they found a subtotal of 43.2, and added on 6.8 to find the sum of 50. Teachers shared their strategies and discussed the SMP(s) they used. See figure 12.6 for samples of teachers' work.

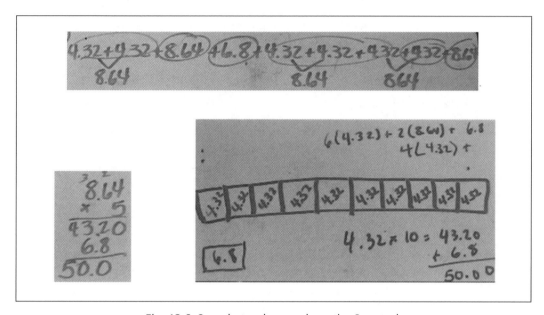

Fig. 12.6. Sample teacher work on the Sum task

■ Teacher Learning Continuum of the Standards for Mathematical Practice

A major focus of the project was a development of the SMPs as habits of mind within both our teachers and their students (National Council of Teachers of Mathematics [NCTM] 2014). In order to achieve this goal, we define teachers as moving through four different stages of a continuum model related to the SMPs, as shown in figure 12.7. At first, teachers come to an awareness of what these standards are. Next, they start to develop an appreciation of the SMPs through participation in mathematical tasks. As one teacher noted, "I do have a poster of the MPs . . . and they are embedded in my . . . curriculum book, but I would not have put my own personal time into truly understanding the importance of the practice standards and how they are applied without being part of this grant." As they become more comfortable and confident with them, they start to interpret and apply the SMPs with their own students. Finally, they move to actively engage their students in discussions and uses of SMPs.

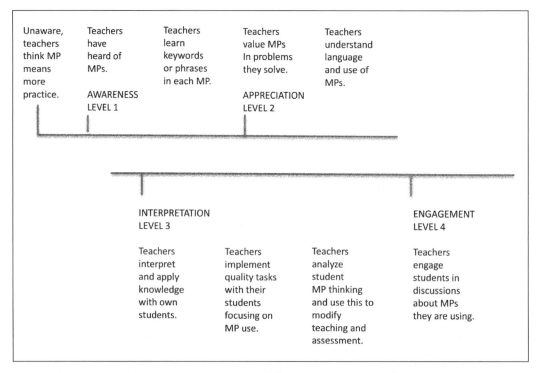

Fig. 12.7. Teacher learning continuum of the Standards for Mathematical Practice

In our early meetings we introduced the teachers to the language of the SMPs through handouts, charts, and tasks. We used specific tasks and videos such as the Slab of Soap task from Illustrative Mathematics (https://www.illustrativemathematics.org/practice-standards/6), so particular SMPs were showcased. As the teachers worked on the task, we asked them to identify each SMP they saw prevalent. They watched the video of students working on the task, and they were able to think about the SMPs from both their viewpoint and what they observed in the student's work and language. Doing this helped teachers learn keywords and phrases associated with each SMP.

A common way to start our early Wednesday night seminars was asking teachers to state the SMPs, individually and as a team, and then provide specific examples of where they observed the SMPs in their classroom that week. During our second JIT seminar, a teacher developed a list of all eight SMPs evident in her class from a week of working on solving problems with whole number operations (fig. 12.8). Through this formative assessment process, we were made aware of the misunderstandings associated with the SMPs, such as the use of math facts to illustrate SMP8 as seen in figure 12.8. This in turn guided our subsequent sessions with teachers. While teachers became more cognizant of the phrasing of SMPs through this activity, they commonly reported that all eight SMPs were present when solving a single task, such as the Sum task in figure 12.5. At this stage, they were not able to easily discriminate the focus within the task.

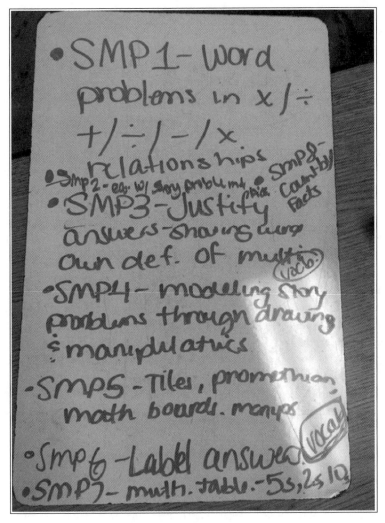

Fig. 12.8. Examples of SMPs in a teacher's classroom

The teachers were now ready to move to Level 2—Appreciation, where they demonstrate an appreciation of the SMPs and start to recognize how they themselves use these habits of mind when solving math problems. One of the teachers stated, "What I find really interesting about these math practice standards, however, is the fact that they span grade levels and in many cases content. . . . I notice myself thinking about these standards as I teach throughout the day, not just while I'm teaching math."

As teachers wrestled to solve problems themselves, they appeared to develop their own habits of mind in their problem solving. In doing so, teachers gain a better understanding of the language associated with the SMPs (e.g., what the language means in practice). Teachers are then ready to start integrating the SMPs into their own teaching and emphasizing the SMPs with their own students. A teacher reflected on this connection between the teacher's own problem solving and classroom implementation, saying, "Once you focus on using and recognizing the Mathematical

Practices, it's *so* much easier to grasp difficult concepts. It's helped *me* master difficult concepts, and it's exciting to share these practices with the children."

We have seen that teachers continue to develop in Level 2—Appreciation, even as they start to move into Level 3—Interpretation, which is using the SMPs with their students. This is represented by the overlap between Levels 2 and 3 in our model (fig. 12.7). Teachers' interactions with the SMPs in Level 2, solving their own mathematical tasks, appears to affect how they engage their students with the SMPs at Level 3. While we have seen that teachers quickly move from not recognizing any of the SMPs to declaring that all eight SMPs are present within a task, with additional problem solving and discussion, teachers are able to better discriminate and declare specific SMPs that are being implemented.

Within Level 3—Interpretation, teachers engage their students in quality mathematical tasks where they focus on looking for SMP use within their students' mathematical work and thinking. A fourth-grade teacher reported to the group that he used the Sum task (fig. 12.5) with his students using three-digit whole numbers instead of decimals, and a student recognized ten copies of 432 and could solve it mentally. The teacher recognized the importance of SMP7 in student reasoning on this task as it exemplifies procedural fluency. Teachers began to analyze student work within the task, with a keen eye on SMP implementation. One teacher commented on how this project had affected her teaching: "Every day I tried to keep math practice standards in mind while planning my instruction." At this point, the teachers' students start to gain an awareness of the SMPs. While we would not expect students to know the SMPs by numbers or exact phrasing, students do start to realize they are constructing a viable argument or making sense of a problem. This is brought about by the attention the teacher pays to the SMPs within his or her classroom. Teachers might hang posters of the SMPs in their classroom, but if the SMPs are never addressed or mentioned, students will not understand or realize the SMPs' purpose. This transformation is evident in a reflection from one of our teachers: "I put up the small 8 posters! I'm being perfectly honest I didn't refer to them at first . . . but then I did. I started noticing them in the lessons. I believe it was because of my own confidence with them. I started pointing to the posters during class and using them."

Within Level 3—Interpretation, teachers are emphasizing the SMPs to their students much as they would a learning objective or content standard throughout a lesson. Teachers start to include tasks and appreciation of the SMPs in their classroom, sometimes beginning with small groups of students. Then teachers come to realize the importance of the SMPs for all students' learning. As one teacher reflected, "At first I was just trying to use the various activities and problems [from the seminars] to push a couple of my higher math students. . . . That changed when I realize [*sic*] the importance of allowing all my students the same opportunities. . . . My lower students blew me away with their reasoning skills. This began to challenge me . . . to make lessons that allowed every student the opportunity to display their mathematical thinking."

Near the end of the project, one teacher wrote, "My participation has made me much more aware of the math practices. I also use and state these practices during lessons to make kids aware of the ways they solve math problems." Another teacher commented, "I have the posters now visible for students. We discuss the MP that we may be using that day and just have them much more aware of their learning process." These statements provide evidence of teachers moving to Level 4—Engagement. In this final stage, teachers engage their students in a discussion about the SMPs and the students are able to meta-cognitively discuss the involvement of the SMPs within their thinking and mathematical reasoning. One teacher mentioned, "I feel like my class had better discussion, they're better at unpacking problems, justifying solutions, and just viewing themselves as mathematicians," which is a hallmark of the SMPs. Students move from an awareness to an appreciation of how the SMPs are a natural part of their process for solving mathematical problems. One teacher reflected on this in reference to SMP1 and SMP7: "This can be amazing to help show the importance of slowing down to analyse [*sic*] a problem rather than reflexively jumping into use an algorithm. . . . Children who learn to see the underlying structure within the base ten system, or the relationships between operations are so well equipped to think flexibly. What I've learned is how teachable this skill actually is, and how rewarding."

At the conclusion of the project, we gave the participants a post-survey. On the same 1-to-4-point scale, participants responded to the prompt "The Common Core Mathematics Practice Standards are evident in my students' interactions" with an average of 3.2 and a standard deviation of 0.4. In addition to this, we also observed a strong improvement when asked to fully name and describe how the teacher would use each SMP in the classroom. As seen in figure 12.9, there was significant growth ($\alpha = 0.001$) in seven of the eight SMPs, with significant growth in SMP4 at the $\alpha = 0.05$ level. The largest changes occurred in SMP5, SMP7, and SMP8.

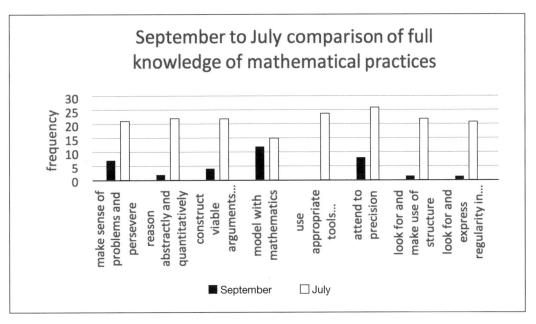

Fig. 12.9. Participant knowledge of SMPs changing throughout the project

Teacher Leadership Model

A key goal of our professional development was to empower teachers so they could sustain what they learned related to the SMPs within our collective partnership and beyond to other colleagues in their districts who did not participate in the project. Through the year we noticed a connection where as teachers move through the Learning Continuum (fig. 12.7), they are also empowered as teachers to learn and lead. As a result of our work, we have developed an Empowerment Model (fig. 12.10) that is cyclic in nature and describes our developmental design. Not all participants became teacher leaders in terms of presentations at our workshops and seminars, but rather they become leaders within their district.

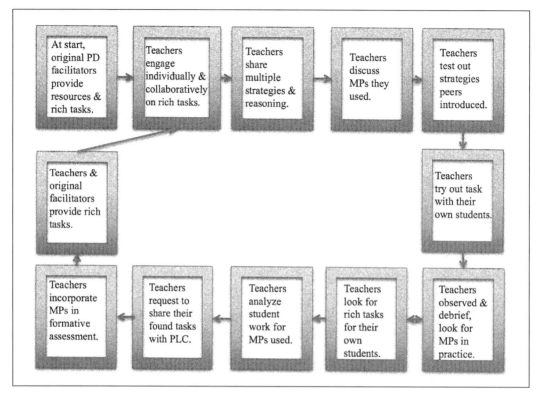

Fig. 12.10. The Empowerment Model for teacher leaders

Initially, we as the mathematics education facilitators provided the resources and purposeful tasks for the teachers. We supported their exploration and modeling, and we engaged the group in productive mathematical discussions about the strategies they used to solve the tasks, as well as the SMPs they engaged in while working on the task. As a result of having this time to wrestle with the task, teachers developed confidence in their ability to try out the tasks in adapted form with their own students. Teachers, both individually or in small groups, adapted the tasks. During this phase, the facilitators observed the teachers in their classrooms. Afterward we would debrief about the learning that took place, as well as the SMPs that were evident in the implementation of the tasks. Teachers analyzed student work as well as their own solution strategies for the tasks related to SMPs. They were encouraged to share what they discovered related to student learning at the JIT seminars. There were numerous instances of teachers sharing specific problems from their print resources in which there were errors or misconceptions. The teachers felt empowered to question, rather than rely on, the classroom resources.

As teachers become more invested in this approach of providing quality tasks related to content with an emphasis on using the SMPs, teachers become the facilitators: leading PD opportunities with their colleagues both within our professional learning community and with other teachers in their schools. A teacher reflected, "Many colleagues hear about activities that I'm doing with students and/or come to me for advice and tasks related to CCSS." This practice-based and classroom-based approach provides just-in-time support. The motivation and encouragement provides an impetus for leadership. The support of the community, increased teacher knowledge, and opportunities for sharing leads to empowerment of the participants (Lightfoot 1986). Teachers were able to informally take on the role of facilitator and teacher-leader in their district. "I have made a point of trying to incorporate some of the information/problems I have learned about from the project by plugging it in directly to our pacing guide. This will allow me to share the ideas and problems with the teachers in my building and district."

■ Moving Forward

Teacher leadership development includes (*a*) the valuing and success in mathematical understanding and reasoning using the habits of mind, (*b*) teacher's growth in pedagogical content knowledge applied in their own classrooms, (*c*) their students exploring mathematical tasks applying the Standards for Mathematical Practice, (*d*) teachers planning and sharing with other teachers informed by student work, and (*e*) leading others in ways of teaching and knowing (Desimone 2009; Doerr, Goldsmith, and Lewis 2010). Based on teacher reflections, our one-year project has addressed and helped our teachers develop within each of these areas: "By gaining a deeper understanding of the mathematical practices through the project I am able to educate others back in my district on them as well, including teachers in my building that don't teach math, teachers at other levels that do teach math, and parents of my students as well."

The structure of our project could be easily transferable to other projects. A key component is frequent and sustained meetings with the teachers throughout the school year as well as in the summer. Another key is the active engagement of the teachers with tasks as learners and providing them the opportunity to share their thinking and reasoning. We believe the Learning Continuum for the SMPs could be framed to any PD for a specific content area.

For ourselves, this project has led us to a new project using a similar structure that focuses on habits of mind and looking at mathematical progressions through the grade levels. We will add teacher mentors to our new project in order to assist new participants in their content and pedagogical development. Mentors will be selected based on their growth in pedagogical content and SMP knowledge and informal leadership they exhibited in previous projects. The mentors will share their own experiences at moving through the different levels on the Learning Continuum (fig. 12.7). They will facilitate tasks and demonstrate interactions with students that are needed to move to the third and fourth level of the continuum. Through the inclusion of the mentors, our PD continues to promote and establish teacher empowerment and to help in creating teacher leaders who will influence classroom activities outside of their districts.

Acknowledgments

The research reported in this article was supported by an ESEA Title IIA Wisconsin Improving Teacher Quality Grant #14-0931. Any opinions, results, conclusions, or recommendations are those of the authors and do not necessarily reflect the views of the ESEA.

References

Boaler, Jo. "Designing Mathematics Classes to Promote Equity and Engagement." *The Journal of Mathematical Behavior* 41 (2016): 172–78.

Desimone, Laura M. "Improving Impact Studies of Teachers' Professional Development: Toward Better Conceptualizations and Measures." *Educational Researcher* 38, no. 3 (April 2009): 181–99.

Doerr, Helen M., Lynn T. Goldsmith, and Catherine C. Lewis. "Mathematics Professional Development." NCTM Research Brief, 2010.

Ernie, Kathryn T., Sherrie J. Serros, Erick B. Hofacker, and Barbara A. Bennie. "Impacting Change in the Common Core Era through a Mathematics Partnership." Joint Meeting of the AMS and the MAA, January 2015.

Heitin, Liana. "Most Math Curricula Found to Be Out of Sync with Common Core." *Education Week*, March 4, 2015. http://www.edweek.org/ew/articles/2015/03/04/most-math-curricula-found-to-be-out.html.

Lightfoot, Sara Lawrence. "On Goodness in Schools: Themes of Empowerment." *Peabody Journal of Education* 63 (March 1986): 9–28.

Loucks-Horsley, Susan, Katherine E. Stiles, Susan Mundry, Nancy Love, and Peter W. Hewson. *Designing Professional Development for Teachers of Science and Mathematics.* Thousand Oaks, Calif.: Corwin, 2010.

National Council of Teachers of Mathematics (NCTM). *Principles to Actions: Ensuring Mathematical Success for All.* Reston, Va.: NCTM, 2014.

National Governors Association Center for Best Practices and Council of Chief State School Officers (NGA Center and CCSSO). *Common Core State Standards for Mathematics.* Washington, D.C.: NGA Center and CCSSO, 2010. http://www.corestandards.org.

Stein, Mary Kay, and Margaret Smith. "Mathematical Tasks as a Framework for Reflection." *Mathematics Teaching in the Middle School* 3, no. 4 (January 1998): 268–75.

Trotter, Terrel. "Normal Magic Triangles of Order *n*." *Journal of Recreational Mathematics* 5 (January 1972): 28–32.

CHAPTER 13

Developing Teachers' Professional Knowledge when Combining Video Clubs with Lesson Study

Jason T. Deal and Gloriana González, *University of Illinois at Urbana-Champaign*

Lesson study and video clubs are two established professional development strategies that encourage teacher learning and professional growth. Lesson study encourages reflection on teaching by promoting a cycle where teachers plan, teach, and then revise a lesson according to the first enactment of teaching. Video clubs encourage teachers to pay attention to new aspects of teaching by providing the opportunity to examine specific moments of teaching or student thinking during the enactment of the lesson. In our study, we examine how these two powerful individual models of professional development could leverage each other's benefits to create additional opportunities for teacher learning. We designed and implemented a two-year professional development intervention combining three strategies—lesson study, video clubs, and discussing animations of classroom instruction. The different strategies in the combined professional development model affected teachers' interactions within each strategy. In this study, we examine how the lesson study revision activity encouraged opportunities for teacher learning during the video clubs. We consider how the lesson study step of revising the lesson provoked teachers to reflect on their teaching using evidence of student thinking in the video club. In addition, we consider how the use of a video club for observation in lesson study allowed teachers to pay attention to details about student thinking because of the capabilities of video. Finally, we discuss how the combined model of professional development could encourage sustainability of lesson study in the United States.

■ Lesson Study and Video Club Models of Professional Development

Lesson study is a professional development strategy where a team of teachers follows four steps: studying the goals of the lesson and the mathematical content, developing a collaborative research lesson to gather evidence about student thinking, teaching the research lesson, and meeting to discuss observations of student thinking. Typically, one teacher teaches the lesson while team members conduct live observations that inform the post-lesson discussion. The lesson study team can revise the lesson following the reflection and repeat the cycle of activities to better suit student learning objectives. A benefit of revising and reteaching a lesson is the opportunity for teacher reflection by incorporating what was observed during the discussion into the lesson plan (Fernandez 2002), examining new understandings about the lesson after the first enactment (Lewis, Perry, and Murata 2006), increasing teacher learning about connecting student thinking to the lesson, and encouraging the idea that instruction should be continually improved (Lewis, Perry, and Hurd 2009). However, sustaining lesson study in the United States is difficult, in part as a result of such logistical challenges in U.S. classrooms as teachers' time available for collaboration, comfort with sharing teaching with colleagues, and the lack of a single curriculum for all schools (Fernandez 2002).

A video club is a professional development meeting where teachers gather to watch and discuss approximately five-minute long video clips of lessons taught by a participating member (Sherin and van Es 2005). Video clubs encourage teachers' attention to detail through a facilitator, who helps to focus the video club discussion on student thinking using evidence from the clip (van Es and Sherin 2008). By participating in video clubs, teachers make more comments over time about students' problem-solving strategies and provide deeper analyses of the videos (Sherin and Han 2004). In addition, teachers who participate in video clubs have shown an increase in their attention to student thinking during instruction (Sherin and van Es 2009). The combination of lesson study and video clubs is promising, because video can allow teachers to view students' actions in detail. For example, teachers can pause and discuss a video when evidence of student thinking is difficult to unpack. Teachers can also replay a video to focus on specific students' actions. These two examples—pausing and replaying a video—would be impossible to do when conducting in-person observations. However, careful attention to detail is an important step for documenting student thinking and informing the process of revising a research lesson for optimizing student learning opportunities. We expected that the need to collaboratively revise the lesson could encourage the teachers to reflect on its first enactment during the video club.

■ A Shared Knowledge Base of Teacher Learning

One theory for examining teacher learning in profession development is a *knowledge base for teaching* (Hiebert, Gallimore, and Stigler 2002). A main goal of developing a knowledge base for teaching is to encourage long-term, sustained professional development that encourages teachers to incorporate research-based knowledge into practice. A method of developing a knowledge base for teaching is for teacher educators to promote transitions from teachers' *practitioner knowledge* into *professional knowledge*. Practitioner knowledge is knowledge about teaching acquired in response to specific instances teachers encounter; connected across the dimensions of content, students, and pedagogy; and typically applied to specific instances in specific classrooms. Because of its specificity, practitioner knowledge cannot be easily shared as professional knowledge with many other teachers. In order to develop into professional knowledge of teaching, teachers' individual practitioner knowledge must become public, shareable with others, and capable of being verified and improved. Professional knowledge is useful because it can be applied more broadly to other instances and shared with colleagues or novice teachers. Additionally, the public nature of professional knowledge allows for continued input and improvement from other teachers who could offer additional insights and suggestions (Hiebert, Gallimore, and Stigler 2002). We focus on how teachers developed professional knowledge of teaching and learning resources (Lewis, Perry, and Hurd 2009). Teaching and learning resources include the development of tasks and lesson plans that encourage high-level, visible student thinking. Providing opportunities for teachers to reflect with one another can elicit practitioner knowledge. More important, teachers' reflections, when engaged in discussions that are centered around issues of practice, can provide opportunities to transform the practitioner knowledge into professional knowledge.

■ A Combined Model of Professional Development

Our study uses data from a two-year professional development program funded by the National Science Foundation that aimed at increasing teachers' noticing and use of students' prior knowledge in problem-based instruction. Six high school geometry teachers across five different high-needs schools participated in the program, although one teacher, Stan (all pseudonyms), withdrew from the study after the fourth session because of outside obligations. We focused on two different topics: *perpendicular bisector* and *dilation*. In year 1, the teachers first discussed animations showing hypothetical scenarios for teaching each topic (González and DeJarnette 2016). They then participated in a lesson study cycle and engaged in video clubs about the lesson. Following the video clubs, the teachers revised the lesson to reteach it during the second year of the program. In year 2, teachers taught the revised lessons and participated in video clubs of the second enactment. This study examines the video club and revision of the perpendicular bisector lesson in year 1.

The Fair Location Lesson

The teachers designed and taught a research lesson that targeted the concept of perpendicular bisector. The lesson, which we will call the fair location lesson, asked students to determine possible locations for a new building located fairly between two schools. The optimal solution to the problem was to construct the perpendicular bisector of the segment connecting the two schools. All of the points on the perpendicular bisector would be equidistant to the schools and thus fair. In the first enactment of the lesson, students were given the locations of the two schools as two points inside a rectangular frame. Some teachers changed the context and some aspects of the lesson to make the problem more relevant to their students. In the version of the lesson we discuss, the two given points were oriented vertically, one above the other. Figure 13.1 shows an example of the worksheet given to the students, used in Alexa and Madeline's lesson. (More information about the lesson can be found at this book's page on NCTM's More4U website.)

Violet City schools are planning to build a shared student center with a skating rink, arcade, and dance hall (with DJ) for after-school hours between Violet High School and Redwood Middle School. They need your help finding three different locations that are a fair placement between each school. Using the map below decide where your three locations would be.

Sketch on the map below where the three locations would be placed.

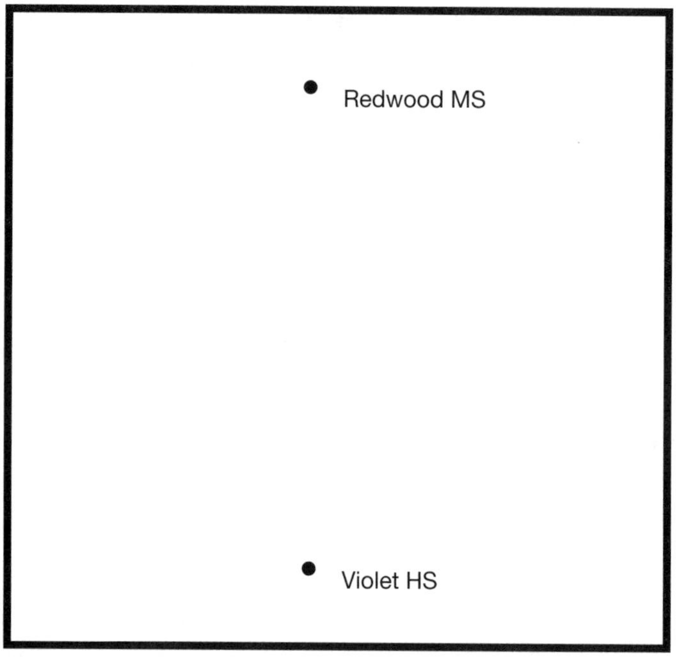

● Redwood MS

● Violet HS

Fig. 13.1. The Fair Location lesson as taught by Alexa and Madeline

■ Teachers' Reflections on the Lesson during the Video Club

During the video club, the goal was to use evidence from the video to discuss student thinking and use of prior knowledge. The goal of the discussion was to identify and discuss student thinking, but the teachers also used the conversation to examine their practice in deeper ways and to consider how they could increase students' mathematical understanding. Table 13.1 summarizes each video clip shown and what comments teachers made about the fair location lesson in each clip.

Table 13.1

Teachers' comments about the lesson during each video club discussion

Session No.	Clip No.	Summary of Clip	No. of Teacher Comments Per Category					Example of Teacher Comment
			Goals	*Type*	*Context*	*Questions*	*Diagram*	
4	1	Students discuss how they are choosing the locations for the athletic complex.	8	0	0	1	0	I guess I just wonder, by using the word "fair" rather than the word "equidistant" or whatever totally skewed the initial interpretation of the problem in the first place.
4	2	Students discuss a method of drawing a "box" with the two schools and the possible locations as vertices.	0	1	0	0	0	I mean, I like the fact that the problem was so open-ended and it, we didn't guide them through a lot, but I just, I think that created more problems for them because they didn't even have a direction of where to go.
5	3	Students find the midpoint and measure horizontally in either direction.	0	0	0	4	20	I wonder too if the orientation of the points hadn't been like north and south but had been skewed if that would have been more difficult because they kind of—
8	4	Students discuss the perpendicular bisector as the "middle street" between the two schools.	0	0	5	1	1	Because they're supposed—the very last question is them—they're supposed to come up with perpendicular bisector. Which that is when, basically I didn't really have to guide, only one group which was a hot mess. I didn't have to guide these guys until the very end. I did my individual closure by talking to them.
8	5	Students discuss how the point would be equidistant even if it was far from the midpoint.	0	0	0	0	0	No comments.
9	6	A student makes overlapping circles to construct the perpendicular bisector and selects the intersection of the circles for her locations.	0	0	0	0	0	No comments.
Total			8	1	5	6	21	

Note. We use an em dash (—) to indicate interrupted text in the transcript.

Overall, the teachers made forty-one comments about either the first enactment of the fair location lesson or possible revisions. The teachers made comments about the lesson while discussing four of the six clips, during sessions 4, 5, and 8. No comments about the lesson were made during the discussion of the final clip shown in session 8 and the clip shown in session 9, which were also the shortest of the six discussions. The teachers primarily discussed the diagram of the lesson, with twenty-one comments. However, they also made multiple comments about the goal of the lesson, the context of the problem, and the type of questions asked, with eight, six, and five comments, respectively. In addition, these comments were generally substantial. For example, Alexa's comment in the fourth session describes characteristics of the problem that shaped students' mathematical understanding during the lesson. These results demonstrate how the teachers' attention to student thinking spurred reflection on the first enactment of the fair location lesson and how they could increase opportunities for students' mathematical understanding.

The teachers' comments about the lesson during each video club were often related to the student thinking that was shown in the video clip. For example, in clip 1, the students discuss how they placed their locations according to what was "fair." The teachers' comments during this discussion focused on the teachers' choice of the word *fair* in the goal of the lesson, as shown by Alexa's comment. In response, Stan suggested, "If we said, like, 'mathematically fair'?" to which Alexa followed with, "And try not to use the word 'equal.'" In this exchange, Alexa connected the students' misinterpretation of the problem to the stated goal of finding "fair" locations. Then, Stan's reply suggested a revision to the lesson according to Alexa's interpretation of student thinking. Alexa's follow-up shows the teachers collaboratively building on their observations of student thinking and using each other's thoughts to consider ways to promote mathematical understanding. During the discussion of this clip that focused on how students addressed the goal of the lesson, eight of the nine teacher comments focused on phrasing the goal. The teachers' other comments about the lesson were similarly related to the content of the video clip in other video club discussions as well. The relationship between the focus of the video clip and the focus of the discussion shows how the teachers were reflecting on the evidence about student thinking when considering the changes to the lesson.

■ Teachers' Reflections Led to a Shared Knowledge Base

In addition to encouraging the teachers to use students' thinking to reflect on their teaching, the video club provided an opportunity for learning by encouraging the transformation of teachers' practitioner knowledge into professional knowledge. During the discussions, the teachers showed all aspects of developing professional knowledge. They made their individual, specific, and detailed reflections about the lesson public, responded to one another's suggestions with suggestions for improvement, and considered new implications for how the lesson affected opportunities for student learning. To demonstrate this, we will focus on an example of how the teachers considered the diagram given for the problem. While planning, the teachers did not pay detailed attention to the diagram, using only the real-world orientation of the points to determine their location inside the frame. During the video club, the teachers became aware of the diagram's importance, commenting on it in three of the four sessions. The conversation focused on the diagram used in Alexa and Madeline's lesson, shown above. The teachers considered three aspects of the diagram in their discussion: the orientation of the two given locations as vertical or offset, a rectangular frame around the points, and a real map of the two locations as a resource. Figure 13.2 shows the progression of the teachers' discussion about the diagram. In the figure, the ovals show the different possibilities for the diagram the teachers brought up during the video club discussions. Each rectangle includes the teachers' evaluations of that aspect of the lesson during the video clubs, numbered in the order they occurred during the video clubs. From the evaluations, teachers made new suggestions about aspects of the lesson to consider, which are connected by arrows.

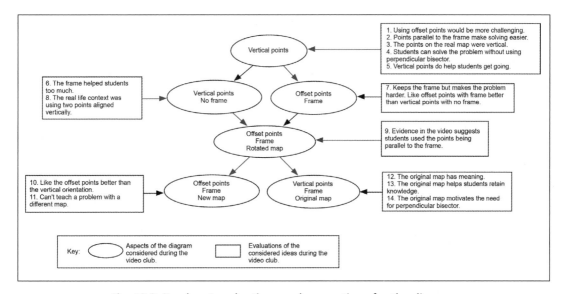

Fig. 13.2. Teachers' evaluations and suggestions for the diagram

In the initial video club discussions, the teachers began by considering only whether or not the points should be oriented vertically as they were in Alexa and Madeline's original enactment. As the teachers evaluated the vertically oriented points, they began to consider how other aspects of the diagram were connected to the orientation. For example, they stated that vertical points might allow students to use the rectangular frame rather than a perpendicular bisector to solve the problem. These evaluations led to suggestions of multiple possibilities for the revised fair location lesson. Following the discussion of the vertical points, the teachers considered two different possibilities: keeping the vertical points and removing the frame, or keeping the frame and rearranging the points to make them offset. While Alexa commented that the map was aligned vertically because of the real-life locations of the points they used in the problem, a different teacher, Gian, commented that he liked the offset alignment better. Based on the comments about using real-life points and offset alignment, Gian then suggested to rotate the original map to make it fit offset points. In the next session, the teachers chose not to rotate the original map. Instead, they considered either using a new map with different points that was shown in a different video or retaining the original vertical orientation with the real-world map. The teachers commented that students would identify more with a map that was contextually relevant. They also described that a contextually relevant map would be useful to help the students retain knowledge and motivate the need for perpendicular bisector.

The teachers' comments about the diagram illustrate how the video club provided opportunities for teacher learning about revising the lesson according to student thinking. The teachers used their practitioner knowledge to reflect on the lesson and consider how to improve their practice. The teachers provided detailed explanations of their thinking by providing support to their suggestions, their comments were concrete changes that could be made to the lesson, and they were specific to the fair location bisector problem. For example, Alexa's assertion about the orientation of the points was supported by the idea that the points were aligned as in the real world, and specifically addressed whether the teachers should change the orientation of the points in the fair location lesson. As the video club progressed, the teachers continued to make these individual comments public, where the suggestions were evaluated by their peers and improved upon with following suggestions. The way in which the teachers' response to one another's comments provoked additional suggestions and evaluations is evidence that their practitioner knowledge became a shared knowledge base of teaching about the lesson. For example, Gian's suggestion to make the points on the map offset incorporated Alexa's desire to use a context from the real world. By making these thoughts about the orientation of the points explicit, the teachers reflected on the connection between the orientation and the frame around the diagram. The teachers had the opportunity to consider broader issues through the discussion as well, such as the connection between the real-world context and the mathematics of a problem when considering whether to use vertical or offset points. Overall, the teachers' consideration of the diagram provides an example of how they made their practitioner knowledge about students' use of the diagram explicit. By making their ideas public, the teachers evaluated each other's suggestions for the revised fair location lesson and developed a joint knowledge base about how students could solve the problem.

■ Discussion

Our findings suggest that the combination of video clubs and lesson study increased opportunities for teacher change and professional growth. During the video clubs, the inclusion of lesson study revision encouraged the teachers to reflect on their teaching through the discussion of students' thinking in relation to the lesson. The use of video clubs for observation in the lesson study process allowed teachers to pay attention to details that may not have been clear otherwise. We also discuss how combining elements of video clubs and lesson study can help address some structural challenges to the individual forms of professional development, encouraging sustainability.

Using lesson study with video clubs supported teacher change by encouraging the teachers to reflect on their teaching and gain a better understanding of how the design of a lesson can affect student thinking. The teachers shared their practitioner knowledge by making public their thoughts about the lesson, which were provoked by specific examples of student thinking from the videos. The teachers developed this knowledge into professional knowledge by applying their observations to make improvements to the lesson, a shareable resource that the teachers continued to improve. For example, when Alexa proposed reconsideration of the word *fair*, she had assessed from evidence in the video that a student had misinterpreted the problem because of that word choice. Additionally, when the teachers noticed evidence that students could use the frame and the vertically oriented points to solve the problem without using perpendicular bisector, they considered how the resources they provided in the lesson affected the students' methods. While the teachers did not incorporate every suggestion into the revised fair location lesson, the discussions considering how changes to the lesson could affect student thinking encouraged the teachers to reflect on what resources they prioritize in a lesson. These examples show that video club discussions about the enactment of the research lesson provoked attention to student thinking and opportunities for collaborative investigation of ways to support student mathematical understanding.

Using video clubs as the observation step of lesson study supported teacher change by allowing teachers to focus on aspects of their teaching that are challenging to notice during the real-time lesson. While teaching a lesson, teachers must understand many students' ideas as they happen, while also paying attention to the logistical issues of managing a classroom. When a teacher misses a student's idea, there is no way to replay exactly what happened the first time. In a video club, on the other hand, teachers can take time to slow down, make sense of students' solutions, rewind, review again, discuss with colleagues, and gather more evidence. Many of the video clubs took over thirty minutes of discussion to understand a two- to five-minute video clip, showing the complexity of understanding student thinking. Attention to detail is especially useful for professional development programs that focus on particular aspects of teaching. As previously stated, during the first iteration of the lesson study lesson, the teachers did not pay particular attention to the design of the diagram when planning. However, after viewing clips that showed how students thought about the problem differently when they were paying attention to different versions and aspects of the diagram, the teachers developed their professional knowledge by sharing their practitioner knowledge of teaching the lesson to consider what choices they could make about the diagram in the revised lesson. During the video club, the facilitators promoted opportunities for the teachers to focus their attention on student thinking (González, Deal, and Skultety 2016). Engaging teachers in the lesson revision process after the video club provided opportunities for the teachers to make changes to the lesson based upon their video club discussions. The combination of video club and lesson study allowed the teachers to increase their understanding of aspects of teaching that are typically difficult to notice while teaching.

We also find that combining video clubs and lesson study could be useful to encourage the sustainability of lesson study in the United States. When using video clubs to review the lesson, there is no need to gather all participating teachers together at the same time during the school day to observe. Additionally, teachers may be more comfortable sharing their teaching publicly when the sharing occurs through video rather than in person. Using video instead of in-person observation could also be useful when gathering teachers from different schools to engage in the lesson study cycle. In our case, we had teachers across multiple school districts. For small schools where there may not be multiple teachers of the same subject, the combination of video clubs and lesson study can support teachers to collaborate with others. As online professional development becomes more prevalent, teachers may even be able to engage in this combination of video clubs and lesson study online.

■ Conclusion

Lesson study and video clubs are important professional development strategies that encourage teachers to increase their attention to student thinking and reflect on their teaching. In our project we found that the combination of lesson study and video clubs allowed each individual strategy to be infused with the benefits of the other. Teachers' comments about the lesson during the video club portion of the professional development were enriched by the common experience of planning and teaching the same research lesson, as well as the need to collaboratively revise the lesson, allowing the teachers to improve their teaching through reflection with a purpose. The use of video to observe student thinking in the lesson allowed the teachers to stop, discuss, review, and examine for evidence in a way they could not collaboratively discuss during a real-time lesson. These discussions provided opportunities for teacher learning through the development of a shared knowledge base (Hiebert, Gallimore, and Stigler 2002). The teachers shared their specific practitioner knowledge of student understanding in the video clubs, as well as knowledge of the content and pedagogy of the common lesson from the lesson study revisions. In doing so, the teachers developed professional knowledge by making their thinking public, and by evaluating and building on each other's ideas to consider revisions to the lesson. In addition, the combined model shows promise as a way to address some of the logistical challenges of lesson study and encourage its sustainability in the United States. While it is not always the case that two good things are equal to the sum of their parts, we are encouraged by the growth shown by teachers through their reflections and discussions, and we encourage professional developers to continue to examine similar combined professional development strategies in the future.

Acknowledgments

The research described in this article was supported by a National Science Foundation grant to the second author for the project entitled "CAREER: Noticing and Using Students' Prior Knowledge in Problem-Based Instruction," Grant No. DRL-1253081. Opinions, findings, conclusions, or recommendations are those of the authors and do not necessarily reflect the views of the National Science Foundation. We appreciate the comments of Enrique Galindo to an earlier version of this chapter. Thanks to the editors, Melissa Boston and Lucy West, and the reviewers of this volume for their valuable suggestions. Thanks to Lisa Skultety and Gabriela E. Vargas, members of the research team, for valuable conversations.

References

Fernandez, Clea. "Learning from Japanese Approaches to Professional Development: The Case of Lesson Study." *Journal of Teacher Education* 53, no. 5 (2002): 393–405.

González, Gloriana, Jason T. Deal, and Lisa Skultety. "Facilitating Teacher Learning when Using Different Representations of Practice." *Journal of Teacher Education* 67, no. 5 (2016): 447–66.

González, Gloriana, and Anna F. DeJarnette. "Designing Stories for Teachers to Notice Students' Prior Knowledge." Unpublished manuscript, University of Illinois at Urbana-Champaign, 2016.

Hiebert, James, Ronald Gallimore, and James W. Stigler. "A Knowledge Base for the Teaching Profession: What Would It Look Like and How Can We Get One?" *Educational Researcher* 31, no. 5 (2002): 3–15.

Lewis, Catherine C., Rebecca R. Perry, and Jacqueline Hurd. "Improving Mathematics Instruction through Lesson Study: A Theoretical Model and North American Case." *Journal of Mathematics Teacher Education* 12, no. 4 (2009): 285–304.

Lewis, Catherine, Rebecca R. Perry, and Aki Murata. "How Should Research Contribute to Instructional Improvement? The Case of Lesson Study." *Educational Researcher* 35, no. 3 (2006): 3–14.

Sherin, Miriam Gamoran, and Sandra Y. Han. "Teacher Learning in the Context of a Video Club." *Teaching and Teacher Education* 20, no. 2 (2004): 163–83.

Sherin, Miriam Gamoran, and Elizabeth A. van Es. "Using Video to Support Teachers' Ability to Notice Classroom Interactions." *Journal of Technology and Teacher Education* 13, no. 3 (2005): 475.

Sherin, Miriam Gamoran, and Elizabeth A. van Es. "Effects of Video Club Participation on Teachers' Professional Vision." *Journal of Teacher Education* 60, no. 1 (2009): 20–37.

Van Es, Elizabeth A., and Miriam Gamoran Sherin. "Mathematics Teachers' 'Learning to Notice' in the Context of a Video Club." *Teaching and Teacher Education* 24, no. 2 (2008): 244–76.

CHAPTER 14

The Development and Use of Student-Learning Data Tools as Formative Mathematics Assessments

David Slavit, *Washington State University Vancouver*

Angie Deuel, *Battle Ground High School, Battle Ground, Washington*

Tamara Holmlund Nelson, *Washington State University Vancouver*

A variety of data about student learning is available to teachers of mathematics, from standardized test results to day-to-day student work. Student-learning data (SLD) can be used to assess the ways in which mathematical practices (National Governors Association Center for Best Practices and Council of Chief State School Officers [NGA Center and CCSSO] 2010) surface during instruction or to monitor specific progress toward skill and concept development. SLD can be a key factor in allowing teachers to make student-centered adjustments to mathematics instruction.

Determining how to use these data to improve instruction and learning might be an arduous task for an individual teacher. There is evidence that analyzing SLD, particularly when done collaboratively, can promote teacher learning and improve instruction (Borko 2004; Horn, Kane, and Wilson 2015). When teachers work collaboratively with data, they will need to negotiate which data matter most, how to construct or find assessments that fit the collective purpose, and how to make sense of and use these data. However, these are not simple problems, and teacher groups often need scaffolding and targeted professional development in order to learn from and use the SLD they collect (Slavit, Nelson, and Kennedy 2009; Jimerson and Wayman 2015).

In this chapter, we describe our work using student-learning data as a central component in mathematics teacher professional development. We explore ways that teacher groups can be supported to effectively collect, analyze, and use SLD. We then identify five teacher practices that can support collaborative efforts to improve instruction.

■ What Is Student-Learning Data?

Teacher inquiry requires evidence, and student-learning data serve this purpose. Student-learning data involve both formative and summative assessments. In general, we consider SLD to be anything that can be captured and examined either for progress toward specific learning targets or as evidence of students' thinking. Student thinking includes initial understandings, conjectures and arguments, problem-solving strategies, or well-formed ideas.

It can be represented in a variety of mathematical, linguistic, and visual representations. Common forms of SLD include student work samples and classroom assessments.

We have identified two specific types of SLD commonly used by teachers—*anecdotal data* and *captured data*. When teachers attend to data without recording or documentation, we consider it *anecdotal data*. The most common example of anecdotal data we observed were teachers' recollections of past instruction. These included specific recounting of instructional segments as well as "feelings" about individual or group student progress. Anecdotal data can be useful, but also fleeting and transient, eventually becoming an impression in a teacher's memory without the possibility of further checking, questioning, or collaborative analysis (Hiebert, Gallimore, and Stigler 2002). While useful in helping to frame an instructional context, anecdotal data can also be unreliable.

Teachers who take the time to document their observations construct a permanent record of their student's progress, making these data more lasting, shareable, and useful. Examples of *captured data* include student work samples, reflective notes, classroom video, and test scores. One teacher group we observed collected samples of student work on *rich mathematical tasks*, which they defined as genuine problems that afford multiple solution strategies as well as concept development (see fig. 14.1a). A series of questions and requests ("What information do you have? What are you trying to figure out? How do you think you will solve this problem? Show your work. What questions do you have about this task?") encouraged students to provide complete responses and mathematical arguments, allowing teachers to delve deeply into the ways their students were thinking (see fig. 14.1b). Another group of teachers collected items related to progress on linear graphing skills by asking students to represent a linear function graphically and then analyze the accuracy of these representations. Both of these examples of SLD reveal aspects of student learning, but they were collected for different reasons and served different purposes. We will discuss these differences more fully in a later section.

Ursala is Undecided

It is urgent that Ursala start at point A and get to point S. She can only travel along the edges of the given graph, either in a southerly (downward) or easterly (rightward) manner. Unfortunately, Ursala is undecided about which path to take.

How many different paths does she have a choice of taking?

Be sure to describe and/or demonstrate how you arrived at your answer. It is not necessary to list every path possible in your answer.

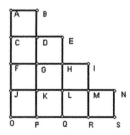

Describe and/or demonstrate how you arrived at your answer in the space below.

How many different paths does she have a choice of taking? _____

Fig. 14.1a. Sample rich mathematics task

Integrated II – Ursula Is Undecided

What information are you given?

Start at Point A and go to Point S. Can only travel on the edges going down or right.

What are you trying to figure out?

The paths that she can take

How do you think you will solve this problem? What will be your strategy?

I will look at the graph, and follow the edges to point S without leaving the edge

Begin work:

What questions do you have about this task?

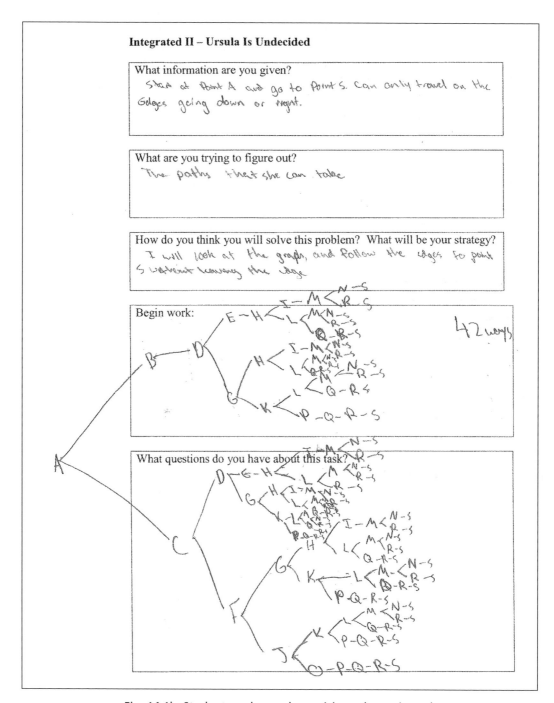

Fig. 14.1b. Student work sample on rich mathematics task

Captured student-learning data can become public objects of collaborative analysis and discussion. In addition to monitoring progress on content-related learning goals, teachers can use these data as evidence related to student-learning goals that can be difficult to define, such as reasoning, modeling, argumentation, and other mathematical practices (NGA Center and CCSSO 2010). In doing so, not only are student outcomes revealed, but teachers' own understandings of these complex mathematical ideas can grow (Borko 2004; Horn, Kane, and Wilson 2015). Together, anecdotal and captured data allow teachers to engage in conversations about mathematics teaching that are grounded in evidence and can provide guidance for future instructional decisions.

■ The Context of Our Work

We have spent over five years studying mathematics and science teachers who have participated in supported collaborated teacher inquiry, most of whom met weekly in professional learning communities. We consider collaborative teacher inquiry to be a systematic process in which teacher groups interrogate their practice through analysis of classroom-based data, usually in the form of student-learning data. Our work began with the Partnership for Reform in Secondary Science and Mathematics (PRiSSM), a three-year, grant-funded professional development (PD) project involving approximately 150 middle and high school mathematics and science teachers from six rural and suburban school districts in the Pacific Northwest. Led by university teacher educators, district instructional leaders, and other area professionals, the project was designed to develop teachers as leaders of content-based professional learning communities. Each year began with a summer academy focused on building community, negotiating instructional beliefs and perspectives, developing inquiry perspectives and skills (with a focus on analysis of SLD), and supporting lead teachers' abilities to organize and facilitate collaborative inquiry processes. The project supported team building, including the development of norms of collaboration (Garmston and Wellman 2013), and provided frameworks for a collaborative inquiry process, with specific focus on a cycle of inquiry that highlights the use of SLD (see fig. 14.2). Teacher teams' negotiation of ideas such as *high-quality mathematics teaching* and *useful student-learning data* were used to build community and focus teachers on problems of practice.

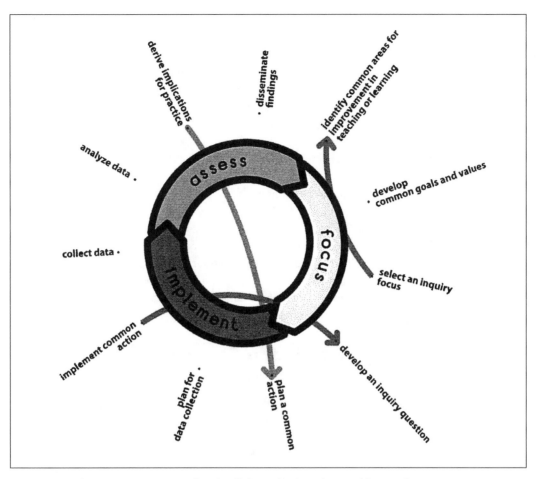

Fig. 14.2. Common cycle of collaborative inquiry used by teacher groups

Our professional development was designed to allow the teacher teams to identify their own dilemmas and questions of practice and then to provide the time and support necessary for them to address these issues. Throughout the year, PRiSSM provided monthly meeting time and a facilitator to assist groups through collaborative inquiry cycles. During these meetings, facilitators supported teachers in decisions related to data collection and analysis, and they provided and supported the use of analytic tools such as coding schemes and rubrics in making sense of and using SLD. For example, a group of high school teachers were systematically led by their facilitator through a process of collectively analyzing student work in order to engage in discussions on mathematical learning goals, become more aligned in their analyses, and consider how these data might affect future instruction (see appendix). During the final year of PRiSSM and beyond, the teachers were asked to self-facilitate their inquiry processes in order to support the long-term sustainability of the PD effort.

We have come to understand through our research and the work of others the various perspectives on student-learning data (Huguet, Marsh, and Farrell 2014), stances toward inquiry (Cochran-Smith and Lytle 2009), and collaborative processes (Little et al. 2003) that can positively and negatively affect the quality of the assessments that teachers develop. Coding the talk in more than 200 recorded teacher meetings, we have found links between the perspectives that teachers take toward student-learning data and the ways in which they collect and use these data. Specifically, teacher groups who seek to verify that their instruction *is effective* tend to collect summative data, and they analyze these data in ways that seek to understand students' current progress. In contrast, teacher groups who seek to make their instruction *more effective* tend to collect formative assessments, and they analyze these data in ways that surface the specific mathematical understandings that students hold (Nelson, Slavit, and Deuel 2012; Slavit, Nelson, and Deuel 2013).

Our analysis revealed the following collaborative practices to be helpful to teacher groups in thinking about the creation and analysis of student-learning data: (1) establishing learning targets, (2) clarifying mathematical content and practices, (3) aligning purpose, (4) focusing on students' mathematical thinking, and (5) professionalizing dialogue. Later in this chapter, we expand on each of these constructs and provide examples of mathematics teacher collaboration that support the development and refinement of these practices.

■ Teachers' Approaches to the Collection and Analysis of Student-Learning Data

We have identified two distinct approaches to the ways in which teachers engage in data collection and analysis, a *proving approach* and an *improving approach*. With a proving approach, interest is on student achievement, and conversations often center on the nature of past instruction and the percentages of students who reach benchmark learning goals as a result of that instruction. Assessment results quite often take the form of summative descriptions (usually numbers and percentages) of students' progress. These assessment results might identify the students who "got it," but they do not provide useful information about students' mathematical thinking, understandings, or practices. As such, evidence-based discussions about future instruction are often narrow and leave little room for change beyond minor adjustments.

In an improving approach, assessments are selected with an attempt to expose students' mathematical thinking and practices. Further, teachers with this approach use these data to guide potential changes to instruction related to specific learning targets. With an improving approach, interest is on student thinking, and conversations often center on the ways in which instruction might be modified to support future learning goals. Teachers who take an improving approach often focus on instructional dilemmas that are complicated and complex. Such dilemmas might not be readily resolved with minor tweaks or surface-level changes, or even within a nine-month school year, so teachers with an improving perspective leave open the possibility for radical changes in their instruction. SLD development and analysis among teachers with an improving approach are driven by a continual wondering, questioning, and searching for deeper understanding of students' thinking and learning (Wells 1999; Cochran-Smith and Lytle 2009).

Supporting teachers in developing an improving stance toward inquiry can be difficult, as such change can require enormous self-analysis and an ability to alter some deeply personal beliefs and ways of thinking. Changes in stance were not witnessed frequently. Our facilitators modeled improving stance behaviors (such as consistently asking "Why?," maintaining a focus on high-level mathematical learning goals and emphasizing relationships between student thinking and instruction) and made teachers increasingly aware of the potential power of such a perspective. Our evidence indicated that another important factor in the development of an improving stance in teachers was having a colleague who consistently modeled this perspective.

■ Processes and Practices That Supported Instructional Change

The decisions teachers make as they begin an assessment process affect what they can learn about students' thinking, which in turn affects the nature of the adjustments made to subsequent instruction. The following processes and practices enabled teachers to collect informative SLD that led to evidence-based instructional modifications.

Establishing Learning Targets

In the creation of SLD, teachers decide the mathematical content on which they want to focus. In several groups we observed, teachers spent significant time clarifying their learning targets, with one group spending an entire year on this process. Together they discussed what it meant for a fourth-grader to understand fractions or a ninth-grader to understand linear growth. Teachers negotiated what they thought understanding would look and sound like at that time and what they wanted it to look and sound like in the future. Using past experience and formative data, teachers anticipated students' possible entryways into the learning experience, and they also described the kinds of assessment responses, language, connections, practices, and products for which they were looking.

One group of high school mathematics teachers spent approximately three months attempting to understand the main learning goals in an Integrated 1 course. The teacher leader of the group used a fishbone activity (fig. 14.3), which allowed the other teachers to place learning goals along the "spines." Process goals such as "group work," "problem solving," and "engagement" were identified, as were more specific mathematical goals such as "geometric transformations," "simple inferences," and "simplifying algebraic expressions." As the list was being constructed, conversations turned to what the goals might look and sound like in classrooms and how the various goals might be related.

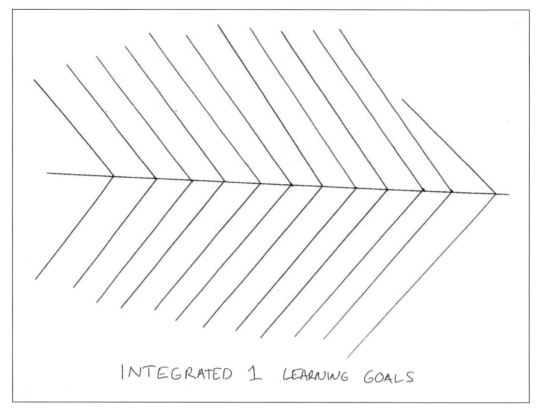

Fig. 14.3. Fishbone activity for negotiating student learning goals

For these teachers, learning target development was not a task of identifying which mathematics should be covered on a test or of reformatting test items. It was a negotiation of what the content meant, what was most important, what it looked like, and into what larger ideas it was embedded. In general, teacher groups that took the time to engage in these challenging and time-consuming conversations more readily produced assessments that generated SLD embedded with information about students' thinking.

Teachers who did not take time to do a shared analysis of student-learning goals produced SLD that had less of an impact on their thinking or decision making about instruction. Some teacher groups discussed topics and goals briefly or not at all before developing their assessments. In this case, the learning goals served as a general label or category for the content topic of the assessment (e.g., "fractions"). This cursory goal development of learning targets often resulted in an assessment tool that provided limited information about students' conceptual understandings or practices or one that assessed something entirely different than what the teachers wanted. The teachers had administered assessments and analyzed data, but they did not have information that would help them advance their own awareness of students' thinking.

Clarifying Mathematical Content and Practices

As teachers discussed learning targets, they were confronted with the reality that big mathematical ideas are composed of principles and a complex set of relationships among concepts, rather than a collection of self-evident discrete facts. Disciplinary terms that have general uses also required clarification. For example, *problem solving* and *modeling* have multiple meanings, and teachers can vary in their usage and understandings of these terms.

Teachers' collaborative learning potential is supported with a shared understanding of central words in their conversation. Several groups we observed made sure that when such words came up in conversation, they paused for a tangential conversation designed to build a collective understanding of these terms. For example, one group spent considerable time deconstructing the phrase *math problem,* a conversation that lasted nearly the entire school year. The act of pausing became a norm in their interaction, and a natural occurrence in their collaboration. Stopping group activity while creating or scoring an assessment takes time, but it results in deeper and more meaningful teacher learning as well as tools that are more precisely focused on desired student-learning goals. When teachers do not have a precise collective understanding of central words and ideas, they are generally working on the same thing but not truly collaborating as a team to deepen their thinking and advance their practice.

Aligning Purpose

When learning goals and content are clarified, it is much easier for teacher groups to align the overall purpose of their assessment. For many groups this began with discussions of "skills vs. concepts" or "We need more problem solving." But as these terms were unpacked, an increased clarity and alignment of purpose regarding the assessments emerged.

As an example, a group of fifth- through eighth-grade teachers in a small, rural school district designed their mathematics assessments using the response to intervention (RTI) model. They created and administered a series of formative assessments for the purpose of identifying individual students' progress toward learning goals as well as surfacing students' understandings of key mathematical topics. Each Friday, the four teachers held special enrichment sessions with selected groups that targeted the mathematical needs of these students at that particular time. The groups contained a mix of students from across the grade levels and focused on a mathematical content area (e.g., ratio and rate) or practice (e.g., problem solving) the teachers were collectively addressing. The teacher team was very careful to design and analyze their assessments in a way that allowed free movement of students up and down the levels of enrichment and to design their weekly sessions in ways that provided appropriate mathematical challenge to every student. The collective purpose of this group of teachers was to ensure challenging and enriching mathematical experiences for *all* students, and they aligned their assessment and instruction to fit this purpose. Beliefs about mathematics, how it should be taught, and what it means to learn mathematics surfaced for these teachers as they worked together to develop and score student assessments. Consider the following excerpt from a weekly session:

Colby: You can go through this on the taxonomy part and it tells you, starting with the basics and going all the way up into higher level thinking. But once again, it's just a matter of being able to, to know what the student knows.

Maggie: So where would that fit in, what will students know and what will students be able to do into what—

Michelle: So it sounds like the same thing you and I had talked about, Serena. Really being able to weed out and focus on what kids really do need to know and get rid of the extraneous stuff—

Amanda: And this is like, that there's different levels of teaching. I didn't want to just blindly follow the lessons, which is what I did last year.

In this brief segment, ideas on how to analyze data and some highly personal beliefs about teaching were shared. Such deeply held beliefs about teaching can drive teachers' decision making and interpretation of events. Spending time to discuss these broader purposes and attempting to align beliefs about teaching not only enhances the collaborative nature of the teacher team, but it also provides clarity and focus to the learning goals and assessments and a more unified approach to the interpretation of SLD.

We observed other teacher groups who did not explicitly share their purpose, rationale, or beliefs about what they were doing. They composed or revised assessment tools without stopping to clarify, individually or for the group, their purpose and rationale. Quite often such groups made narrow implications about what the data revealed and used these implications for short-term planning. However, when teachers revealed their beliefs about what they wanted to do and why, and when some agreement was established, there was a cohesive purpose between group members. What they wanted their SLD to reveal became clearer, and their collaborative work became more aligned. Further, even when such groups created an assessment tool they felt was inadequate or when full agreement was not reached, the teachers still felt the process was beneficial because it tightened their alignment and made all subsequent conversations more productive and precise.

Focusing on Students' Mathematical Thinking

Developing SLD tools to reveal student thinking can be accomplished in a variety of ways, including efficient and straightforward means. One group of middle school teachers simply added a space for students to explain their thinking after their multiple-choice selection. This format showed teachers that sometimes students selected the correct answers but used faulty reasoning or held limited conceptual understanding. This information was then used to rethink their collective approach to teaching this concept. Another group of teachers built on their prior work of identifying key learning targets to engage in more focused discussions about the nature of the mathematical knowledge and thinking they hoped to develop. This group exhibited a mixture of perspectives related to mathematical thinking, based on their interpretation of the data. Some of the teachers in this group interpreted data from a proving perspective, making statements such as "I'm finding kids I thought might be pretty low aren't actually as low as I thought." However, other teachers discussed the various ways they observed students doing mental mathematics, or they shared the various strategies students used to solve problems. They then used this information to increase the mathematical challenge of the learning experiences in line with these observed understandings and practices.

One group of high school mathematics teachers collaboratively developed an SLD tool to support their classroom enactment of group problem solving (table 14.1). The tool also supported their data collection and analysis efforts. This tool prompted the teachers to clarify learning goals and then pay special attention to the solution strategies observed. Not only did this support their collective instruction, it provided a common lens through which to think about important student learning goals and through which they collaboratively analyzed data.

Table 14.1

Instructional and observational protocol for mathematical problem solving and group work

	Students	Teacher
Before group work	• Understand expectations of task • Work individually on the problem	• Make expectations of task clear • Efficient group assignment and formation • Provide enough quiet time
During group work	• Close proximity • Math Talk (ask questions, clarify thinking) • Work together (focus on same problem at same time) • All in agreement (?) on solution/strategy	• Identify key solutions/strategies to bring to whole class discussion
After group work	• Individual reflection/accountability • Whole class share strategies/solutions	• Prepared with questions to ask during presentations

Professionalizing Dialogue

Our final collaborative practice involves the approaches teachers take to the interactions in which they engage. Teacher professionalism has an increasingly collaborative nature:

 Mathematics teachers are professionals who do not do this work in isolation. They cultivate and support a culture of professional collaboration and continual improvement, driven by an abiding sense of interdependence and collective responsibility. (National Council of Teachers of Mathematics [NCTM] 2014, p. 99)

Professional collaboration is closely tied to the relationships and norms of interaction that exist inside a teacher group. Specifically, we found that teacher groups increased the professional nature of their interactions by regulating their conversation in two important ways: They remained on task, and they respectfully challenged or sought clarification from each other.

First, teacher groups who engaged in professional dialogue were able to maintain focus and avoid conversations that derailed them from deeper SLD discussion. Several groups we observed lost focus by veering to talk about student characteristics (being unmotivated or unorganized), department business (scheduling activities, curriculum issues, or ordering materials), or events of the day. Successful groups recognized when they had gone off task and quickly refocused; at times this was the task of the facilitator, but groups that developed this norm were able to refocus in spontaneous ways.

Second, teacher groups who exhibited professional interactions did not accept statements on face value, nor did they leave confusing or debatable comments unchecked. They had an expectation that probing questions about content, learning targets, purpose, and instruction should be a regular part of the professional conversations teachers have. These teachers probed for deeper, clearer meanings and developed the norm of asking and answering questions such as, "Do we understand ____ the same way?" "How do you think kids will think about this problem/idea?" "Why is this the best assessment tool to get what we want?" and "Is there another way to accomplish this?" As important, these teachers developed the norm of reflecting on and addressing the questions and concerns of their colleagues. Teachers who took a professional approach to their interactions sought clarity and justification from others, and they did not just politely accept a statement or fail to reflect on what was being said (Nelson et al. 2010). Teachers who held each other accountable and required justifications for their decisions sharpened their own thinking and fostered a work environment where student learning was discussed in more explicit terms.

■ Conclusion

The development and use of student-learning data tools is a complex process, but it is also one that can be a resource for improving teaching, particularly in collaborative settings. We argue that teachers who work with student-learning data should be engaged in collaborative practices that highlight content and learning goals that are purposefully aligned, and they should then work to achieve clarity on the precise nature of the mathematical content and practices on which to focus. The ability of teachers to interact professionally during these activities mediates the power of this work.

The above five practices require dedication, intellectual support, and time. Collaborative teacher activity that seeks to meaningfully affect future instruction through the creation and analysis of SLD must be supported in several key ways. These include (1) the provision of adequate time for ongoing collaborative work, (2) the freedom to take risks in assessment choices, (3) technical classroom assessment support, and (4) intellectual supports necessary to engage in purposeful, content-rich discussions of learning goals and student thinking.

The power of student-learning data lies in its use. Teacher collaboration around SLD can significantly increase its potential power, and it can sharpen mathematics instruction around the precise needs of students. When supported, teachers are quite capable of engaging in productive collaborative practices that can develop student-learning data to improve mathematics instruction.

References

Borko, Hilda. "Professional Development and Teacher Learning: Mapping the Terrain." *Educational Researcher* 33, no. 8 (2004): 3–15.

Cochran-Smith, Marilyn, and Susan L. Lytle. *Inquiry as Stance: Practitioner Research for the Next Generation.* New York: Teachers College Press, 2009.

Garmston, Robert J., and Bruce M. Wellman. *The Adaptive School: A Sourcebook for Developing Collaborative Groups.* Lanham, Md.: Rowan & Littlefield, 2013 (original publication date 1999).

Hiebert, James, Ronald Gallimore, and James W. Stigler. "A Knowledge Base for the Teaching Profession: What Would It Look Like and How Can We Get One?" *Educational Researcher* 31, no. 5 (2002): 3–15.

Horn, Ilana Seidel, Britnie Delinger Kane, and Jonee Wilson. "Making Sense of Student Performance Data: Data Use Logics and Mathematics Teachers' Learning Opportunities." *American Educational Research Journal* 52, no. 2 (2015): 208–42.

Huguet, Alice, Julie A. Marsh, and Caitlin C. Farrell. "Building Teachers' Data-Use Capacity: Insights from Strong and Developing Coaches." *Education Policy Analysis Archives* 22, no. 52 (2014): 1–31.

Jimerson, Jo Beth, and Jeffrey C. Wayman. "Professional Learning for Using Data: Examining Teacher Needs and Supports." *Teachers College Record* 117, no. 4 (2015): 1–36.

Little, Judith Warren, Maryl Gearhart, Marnie Curry, and Judith Kafka. "Looking at Student Work for Teacher Learning, Teacher Community, and School Reform." *Phi Delta Kappan* 85, no. 3 (2003): 184–92.

National Council of Teachers of Mathematics (NCTM). *Principles to Actions: Ensuring Mathematical Success for All*. Reston, Va.: NCTM, 2014.

National Governors Association Center for Best Practices and Council of Chief State School Officers (NGA Center and CCSSO). *Common Core State Standards for Mathematics*. Washington, D.C.: NGA Center and CCSSO, 2010. http://www.corestandards.org.

Nelson, Tamara Holmlund, Angie Deuel, David Slavit, and Anne Kennedy. "Leading Deep Conversations in Collaborative Inquiry Groups." *The Clearing House* 83, no. 5 (2010): 175–79.

Nelson, Tamara Holmlund, David Slavit, and Angie Deuel. "Two Dimensions of an Inquiry Stance toward Student-Learning Data." *Teachers College Record* 114, no. 8 (2012): 1–42.

Slavit, David, Tamara Holmlund Nelson, and Angie Deuel. "Teacher Groups' Conceptions and Uses of Student-Learning Data." *Journal of Teacher Education* 64, no. 1 (2013): 8–21.

Slavit, David, Tamara Holmlund Nelson, and Angie Kennedy, eds. *Perspectives on Supported Collaborative Teacher Inquiry*. New York: Taylor & Francis, 2009.

Wells, Gordon. *Dialogic Inquiry: Towards a Socio-Cultural Practice and Theory of Education*. Cambridge, U.K.: Cambridge University Press, 1999.

Appendix

Collaborative Inquiry Meeting Facilitation Protocol

Part 1: Scoring Student Work (30 minutes)

Facilitator should select 5–6 papers that the group will score together during this part.

Facilitator: Elicit and/or state the **purposes** of scoring student work together:

- Test and refine rubric
- Develop common agreement regarding criteria
- Develop consistency among teachers regarding scoring tasks

Process: Round Robin

- Each teacher should read and score each paper in the group. Record the score, rationale for the score, and any questions or comments related to the rubric.
- After all have scored and recorded, discuss each paper individually until agreement is found regarding the score.
- Modify the rubric as needed based on observations made during the scoring process.

Part 2: Analyzing Student Work (45 minutes)

Teachers should bring a class set of student work for this part.

Facilitator: Elicit and/or state the **purposes** of analyzing student work together:

- Determine the nature and extent of student understanding
- Clarify learning expectations
- Determine the implications for instructional practice and effectiveness

Facilitator: How are these purposes related to our inquiry question? *Make sure teachers recognize that one goal of this activity is to consider how they might modify the group-work lessons to improve student performance on this and other rich, problem-solving tasks.*

Anticipate:

- Identify the important mathematical ideas in the task and alignment to standards.
- List the types of strategies and/or solutions you expect to see.
- Clarify additional criteria pertinent to the task (e.g., communication)

Process:

- Ask each teacher to **randomly** select 3 papers from their class set to work with. Label them in the top right corner with teacher initials and paper #(1, 2, 3).

- All teachers select their paper #1 to review and record the following on their own student analysis chart:

  — Rank the paper as High, Medium, or Low

  — List evidence based on criteria:

    ♦ What evidence of mathematical understanding?

    ♦ What strategies does the student use?

    ♦ How does the student communicate their understanding?

  — Pass #1 papers around the group so that all have been analyzed by each member.

  — After all have reviewed #1, the group should compare their evidence and ranking and resolve discrepancies.

  — Repeat with set #2 (and #3 if there is time).

  — Organize the analyzed papers into three sets according to their rank.

  — As a group, review each stack:

    ♦ Identify any trends that seem to be emerging. Teachers may want to review their remaining work samples to see how consistent their observations are (finding something in two papers does not constitute a trend).

    ♦ Identify and plan instructional changes, modifications, and supports that will increase student performance related to the standard and PLC Inquiry.

CHAPTER 15

Using Formative Evaluation to Support Teachers in Increasing Student Reasoning

Kathleen Melhuish, *Texas State University, San Marcos*
Eva Thanhieser, *Portland State University, Portland, Oregon*

In this chapter, we introduce an observation tool designed to capture instances of high-level student reasoning and the corresponding teacher moves/actions that promote such reasoning. The Mathematically Productive Habits and Routines Tool (MPHR) was developed as part of a large quasi-experimental study addressing the efficacy of Teacher Development Group's studio model professional development (PD) (Foreman 2010). The tool was developed with several simultaneous purposes in mind: (1) as a research tool for collecting data about what is occurring in classrooms with respect to teaching and student reasoning, (2) as a learning tool where teachers and school leaders can learn more about best practices for teaching and learning mathematics, and (3) as a tool for teachers and school leaders to use to reflect on their classrooms and grow in their practice. This chapter focuses primarily on the third purpose.

■ The Context for the Observation Tool

The theory of action underlying our work depends on four principles (Foreman 2013):

1. *Students' reasoning and sense making about core math content (and its trajectory) must guide all teaching actions and decisions.* Building on students' current understanding and their reasoning and sense making is essential for students to build a coherent understanding (Bransford, Brown, and Cocking 1999) and promote learning (Lampert et al. 2013).

2. *All students are capable mathematical thinkers. Their mind-sets and identity as mathematicians are central to success.* Students who see themselves as capable mathematical thinkers are able to develop their mathematical understanding (National Research Council 2001). Students with growth mind-sets are more likely to improve their mathematical understanding (Dweck 2007).

3. *Cognitive demand always matters.* Cognitive demand refers to the kind of thinking processes involved in solving the task (Stein et al. 2009). If we want students engaging deeply with mathematics, teacher actions should promote high cognitive demand through focusing on reasoning rather than correct/incorrect answers (Stein and Lane 1996).

4. *Planning always matters. Public, collaborative planning and coached "live" rehearsals make the invisible aspects of mathematically productive teaching visible.* Teacher reflection is necessary for transformative teaching (Arzt and Armour-Thomas 2002). This involves the thoughts teachers have before, during, and after the actual enactment of a lesson (p. 7). Through shared observation, teachers may be motivated to improve their own teaching and have a "common referent" to reflect on pedagogy (Lewis, Perry, and Hurd 2009).

We believe that all students should have access to *powerful mathematical practices*, as in the Common Core State Standards for Mathematical Practice (National Governors Association Center for Best Practices and Council of Chief State School Officers [NGA Center and CCSSO] 2010), *powerful mathematical understanding*, and continuous engagement in a *culture of sense making and reasoning*. We not only attend to students and teachers but also view school leaders as providing an essential mechanism of support and development of a school culture that promotes productive classrooms.

We present the tool as a product of our current research to illustrate its utility to (1) work with school leaders in observing and reflecting on classroom visits as well as planning feedback for teachers and (2) work with teachers in observing and reflecting on classroom observations (their own or others').

■ The Structure of the Observation Tool

We developed the MPHR instrument to capture the critical components of mathematically productive classrooms in accordance with a large body of research (Cuoco, Goldenberg, and Mark 1996; Stein et al. 2008) on which our theory of action is based. To that end, the instrument covers both how students engage in mathematics and what teachers do, thus allowing for powerful reflecting on the connection between teacher moves and student engagement. The instrument is divided in four categories: Students—*Mathematical Habits of Mind and Interaction*, Teaching—*Mathematically Productive Teaching Routines*, Teaching—*Catalytic Teaching Habits*, and Lesson—*Cognitive Demand* and *Connection to Learning Targets*. See figure 15.1 for a screenshot of our in-development tablet application version of the tool. In this chapter, we focus on the student and teaching categories.

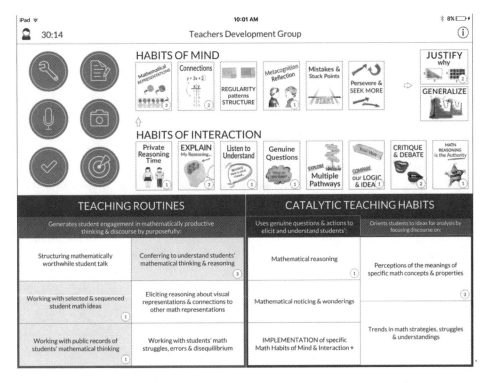

Fig. 15.1. Screenshot of the observation tool from an in-development iPad™ application (reproduced with permission from Teachers Development Group, West Linn, Oreg.)

The Habits of Mind (HoM) and Habits of Interaction (HoI) are established ways that students can engage with mathematics at a deep level. The HoM are how students think and make sense of mathematics, and the HoI are the ways in which students interact to allow for those powerful ways of thinking. The core habits of justifying and generalizing are presented at the top of the tool. We posit that these are the essential habits to make sense of mathematical ideas. The remaining HoM are the tools needed to do this successfully; these include making connections, using representations, and engaging in metacognition and reflection. The HoI that support engagement in these HoM include habits such as private reasoning time, critiquing and debating, and asking genuine questions. This chain of dependence is reflected in classrooms where, in order for students to justify and generalize, students interact in ways that allow for deep engagement, access, and analysis of ideas.

In the teaching categories, we focus at two levels: extended routines (Mathematically Productive Teaching Routines) and the smaller moves that live within these routines (Catalytic Teaching Habits). The Mathematically Productive Teaching Routines (MPTR) are the following:

1. Structuring student mathematical talk

2. Working with selected and sequenced mathematical ideas

3. Working with public records of students' mathematical thinking

4. Conferring to understand students' mathematical thinking

5. Working with students' visual representations

6. Working with students' mathematical struggles and misconceptions

Catalytic Teaching Habits (CTH) then serve two major purposes: researching student thinking and orienting students to mathematical ideas for analysis. For purpose 1, researching student thinking, the CTH are: Using purposeful, genuine questions and actions to (1a) reveal students' mathematical reasoning, (1b) reveal students' perceptions of the meanings of math concepts/ideas, (1c) elicit students' noticings and wonderings, (1d) foster student engagement habits of mind, and interaction, and (1e) monitor for trends in students' mathematical thinking. For purpose 2, orienting students to ideas for analysis and/or comparison, the CTH are: (2a) eliciting/working with mathematical contradictions, (2b) asking one or more students to re-voice another's math reasoning, (2c) making public a specific line of math reasoning, (2d) asking students to identify the mathematical structure(s) involved in one or more strategies, and (2e) providing/asking for mathematical evidence of student use of a specific habit of mind or interaction. The teaching routines lead to high levels of students engaging in mathematical reasoning when paired with specific CTHs that promote such reasoning. See figure 15.2 for an illustration of how the components interconnect and depend on our theory of action. For examples of the classroom interaction dependencies, we provide vignettes in the section that follows.

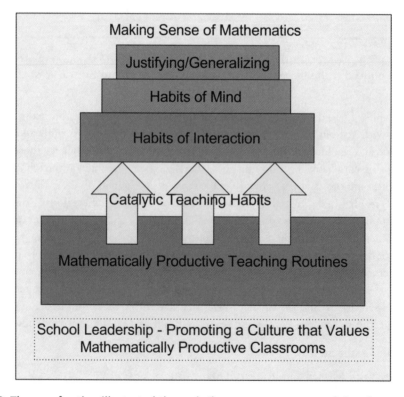

Fig. 15.2. Theory of action illustrated through the core components of the observation tool

■ Research Observation Tools as Formative Evaluation Tools

Validated research tools can be boundary objects (Stein and Coburn 2008) and as such serve multiple purposes; for example: determining the effectiveness of interventions, and also helping teachers (and leaders) "create, learn, and reflect on practice" (Coburn and Stein 2010). The MPHR tool serves the dual purposes of measuring PD implementation and providing a means for *formative evaluation*. We use this construct in a way parallel to formative assessment. Formative evaluation differs from traditional summative evaluations in that the purpose is not to rate a teacher for some final purpose but rather to provide ongoing opportunities for learning and reflection on *teaching* and provide school leadership with insight into what their teachers' professional learning needs are. Adapting Nicol and Macfarlane-Dick's (2006) synthesis of formative assessment literature and formative evaluation with the MPHR tool—

1. helps clarify what good performance is (goals, criteria, expected standards);

2. facilitates the development of reflection in teaching;

3. delivers high-quality information to teachers about their teaching and student learning;

4. encourages teacher leaders and teacher dialogue around teaching/learning;

5. encourages positive motivational beliefs and self-esteem;

6. provides opportunities to close the gap between current and desired performance; and

7. provides information to school leaders that can be used to help shape their support of teachers.

By keeping the focus on the quality of student mathematics engagement and teaching moves, we keep the focus on teaching rather than on teachers, and we concretely connect teaching to what is actually going on with students. These connections provide the lens for growth and reflection and the tools to increase student reasoning through specific and targeted teaching routines and moves.

■ The Creation and Validation of the Observation Tool

The MPHR tool was developed to reflect the critical components of a research-based mathematics PD aimed at promoting high levels of student mathematical reasoning through regular use of mathematical habits of mind and interaction. The PD-promoted habits and routines are connected to a large body of research corresponding to best practices in teaching (Stein et al. 2008), promoting accountable talk (Michaels, O'Connor, and Resnick 2008), maintaining high cognitive demand (Henningsen and Stein 1997), and following the National Council of Teachers of Mathematics's (NCTM) *Principles to Actions* (2014).

The tool was developed and refined through piloting across various grades 3–5 elementary classrooms in a subset of schools from a midsize urban district. Once the categories and their relationships to one another were stabilized, members of the research team measured implementation of the PD across twelve elementary schools participating in the study's PD. Through collecting these data, lessons were categorized based on the quality and quantity of student reasoning and supporting teaching moves with scores of none, minimal, low-medium, high-medium, and high. In order to validate the tool, these levels were then correlated with two sources: teacher lessons coded using the Mathematical Quality of Instruction instrument (Hill 2010) and the PD facilitator's ratings of teacher implementation (Melhuish and Thanheiser, forthcoming).

In addition to research purposes, the tool has been tested with school leaders and groups of teachers reflecting on lessons. Our PD facilitators have taken principals and coaches into teachers' classrooms at schools across the country. After the observations, the facilitators and coaches use the tool to make sense of what they saw in the classroom, identify teacher-learning needs, and reflect on how leadership can support teacher growth. Additionally, as part of the PD, teachers jointly observe a colleague's lesson and use the tool to reflect on what occurred in the classroom. They place careful attention first to what the students did and to what habits of mind and/or habits of interaction they used, and then to how that connects to various mathematically productive teaching routines and catalytic teaching habits. In this way, the tool served to strengthen teachers' understanding of the mechanisms for promoting mathematically productive classrooms. In the next section, we elaborate on using the tool in this manner with two vignettes based on classrooms we have observed.

■ Illustrations of Tool Usage from Our Research Schools

We present two vignettes of contrasting fifth-grade classrooms. Both vignettes and accompanying reflections are based on our observations of several classrooms and as such represent a synthesis of multiple observations. They provide brief glimpses into hypothetical classrooms representative of those in our case study schools. Additionally, we pair our discussion of the classrooms with quotes from principals and teachers in our project reflecting on classrooms that served to inform our vignettes. The principal and teacher quotes come from three sources: principal reflections after entering teacher classrooms, discussions among teachers after watching a common lesson, and teachers' written reflections after engaging in these activities. The formative impact of the tool lies in its ability to capture the relationship between teaching moves and student reasoning levels, and so we focus heavily on these relationships. We provide two examples of the launch and beginning of a task where students engage in exploring the following expression: $8 \div {}^3/_4$. For each vignette, we pair the transcript with the habits and routines being used by both students and teachers. After each vignette, we spend some time looking at these connections and outlining how school leaders or other teachers observing lessons might use the tool.

When working in schools, we have a series of questions to help observers debrief reflections. The first focus is making sense of what they saw. We begin with a focus on students: *What sort of habits were students engaged in? Did the students arrive at justifying or generalizing mathematical ideas?* By starting reflections in this manner, we found that school leaders and teachers were able to focus on student reasoning first rather than on other aspects of the classrooms or on evaluating teacher actions without connection to student reasoning. The next question focuses on the teacher actions: *What teaching routines and catalytic teaching habits lead to students engaging in the habits?* This directs the analysis of teacher moves toward their immediate impact on student reasoning. The second focus is identifying teacher learning needs and opportunities for growth. Effective questions include ones such as these: *What catalytic teaching habit could promote more student engagement in [enter habit of interest here]? How can a teaching routine be leveraged or added to increase student reasoning? What in the lesson could be justified and/or generalized and how can teaching habits and routines support students in achieving that reasoning?*

Vignette #1

The first vignette illustrates the opening of a lesson focused on making sense of dividing a whole number by a fraction with particular attention to the meaning of the remainder. In this classroom, the teacher opens with the task $8 \div \frac{3}{4}$. She further prompts her students to use a visual representation to make sense of the problem. Figure 15.4 (on the following page) provides a transcript of the start of this class along with the corresponding habits and routines connected to the observation tool. The CTH are preceded by black diamonds; the teaching routines ("Structures Student Math Talk," etc.) are in the other dark boxes; and the student habits ("Private Reasoning Time," etc.) are in white boxes. The launch includes focus on using a model for division. A similar model can be found in figure 15.3. Students draw 8 circles and divide each in fourths. Then they count out $\frac{3}{4}$ successively (see the dark and medium gray quadrants in fig. 15.3) with two pieces left over (see the light gray on the right side of the eighth circle in fig. 15.3). Two possible interpretations of the remainder emerged: $\frac{1}{2}$ of 1 and $\frac{2}{3}$ of $\frac{3}{4}$. The lesson continued by focusing on a student question as to the meaning of the remainder in this problem. This question served as the launching point for the remainder of the lesson where students critiqued and debated the two potential remainder interpretations: $\frac{1}{2}$ or $\frac{2}{3}$.

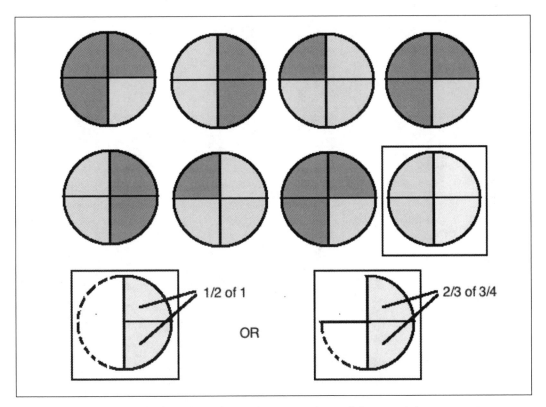

Fig. 15.3. Model of $8 \div \frac{3}{4}$ with two interpretations of the remaining two parts

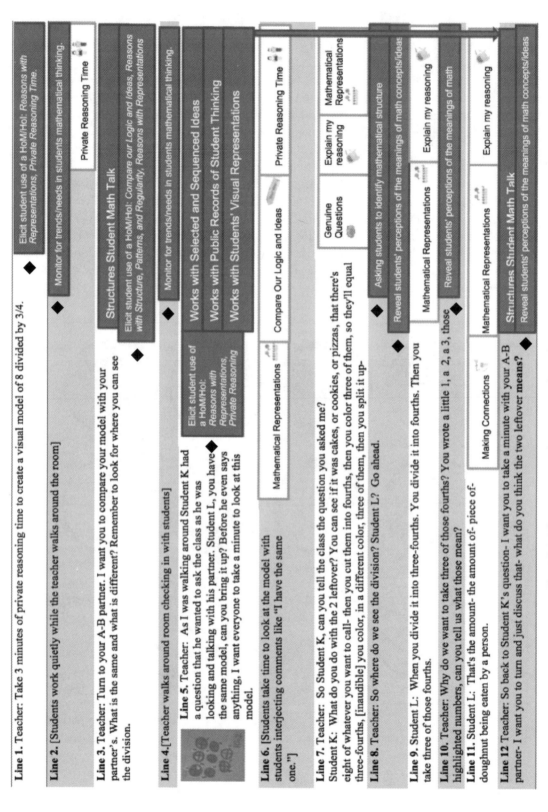

Fig. 15.4. Vignette #1 and corresponding observation tool categories

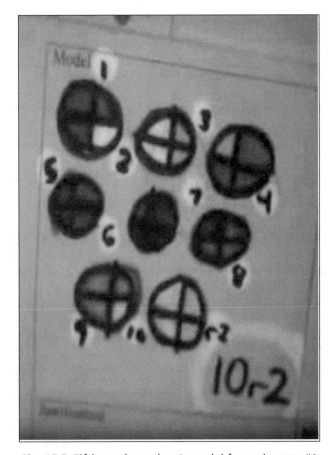

Fig. 15.5. Fifth-grade student's model from vignette #1

The first vignette was rich in terms of students engaging in habits, teaching routines, and teaching habits (see fig. 15.5 for an example of a student's model). This teacher frequently not just used routines but also leveraged CTH within the routines. This led to students engaging in genuine reasoning where they made sense of a problem using representations connected to meaning, and they asked genuine questions that eventually led to rich mathematical exploration and learning.

Debrief Focus #1: What was the nature of student reasoning and how did teacher habits and routines promote this reasoning?

The teachers and school leaders in our project always begin by addressing the formative evaluation goal of providing high-quality information about the teaching and learning in the classroom. This occurs through reflection on what happened in terms of student reasoning and how the teaching supported the reasoning. In vignette 1, there are several strong examples of how teaching actions connected to student reasoning. This teacher repeatedly went back to the underlying meaning of mathematical ideas (lines 3, 8) and to what we identify as part of the structure of mathematics. When the teacher had students talk to their partners, she used the mathematically productive teaching routine of Structuring Student Mathematical

Talk (MPTR 1) in order to promote productive mathematical discussion (see fig. 15.6a for an illustration). She used a Catalytic Teaching Habit when she prompted them to *compare* (CTH 1d) their ideas through looking at what is the same and different and *reason with structure* (CTH 1d) via attending to the meaning of division. In her reflection, the teacher stated that these actions led to a student asking a *genuine question* about what the remainder means. During whole-class discussion, the teacher engaged in many mathematically productive routines. For example, she worked with *student visual representations* (MPTR 5) (see fig. 15.6b for an illustration). In the process of doing this, she pressed for students to find where the division was in the problem, connecting the catalytic teaching habit of *identifying structure in student ideas* (CTH 2d). This led to the student *reasoning with a representation*, and *explaining his reasoning* through *connecting* the model to the story context.

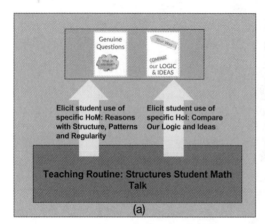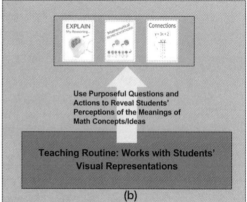

Fig. 15.6. Teaching routines, catalytic teaching habits, and
student habit relationships from vignette #1

Teachers and principals in our project explicated these types of connections. For example, one principal reflected that "it was a kind of a public record [MPTR 3], but she had, because there were some examples of students' thinking up there on the board. So, with that, also some probing to reveal students' mathematical reasoning and understanding [CTH 1a], with that, and that just had led to, the students also sharing out their perceptions of the meaning and the math, and other ideas." An observing teacher reflected (on a full lesson), "I noticed that she was . . . elicit[ing] students' mathematical noticings and wonderings [CTH 1c] about . . . the representations [HoM], making connections [HoM] to and about the representations . . . and they did that through some critique and debate [HoI] and explaining [HoI]. And that all led to those justifications [HoM] that they were making." By the end of the project, both the principal and teachers were able to notice the dependencies that eventually led to high-level student reasoning.

Debrief Focus #2: Opportunities for leader and teacher professional learning

The students in this lesson excerpt engaged in high-level reasoning through using models, connecting to the meaning of division, and trying to make sense of the remainder in this problem. In addition to providing rich information about what occurred in the classrooms, the leaders and teachers always focused on the formative evaluation purpose of professional growth by focusing on next steps for increasing student reasoning. The teachers and principals in our project reflected on the degree to which students engage in the habits of mind and whether or not they are reaching the capstone habits of justifying and generalizing. Consider the following formative plan put forth after a classroom observation by one of our principals: The principal would start with asking the teacher *What are you noticing about [student understanding/habits]* in order to understand what the teacher is noticing and to encourage self-reflection, *because that gives us information about what she's seeing.* In a classroom such as the one in the vignette, students are engaging in high-level reasoning, so the next step to focus on is reaching the capstone habits of justifying and generalizing: *How do we, so students are able to eventually take their understanding and [generalize] it from one question to another . . . What would that look like and sound like?* The focus is for this teacher to reflect on moving the mathematics beyond the specifics of this problem to a generalizable statement. Notice the principal's formative evaluation is focused on (1) what students are doing, (2) what higher-level reasoning would look like and sound like in the classroom, and (3) how the teacher can support it. In terms of the sample vignette, the resulting conversation may focus on what a targeted generalization might be, such as "the remainder is always what proportion of the divisor is left." If students are to generalize, they need multiple examples and the opportunity to notice and make sense of regularity. A targeted teaching move to promote generalizing might be CTH 1c, eliciting students' noticings and wonderings. Through the conversation with a principal, a coach, other teachers, or self-reflection, thinking about targeting a generalization provides opportunities for the classroom teacher to think deeply about the mathematics content, anticipate what students might say or do in response to a task, and plan for what teaching actions might support the emergence of a generalization.

Vignette #2

The second vignette reflects another fifth-grade classroom that similarly uses $8 \div {}^3/_4$ as a launching point for the lesson. The focus in this lesson is using the procedure of flipping and multiplying to find the quotient. The beginning of the lesson can be found in figure 15.7, along with corresponding observation tool categories. After the shared classroom vignette, the lesson focuses on practicing the procedure of flipping and multiplying on additional problems.

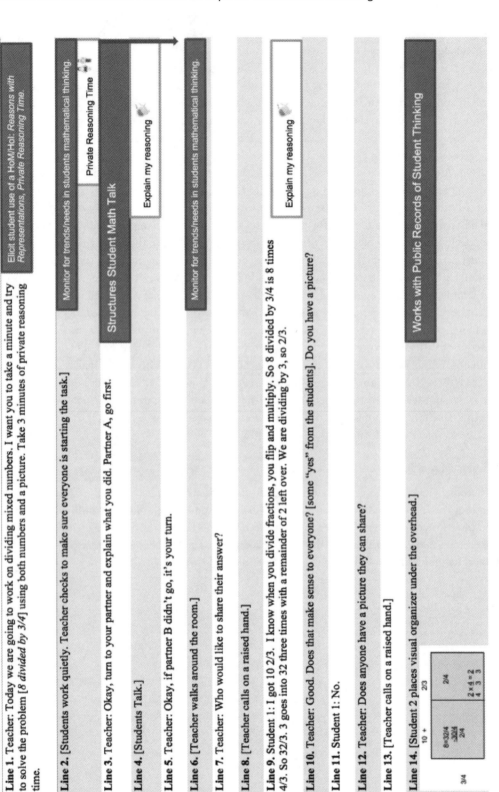

Elict student use of a HoM/HoI: *Reasons with Representations, Private Reasoning Time.*

Line 1. Teacher: Today we are going to work on dividing mixed numbers. I want you to take a minute and try to solve the problem [8 *divided by 3/4*] using both numbers and a picture. Take 3 minutes of private reasoning time.

Monitor for trends/needs in students mathematical thinking.

Private Reasoning Time

Line 2. [Students work quietly. Teacher checks to make sure everyone is starting the task.]

Structures Student Math Talk

Line 3. Teacher: Okay, turn to your partner and explain what you did. Partner A, go first.

Explain my reasoning

Line 4. [Students Talk.]

Line 5. Teacher: Okay, if partner B didn't go, it's your turn.

Monitor for trends/needs in students mathematical thinking.

Line 6. [Teacher walks around the room.]

Line 7. Teacher: Who would like to share their answer?

Line 8. [Teacher calls on a raised hand.]

Explain my reasoning

Line 9. Student 1: I got 10 2/3. I know when you divide fractions, you flip and multiply. So 8 divided by 3/4 is 8 times 4/3. So 32/3. 3 goes into 32 three times with a remainder of 2 left over. We are dividing by 3, so 2/3.

Line 10. Teacher: Good. Does that make sense to everyone? [some "yes" from the students]. Do you have a picture?

Line 11. Student 1: No.

Line 12. Teacher: Does anyone have a picture they can share?

Line 13. [Teacher calls on a raised hand.]

Works with Public Records of Student Thinking

Line 14. [Student 2 places visual organizer under the overhead.]

Fig. 15.7. Vignette #2 and corresponding observation tool categories

This vignette provided a starkly different classroom, with some positive things occurring. Students had time to think about the problem and were asked to share their ideas. However, students engaged minimally with Habits of Interaction, and they did not engage with the Habits of Mind.

Debrief Focus #1: What was the nature of student reasoning and how did teacher habits and routines promote this reasoning?

Within this vignette, students explained their procedures and used private reasoning time. These habits of interactions were linked tightly with the teacher questions, including explicit prompting to take private reasoning time (CTH 1e). Students also explained their reasoning (in terms of procedures) which followed structuring talk by having the students turn and talk to their neighbors (MPHR 1). However, the teaching routines and CTH occurred in isolation (see fig. 15.8 for an illustration). One principal reflected, "She was working with public records [MPTR 1] and turn and talk with your neighbor [MPTR 1]. . . . The vast majority of kids as I was walking around were just [procedurally] solving it so I'm making an assumption that they already have a generalization . . . doing computation. Compared to a generalization [HoM] [or] currently trying to make a connection [HoM]." The principals and teachers in our project spent a great deal of their time reflecting on whether students moved beyond procedures. This principal's reflection was representative of teacher, coach, and principal observations of classrooms similar to vignette #2. The principal noticed the use of a routine but also that students generally were not engaging in higher-level reasoning.

Debrief Focus #2: Opportunities for leader and teacher professional learning

At this point, the teacher is engaging students and providing opportunities for them to contribute to the mathematics lesson. However, these opportunities are not always rich. As in the first vignette, the professional growth purpose of formative evaluation remains focused on raising the level of student reasoning. In this case, that may focus on promoting the use of any HoM. One participant suggested CTH 1b—"pressing for student perceptions of meaning, concepts, and ideas"—as a teaching move that may lead to higher reasoning. An important emphasis of this reflection is how using the teaching routines can lead to richer student mathematics when they are paired with catalytic teaching habits. In addition to the above suggestion, this might include asking for a model that visually represents the problem (such as in fig. 15.3) and connects to the meaning of division (the visual the student presented served more as a graphic organizer). Another move is prompting students to share reasoning in terms of not just explaining their procedure but also explaining why it works (CTH 1d: explaining). There are a number of paths this discussion could take. The key aspects of the formative evaluation include richly describing the student discourse, reflecting on the teaching routines and habits that can alter the level of student reasoning, and finding an accessible and doable next step. By concretely addressing structuring the talk, the teacher can think about how to incorporate mathematically minded questions in partner talk in order to have students make connections and leverage representations. This again provides the opportunity for the teacher to think deeply about the mathematics (the meaning of division and how that relates to the remainder) and about pedagogical moves that may lead to students deepening their own mathematical understanding.

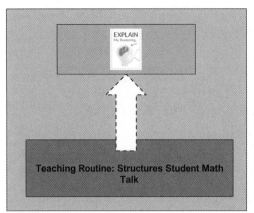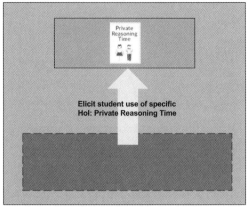

Fig. 15.8. Teaching routines, catalytic teaching habits, and
student habit relationships from vignette #1

■ Comparing across the Vignettes in Terms of Formative Evaluation

Vignette #1 and #2 provided contrasting classrooms to illustrate how the MPHR tool can serve as a means for formative evaluation in classrooms with a variety of levels of student reasoning. In both cases, the tool focused on noticing positive teacher moves and student interactions, such as students explaining their reasoning and the teacher providing private reasoning time. However, connecting explicitly among CTHs, MPTR, and student habits of mind and interaction resulted in different types of learning. In the case of the first classroom, this teacher can reflect on what actions successfully promoted high-level reasoning in order to promote continued use of best practices. Additionally, we have found that teachers who observe classrooms with richly connected teaching moves and high student reasoning were able to appreciate and reflect about building such connections into their classrooms. For example, one teacher in our project shared this personal teaching goal: "Pressing for student perceptions of the meanings of ideas by having them explain their work, their classmate's work, and through my questioning of students." In contrast, the lack of connection among MPTRs, CTHs, and the resulting level of student reasoning in the second classroom types allows for rich reflection about how these can be connected in order to improve the level of student reasoning. For example, one teacher (whose classroom was reflected in vignette #2) noted a personal teaching goal that focused specifically on including the missing CTHs: "My intention for my next lesson is to refine my probing to better understand their mathematical reasoning [MPTR 4: CTH 1a]. Also, press for meaning of math concepts [CTH 1b]." Many of the other participating teachers explicitly put forth the building of "triangles" [connections among MPTRs, CTHs, and MoH/Is) as their teaching goal.

The primary focus in the second classroom is raising the level of student reasoning from reasoning with procedures to reasoning with procedures *connected to mathematical meaning*. In contrast, the first lesson is well connected to meaning but provides learning opportunities in terms of moving up the reasoning hierarchy to generalizing. The observing teachers, the classroom teachers, and the leaders in our project have used this as a focus. For example, several teacher goals reflected this move towards generalization with suggestions of "Will this always work?" being a guiding question in lessons, and with conscious thinking on how to raise levels of student reasoning such as one teacher noting, "I want to pay attention to the discourse type of my students so I can think about how to move them into the levels of justifying and generalizing."

In both types of classrooms, the tool provides a means for reflection, analyzing the connections between teaching and student reasoning. The opportunities for learning always focus first on student reasoning and then on how teachers can promote that reasoning. In vignette #1, student reasoning can move from procedural to conceptual with a concentrated focus on mathematical meaning. In vignette #2, student reasoning can go from meaningful but specific to the more advanced mathematical practice of generalizing. By focusing on student reasoning first and foremost, teacher planning goals then reflect ways they can foster higher level reasoning through careful attention to teaching routines and actions.

■ Conclusion

The vignettes above reflect many of the classrooms we have studied at the elementary level and the usefulness of the tool with respect to formative evaluation. We have found that change occurs when it is incremental, supported, and doable. The MPHR tool provides a lens to focus reflection and formative evaluation on the connections between teaching actions and student reasoning. The tool covers a lot of ground, but each habit and routine provides an impetus for reflection and formative evaluation. The Mathematically Productive Teaching Routines and Catalytic Teaching Habits provide tools for keeping student reasoning high. By focusing on these aspects of teaching, formative evaluation can be targeted in a way that can take a similar lesson and raise the level of student reasoning through purposeful actions of the teacher. In our vignettes, Teacher 1, who has a productive classroom, may focus on having students discover the generalizable mathematical idea and what teaching actions may promote this. Teacher 2 might consider some basic CTH that could be used to raise the level of discussion when talking with partners. Altering pedagogy to promote student reasoning is a complex process, and the MPHR is a tool for providing formative evaluation and specific, *doable* changes that teachers can implement to develop richer classrooms.

We have found that the MPHR has led to both school leaders and teachers being able to focus on (1) student reasoning and (2) connected teaching actions. As a result, our teachers are developing better conceptions around productive classrooms and on which small changes can affect the cognitive level of engagement. In fact, the teachers in our project have consistently integrated the tool into their action steps for planning and reflecting on classrooms between PD cycles. Furthermore, principals and coaches have similarly used the tool as a means for supporting teachers. We have found this tool useful in observations as short as ten minutes because of the broad coverage and nuanced attention to different aspects of productive classrooms. We take the view that teaching observations are for teachers' professional development and learning rather than summative evaluations. Formative evaluation tools provide a means for teacher reflection and a chance for leadership to directly support their teacher's needs. In our two vignettes, we illustrated two ways a classroom teacher might be supported (or self-reflect) with our tool: (1) moving student reasoning from specific cases to general and (2) increasing student reasoning from rote procedures to procedures connected to meaning by leveraging specific teaching actions. In both cases, the classroom teachers have the opportunity to reflect both on their pedagogy and on the mathematics in order to continue their professional growth.

References

Artzt, Alice F., and Eleanor Armour-Thomas. *Becoming a Reflective Mathematics Teacher: A Guide for Observations and Self-Assessment.* Studies in Mathematical Thinking and Learning Series. Mahwah, N.J.: Lawrence Erlbaum Associates, 2002.

Bransford, John D., Ann L. Brown, and Rodney R. Cocking. *How People Learn: Brain, Mind, Experience, and School.* Washington, D.C.: National Academies Press, 1999.

Coburn, Cynthia E., and Mary Kay Stein. *Research and Practice in Education: Building Alliances, Bridging the Divide.* Lanham, Md.: Rowman & Littlefield Publishers, 2010.

Cuoco, Al, E. Paul Goldenberg, and June Mark. "Habits of Mind: An Organizing Principle for Mathematics Curricula." *The Journal of Mathematical Behavior* 15, no. 4 (1996): 375–402.

Dweck, Carol S. "The Secret to Raising Smart Kids." *Scientific American Mind* 18, no. 6 (2007): 36–43.

Foreman, Linda. "About the Mathematics Studio Program." Teachers Development Group. 2010.

Foreman, Linda. *Best Practices in Teaching Mathematics: How Math Teaching Matters.* West Linn, Oreg.: Teachers Development Group, 2013.

Henningsen, Marjorie, and Mary Kay Stein. "Mathematical Tasks and Student Cognition: Classroom-Based Factors That Support and Inhibit High-Level Mathematical Thinking and Reasoning." *Journal for Research in Mathematics Education* 28, no. 5 (1997): 524–49.

Hill, Heather. "Mathematical Quality of Instruction (MQI)." Coding tool. 2010.

Lampert, Magdalene, Megan Loef Franke, Elham Kazemi, Hala Ghousseini, Angela Chan Turrou, Heather Beasley, Adrian Cunard, and Kathleen Crowe. "Keeping It Complex Using Rehearsals to Support Novice Teacher Learning of Ambitious Teaching." *Journal of Teacher Education* 64, no. 3 (2013): 226–43.

Lewis, Catherine C., Rebecca R. Perry, and Jacqueline Hurd. "Improving Mathematics Instruction through Lesson Study: A Theoretical Model and North American Case." *Journal of Mathematics Teacher Education* 12, no. 4 (2009): 285–304.

Melhuish, Kathleen, and Eva Thanheiser. "Measuring Fidelity of Implementation in a Large-Scale Professional Development Efficacy Study." In *Proceedings of the 38th Annual Meeting of the North American Group of Psychology in Mathematics Education* (forthcoming), Tucson, Ariz.

Michaels, Sarah, Catherine O'Connor, and Lauren B. Resnick. "Deliberative Discourse Idealized and Realized: Accountable Talk in the Classroom and in Civic Life." *Studies in Philosophy and Education* 27, no. 4 (2008): 283–97.

National Council of Teachers of Mathematics (NCTM). *Principles to Actions: Ensuring Mathematical Success for All.* Reston, Va.: NCTM, 2014.

National Governors Association Center for Best Practices and Council of Chief State School Officers (NGA Center and CCSSO). *Common Core State Standards for Mathematics.* Washington, D.C.: NGA Center and CCSSO, 2010. http://www.corestandards.org.

National Research Council. "Adding + It Up: Helping Children Learn Mathematics." Edited by Jeremy Kilpatrick, Jane Swafford, and Bradford Findell. Mathematics Learning Study Committee, Center for Education, Division of Behavioral and Social Sciences and Education. Washington, D.C.: National Academy Press, 2001.

Nicol, David J., and Debra Macfarlane-Dick. "Formative Assessment and Self-Regulated Learning: A Model and Seven Principles of Good Feedback Practice." *Studies in Higher Education* 31, no. 2 (2006): 199–218.

Stein, Mary Kay, and Cynthia E. Coburn. "Architectures for Learning: A Comparative Analysis of Two Urban School Districts." *American Journal of Education* 114, no. 4 (2008): 583–626.

Stein, Mary Kay, and Suzanne Lane. "Instructional Tasks and the Development of Student Capacity to Think and Reason: An Analysis of the Relationship between Teaching and Learning in a Reform Mathematics Project." *Educational Research and Evaluation* 2, no. 1 (1996): 50–80.

Stein, Mary Kay, Margaret S. Smith, Marjorie Henningsen, and Edward A. Silver. *Implementing Standards-Based Mathematics Instruction: A Casebook for Professional Development.* New York: Teachers College Press, 2009.

Stein, Mary Kay, Randi A. Engle, Margaret S. Smith, and Elizabeth K. Hughes. "Orchestrating Productive Mathematical Discussions: Five Practices for Helping Teachers Move beyond Show and Tell." *Mathematical Thinking and Learning* 10, no. 4 (2008): 313–40.

CHAPTER 16

The Iceberg Model:
Rethinking Mathematics Instruction from a Student Perspective

David C. Webb, *University of Colorado Boulder*

The choices we make for teaching mathematics are influenced by a variety of factors; these include our prior experiences learning mathematics (Lortie 1975), our mathematical knowledge for teaching (Ball, Thames, and Phelps 2008), our interpretation of priorities articulated in content standards, and our assumptions about the needs of our students. The perceived affordances and constraints of the school context also play into decisions regarding the use of instructional resources, technology, and assessments. Unfortunately, we often plan, teach, and assess without fully articulating our conceptions about how students learn mathematics. Keeping these conceptions implicit can leave many of our decisions to the design of the instructional resources we use. To be a reflective practitioner (Schön 1983), it is critical to consider how we learn mathematics and the ways in which the design of resources supports the various forms of mathematical reasoning articulated in the Standards for Mathematical Practice (National Governors Association Center for Best Practices and Council of Chief State School Officers [NGA Center and CCSSO] 2010).

To help teachers make informed instructional decisions, researchers at the Freudenthal Institute developed the Iceberg model as part of a professional development program to support primary level special education teachers working with students in mathematics (Boswinkel and Moerlands 2002). The Iceberg model is a metaphor that communicates the role of contexts, models, representations, and strategies in the development of student understanding of mathematics. The beauty of the model is that it can be used at all levels of mathematics and in other scientific disciplines. It can be used to support curriculum developers in their design of instructional materials, and it can also support teachers in their instructional planning, formative assessment, and reflection on ways to support student learning. The purpose of this chapter is to illustrate how the Iceberg model can be used as a basis for planning, instruction, and assessment in ways that promote individual and collaborative reflection. For almost any mathematics topic, teachers draw upon their knowledge and experiences with the content domain of interest to co-construct and share contexts, strategies, and representations that reflect their collective understanding of how the content domain is developed.

■ The Iceberg Model

To convey the various ways mathematical representations are related and used to support the mathematical learning of formal mathematical goals, the concept of an iceberg can be used. The tip of the iceberg represents the goal: Often this is a formal representation, such as two-digit multiplication, finding the area of a triangle, or solving systems of equations. Beneath the iceberg's tip is its much more substantial volume, which contains various informal and pre-formal mathematics representations that are related to the formal mathematical goal. This iceberg of mathematics representations is also organized a particular way, with contexts that support students' informal reasoning at the bottom of the iceberg. Then, above the informal level in the middle of the iceberg, are pre-formal models, representations, and strategies that are related to the goal (cf. Gravemeijer 1994). Essentially, beneath the tip of the iceberg is its substance — i.e., the "floating capacity" of the iceberg that serves as the basis for understanding the mathematics represented at the tip of the iceberg. This floating capacity includes reasoning with related contexts (informal) and the use of models, tools, representations, and strategies (pre-formal).

To exemplify the different characteristics of informal and pre-formal reasoning, and the contexts and representations that could be used to elicit such reasoning, an iceberg for systems of equations is given in figure 16.1. A representation of a more formal goal, solving a system of equations with two unknowns, is shown in the tip of the iceberg. Even though there are many different variations of systems of equations that could be placed here that favor different solution strategies, this example is only meant to suggest that the contexts and representations "below the water line" should support students' understanding of the skills and concepts needed to find a solution to this system.

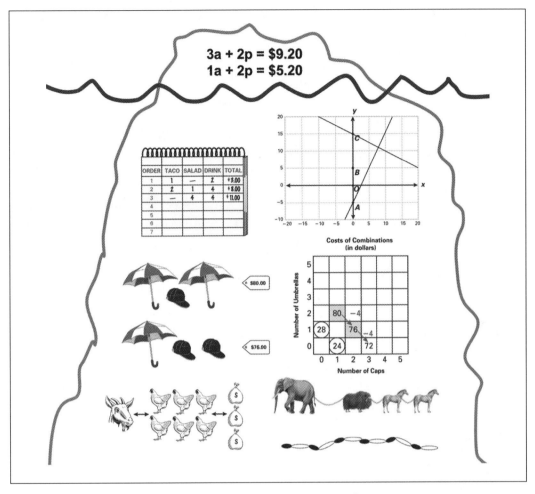

Fig. 16.1. An iceberg for solving systems of equations
(Graphics adapted from Kindt et al. 2006, and Webb, Hedges, and Abels 2010;
by courtesy of Encyclopaedia Britannica, Inc., used with permission)

Using Contexts to Promote Informal Reasoning

Across the bottom of figure 16.1 are three examples of various contexts that could be used
to elicit informal student reasoning. Students are often asked to learn and use mathematical
procedures without any opportunity to relate such procedures to relevant contexts. The
representation on the left can be used to model a story describing a bartering situation. The
bartering context can be used to suggest exchanges of products with equal value — for example,
one goat can be traded for six chickens, which can be traded for three bags of salt. Bartering is
a context that is accessible for young students who have experience in trading games, cards, and
the like. The bartering context also elicits informal reasoning for the mathematical principles
of equivalence and substitution. However, even for those students who do not have such
experiences with trading, the context is something that they can make sense of and role-play

in the classroom. This context also leads to discussions that include the phrase "I can trade two sheep for four bags of corn," an example of informal reasoning for these principles. Even though it may not be immediately apparent how bartering relates to systems of equations, the example given at the tip of the iceberg can be interpreted as "When I add two adult tickets (A), the total cost increases by four dollars." In this way, identifying and providing students opportunities to engage in informal reasoning can support alternative interpretations of formal, symbolic representations.

Further to the right is a beaded necklace that is meant to suggest a different contextual representation of an equations—e.g., a necklace with 6 black and 6 white beads is 21 centimeters. This context could lead to representations of systems of equations using two different length necklaces using the same two beads in different patterns. The other example that supports informal reasoning is the tug-of-war context, which can be used to suggest equality (a tie) and inequality (who will win or lose). Multiple examples of tug-a-war situations can be used to motivate substitution strategies to figure out which combinations of animals are the strongest.

Pre-formal Models and Strategies to Promote Sense Making

Moving up the iceberg, we transition to two layers of pre-formal representations that focus more on models and strategies that support student understanding of the formal strategies for solving systems of equations (e.g., elimination method, substitution method, and matrix-based methods). Even though these models can be used without reference to a context, the examples offered for this iceberg all refer to some context. In fact, in some cases pre-formal models can emerge from a problem context. For example, a download bar for computer software can lead to student use of a percent bar in many other contexts. A fair share context for distributing equal pieces of fruit tape can lead to student use of fraction bars. Nevertheless, whenever possible, pre-formal models should be used across multiple contexts to support student generalization of the main features of each model so that the model is not connected to just one context. The purpose of a pre-formal model is that it provides greater mathematical structure. They also provide ways for students to make connections between problem contexts and more formal, symbolic mathematical abstractions and procedures. As the need for more generalizable strategies emerge, formal strategies are then introduced and explicitly related to students' prior experiences with the informal strategies and pre-formal models (Webb and Abels 2011).

The model that includes caps and umbrellas is a complete visual representation of systems of equations to promote strategy development. (Note that this is different from the contexts used to focus on one equation in the examples in the informal level.) Notice how the caps, umbrellas, and price tags are organized so that each set of objects and its corresponding price can be read horizontally. This model also organizes two "equations" and two "unknowns," depicted visually. The unknowns in this case are the price of each object. This example motivates solution strategies that relate to valid equation-based methods. For example, with the caps and umbrellas, both sets can be combined, resulting in a new set of six caps and six umbrellas, which would cost 156 dollars. This would parallel the equation-based strategy of adding two equations together. Notice how the model helps students validate the potential strategy. It invites students to consider possibilities and justify why that might work, symbolically. Another way to interpret the caps and umbrellas task is by creating new sets through exchanges of caps and umbrellas. By looking at the given information, students often see that they can create a new set below the one umbrella and two caps, since replacing an umbrella with a cap reduced the price of the set by four dollars. So a new set with three caps should be priced at $72. Hence, the price of each cap should be $24. Similarly, a new set of three umbrellas could be made using the same principle. This pre-formal model and strategy for solving a system of equations typically makes more sense to students, and in this case is more efficient than a formal strategy that involves rewriting the sets as equations and solving the system using either elimination or substitution.

To the right of the caps and umbrellas is a combination chart. This is a pre-formal model that includes values for combinations of different quantities of two objects. This model supports numerical examination of the exchange principle. As you move across the combination chart horizontally, vertically, or diagonally, different shifts occur in the sets of objects represented and their total value. Moving horizontally from left to right is an increase in the number of objects represented by the horizontal axis. Similarly, moving up vertically is an increase in the number of objects represented by the vertical axis. A diagonal move, however, involves a change in the number of both objects. For example, moving down one cell and to the right one cell—i.e., down one over one—decreases the number of umbrellas by one and increases the number of caps by one, resulting in a total decrease in value of four dollars. The combination chart illustrates related decreases (or increases) in the value for each new set that is found with a move across the chart. Larger moves can be explored, like the L-shaped move of a knight on a chessboard—e.g., down one cell and to the right or left by two cells. This pre-formal model offers students an opportunity to make sense of relationships represented by equations with integer solutions. With a system of equations, the two cells representing the value of two equations visually shows the exchange in objects and the related change in value. Solutions to systems of equations involve making moves to the horizontal or vertical edge of the combination chart, reducing the number of objects for one of the variables to zero, and then solving for the value of the other variable. The combination chart in figure 16.1 shows diagonal moves to the horizontal axis to find the value of three umbrellas is $72, or $24 for each umbrella.

The two pre-formal models just under the waterline include notebook notation and graphical solutions. Notebook notation has the simple appearance of a table or spreadsheet, but the rows have more specific meaning as they are used to represent the coefficients of each situation or set that is represented. In the example given, the columns represent the number of each item in a menu (e.g., taco, salad, and drink) and the column on the right represents the total value. Each row can be added, multiplied, divided, or subtracted. Students use different operations and combinations given in the model to create new rows that eventually are reduced to having only one for one of the objects and zero of the rest of the objects. Notebook notation is essentially a pre-formal model that can lead to matrix-based solution methods. Notebook notation can also support solving systems of equations with more than two variables, whereas the combination chart only supports solutions for systems of equations involving two variables.

The graphing method is categorized as a pre-formal strategy in the iceberg since it is not a general approach that can find an exact solution for all systems of equations for two variables (unless one is using technology-based tools). The graphing method helps students understand how relationships between pairs of linear equations can result in one solution, no solutions, or an infinite number of solutions, even though each equation may have an infinite combination of solutions.

■ Making Mathematics Icebergs

The process of creating icebergs to represent the important contexts and representations for a mathematics topic is a process that involves individual reflection and collaboration. From the perspective of the individual, creating an iceberg first motivates reflection on the underlying strategies, representations, and contexts that have been experienced either when learning or teaching that topic. Beyond these firsthand experiences, it is also important to review available instructional materials for other potential examples of informal and pre-formal representations for the selected content domain. Even then, while individual reflection is an important and necessary start, some of the most productive experiences in building icebergs can be found through collaborating with colleagues and drawing upon each other's collective experiences and perspectives to identify relevant contexts, models, and strategies. The construction of a mathematics iceberg is an opportunity to identify useful contexts that can be used to introduce a topic and a chance to discuss the pros and cons of pre-formal representations and alternative strategies that have been used with students. Even though the end product of a completed iceberg is a useful summary that can serve as a future reference to inform instructional planning and assessment, the sharing of personal experiences about the ways the various contexts and models have been used, or could be used, is an opportunity for professional learning that lies at the intersection of mathematics content, student learning, and classroom practice.

The iceberg shown in figure 16.2 was co-constructed by mathematics teachers as part of a regional workshop focused on formative assessment (Webb 2009). Keep in mind that this iceberg is not a complete representation of what could be included in an iceberg for graphing polynomials. This is partly due to the time constraints the teachers had to develop the iceberg, but it is also a result of what this group of teachers was able to draw upon to organize their informal and pre-formal representations. The contexts noted in the informal category include projectiles, roller coasters, wave forms, and boogie dancing! The pre-formal category includes their conceptions of key models and strategies that could be used to inform students' understanding of graphing polynomials. One of these concepts includes knowing the difference in shape between polynomials with odd and even degrees. Even though this is not a model per se, it is information about graphing polynomials that could support student graphing.

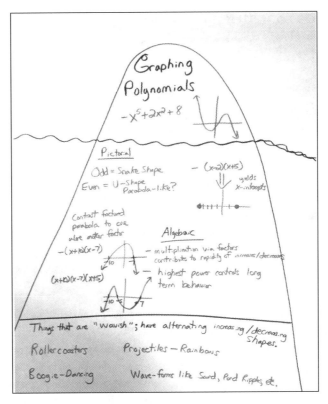

Fig. 16.2. An iceberg for graphing polynomials

This iceberg also reveals the absence of other pre-formal models and strategies that could be discussed, such as the relationship between linear and polynomial functions. (However, it is also worth noting that figure 16.1 is, similarly, not a comprehensive iceberg for systems of equations.) For the polynomial iceberg, students could explore how the graph of the given polynomial function, $y = x^3 + 2x^2 - 5x - 6$, can be constructed from the multiplication of related linear functions that are the polynomial's factors. This exploration could be explored dynamically with graphing calculators or online graphing tools. As students add linear factors to the graphed function, they can observe how $(x + 1)$, $(x - 2)$, and $(x + 3)$ contribute to changes in the shape of the polynomial's graph. In this way, teacher reflection on and analysis of constructed icebergs can often reveal the need to turn additional instructional resources in print or on the web to identify any other representations that could be considered.

It is worth considering why this activity was used for a workshop focused on formative assessment. If formative assessment is the process of using information gathered from students to inform subsequent instruction, the informal and pre-formal representations provide a blueprint for potential instructional pathways to develop a new topic or review concepts that are not well understood (Webb 2010). As discussed by Black and Wiliam (1998), Hattie and Timperley (2007), and others, formative assessment has been described through the formulation of three questions: *Where are you going? Where are you now?* and *How are you going to get there?* The tip of the iceberg is where you are going. Your assessment of students is where they are now. The iceberg helps articulate how you are going to get there.

From Icebergs to Instructional Sequences

Even though the Iceberg model focuses on relevant contexts and representations, it can also be used to identify key activities that should be included in instructional sequences. As teachers transition from the construction of icebergs to the development or revision of instructional sequences, they often propose different pathways through the iceberg that involve informal and pre-formal representations in addition to other activities that incorporate various Standards for Mathematical Practice, academic language, and other important goals for the topic. One of the tensions teachers constantly need to manage is the desire to pursue a topic more deeply and the pressure to move onto other important topics in the curriculum. To help manage this tension, the iceberg offers a summary of essential representations that have been used by colleagues to support the sense making and fluency for specific formal mathematics goals. Teachers encounter this tension when time runs short as they are teaching a unit and they need to decide on activities that might need to be deemphasized or cut. The process of developing and deliberating mathematical icebergs can support the prioritization of contexts and models that students should experience and use.

■ Summary

This chapter offers a practical application of a model that synthesizes mathematics content, curriculum design, and research on student learning. The Iceberg model can be used as the basis of professional development activities that motivate individual and collaborative reflection on the role that contexts and representations play in the development of student understanding of mathematics. The building of mathematical icebergs invites teacher reflection on how mathematics topics are developed. This process also invites collaboration: As teachers propose contexts and pre-formal models and strategies to be sketched in the iceberg, those models that are less familiar to the group can be discussed, exemplified, and deliberated so that colleagues can benefit from these new ideas. In this way, all teachers bring their prior knowledge and experience to bear to support the construction of the iceberg, but the discussion and further reflection that ensues is a critical part of the activity. This process invites teachers into the process of instructional design, using a principled approach that is grounded in how students learn mathematics (cf. Fuson, Kalchman, and Bransford 2005, p. 230).

As noted at the beginning of this chapter, this activity has been used as part of professional development activities for primary, secondary, and postsecondary mathematics teachers. Some teachers have used the iceberg as an organizing principle for revising a unit or an entire course as a way to improve its mathematical coherence and opportunities for student learning (e.g., Peck and Matassa 2016). As mathematics departments adopt and use instructional resources, the extent to which those resources include informal and pre-formal representations could be considered by extending this work to analyze materials and textbooks regarding the ways in which informal and pre-formal reasoning are addressed. Resources that lack some essential representations, but are otherwise useful, can then be adapted with other resources to support teachers' achievement of their instructional goals.

The more that teachers are familiar with potential representational pathways for a given domain, the more likely they are to engage in goal-oriented instructional planning and respond to students in ways that are developmentally consistent with how students learn mathematics. Once teachers understand the role of contexts and models to support informal and pre-formal reasoning and use instructional activities to elicit such reasoning, they begin to integrate these approaches into their planning, instruction, and assessment. Such approaches both inform and affirm their work as instructional designers.

References

Ball, Deborah Loewenberg, Mark Hoover Thames, and Geoffrey Phelps. "Content Knowledge for Teaching: What Makes It Special?" *Journal of Teacher Education* 59, no. 5 (2008): 389–407.

Black, Paul, and Dylan Wiliam. "Assessment and Classroom Learning." *Assessment in Education* 5, no. 1 (1998): 7–74.

Boswinkel, Nina, and Frans Moerlands. "Het topje van de ijsberg" [The top of the iceberg]. In *Nationale Rekendagen, een praktische terugblik* [National Conference on arithmetic, a practical view], edited by Karel Groenewegen, pp. 103–14. Utrecht, The Netherlands: Freudenthal Institute, 2002.

Fuson, Karen C., Mindy Kalchman, and John D. Bransford. "Mathematical Understanding: An Introduction." In *How Students Learn: History, Mathematics, and Science in the Classroom,* edited by M. Suzanne Donovan and John D. Bransford, pp. 217–56. Washington, D.C.: National Academies Press, 2005.

Gravemeijer, Koeno. "Educational Development and Developmental Research in Mathematics Education." *Journal for Research in Mathematics Education* 25, no. 5 (1994): 443–71.

Hattie, John, and Helen Timperley. "The Power of Feedback." *Review of Educational Research* 77, no. 1 (2007): 81–112.

Kindt, Martin, Monica Wijers, Mary S. Spence, Laura J. Brinker, Margie A. Pligge, Jack Burrill, and Gail Burrill. "Graphing Equations." In *Mathematics in Context,* edited by Wisconsin Center for Education Research & Freudenthal Institute. Chicago: Encyclopædia Britannica, Inc., 2006.

Lortie, Dan Clement. *Schoolteacher: A Sociological Study.* Chicago: University of Chicago Press, 1975.

National Governors Association Center for Best Practices and Council of Chief State School Officers (NGA Center and CCSSO). *Common Core State Standards for Mathematics.* Washington, D.C.: NGA Center and CCSSO, 2010. http://www.corestandards.org.

Peck, Fred A., and Michael Matassa. "Reinventing Fractions and Division as They Are Used in Algebra: The Power of Preformal Productions." *Educational Studies in Mathematics* 92, no. 2 (2016): 245–78.

Schön, Donald A. *The Reflective Practitioner: How Professionals Think in Action.* London: Temple Smith, 1983.

Webb, David C. "Designing Professional Development for Assessment." *Educational Designer* 1, no. 2 (2009): 1–26.

———. "Collaborative Design of Instructional Sequences: Teacher Developed Support for Formative Assessment." *Procedia—Social and Behavioral Sciences,* 9 (2010): 153–57.

Webb, David C., and Mieke Abels. "Restrictions in Algebra." In *Secondary Algebra Education: Revisiting Topics and Themes and Exploring the Unknown,* edited by Paul Drijvers, pp. 101–18. Boston: Sense Publishers, 2011.

Webb, David C., Teri Hedges, and Mieke Abels. "Comparing Quantities" [Teacher Guide]. In *Mathematics in Context,* edited by Wisconsin Center for Education Research & Freudenthal Institute. Chicago: Encyclopaedia Britannica, Inc., 2006.

PART IV

Enhancing Mathematics Teaching across Multiple Stakeholders

Introduction

Michael D. Steele, *University of Wisconsin–Milwaukee*

In a wide-ranging review of the research on teacher professional development, Wilson and Berne (1999) note three commonalities in effective teacher learning opportunities: they involved communities of learners working to reconceptualize teaching practice; the learning was active in nature; and teachers' interactions with one another were at the core of the learning activities. In the context of teacher preparation, scholars have argued for the importance of creating meaningful bridges between mathematics content and methods courses, and between the university and K–12 school contexts (Grossman, Hammerness, and McDonald 2009; McDonald, Kazemi, and Kavanagh 2013). Analyses of teacher professional development effectiveness have emphasized the importance of long-term sustained programs (such as the National Science Foundation Math Science Partnership programs) that build professional learning communities (Fulton and Britton 2011). The four chapters in this section describe collaborations in teacher preparation and professional development that seek to build professional communities by bridging traditional divides to bring stakeholders together to improve student learning outcomes.

The first two chapters explore the affordances of professional learning communities that endure and sustain over time. In **Collaborating in a School-University Partnership: A Focus on Preservice Teachers' Learning about Mathematics Curriculum**, Lloyd, Coon-Kitt, Margusity, Romig, and Hall take us into the preservice mathematics teacher preparation world. This work takes place in a longstanding partnership in the form of a professional development school (PDS). The focus of the collaboration was the work of selecting and adapting mathematical tasks, a topic in the authors' elementary mathematics methods course to be implemented across K–4 classrooms in the PDF. The work in this chapter illustrates the learning opportunities and affordances of a tight PDF connection. University instructors, coaches, and student teaching interns collaborated together to provide K–4 students with richer learning opportunities than the adopted curriculum would have otherwise afforded. Moreover, coaches and student teaching interns made use of a "carousel brainstorming" format to identify high-leverage instructional strategies that could be put into use with students. The coaches, interns, and university teacher educators emerged from these discussions with stronger and shared understandings of instructional practices that supported rich student learning.

In the second chapter, **Working Together to Enhance Children's Understanding of Fractions**, Monson, Ahrendt, and Cramer describe how a long-term university-district collaboration came to focus on supporting a group of third-grade teachers in implementing a research-based mathematics curriculum. The university-based research group had a long and successful history partnering with school districts for over three decades, which included work with the district described here. In this analysis, the authors describe how the partnership tackled an important problem of practice: the need to adapt a research-based curriculum related to fraction learning from fourth grade to third because of changes in the state standards. Using the existing professional learning community, researchers and teachers collaborated on the design of new lessons and facilitated structured reflections on them with teachers. This collaboration supported a more coherent fidelity of implementation and improved student outcomes. Three key elements emerged that contributed to the success of the efforts: trust and respect through the preexisting long-term collaboration, a clear focus on a manageable goal, and a lack of hierarchy in the working relationships. This illustration underscores the importance of establishing and fostering professional learning communities and finding creative ways to co-evolve their goals accordingly as needs change.

In **Cross-Sector Collaboration to Improve Teaching and Learning through Focused Inquiry**, Coomes, Alvin, and Olson describe the ways in which high school, community college, and university mathematics instructors crossed divides to address issues of transition to college. In particular, these mathematics educators were focused on critical thinking, habits of mind, deep learning, and metacognition to strengthen students' abilities to transfer skills and practices from one sector to the next. The collaboration began with an explicit focus on establishing shared values and collective ownership of the broad challenges and on developing processes and protocols for talking about mathematics teaching and learning. The cornerstone of the collaboration involved observation visits across sectors (e.g., high school teachers visiting community college classrooms, university professors visiting high school classrooms) using a common observation protocol to guide the analysis of instruction. The shared values and observation lenses allowed instructors across sectors to see more commonalities in their contexts than differences, which in turn afforded opportunities to identify and work on more fine-grained problems of practice. The specific case of the algebra study group given here affords a deep look into the iterative nature of this professional collaboration, grounded in the shared values, through cycles of inquiry, data collection, instructional improvement, and the identification of new problems of practice.

In the final chapter of the section, **Multiple Perspectives on Collaborative Teaching: Mathematicians, Mathematics Teacher Educators, and Students**, Bénéteau, Bleiler-Baxter, Kersaint, Krajčevski, and Thompson provide an intimate view of the collaborations of two mathematicians and two mathematics teacher educators in co-facilitating mathematics content and methods courses. Although there are several such analyses in this volume of the affordances and challenges of co-instruction across the mathematics-education worlds, this chapter introduces a novel data source: the perceptions of the preservice teachers who were students in the course. This unique voice, alongside the first-person perspectives of the four instructors and graduate student observing the courses, provides tremendous insight into this cross-sector collaboration and its effects on student learning. The authors make use of Tzur's (2001) frames of *learning to teach mathematics* and *learning to teach teachers* to describe the differences in each constituency's perspectives as they worked in pairs to collaborate. They note a transition from learning to teach mathematics to learning to teach teachers, and they describe in detail the ways in which their planning, enactment, and reflection conveyed a transition across those roles. The reactions of preservice teachers about perceived disagreements between the co-instructors presents a fascinating view that stands in contrast to the ways planning conversations actually unfolded between mathematicians and mathematics teacher educators. For example, preservice teachers perceived the mathematics teacher educator in a content course as responsible for planning for the use of mathematics technology and the mathematician as responsible for the delivery, when in fact it was the mathematician who was responsible for creating the content and technology demonstrations. The voices of the preservice teachers in this study raise critical and meaningful issues about our perceptions of mathematician/mathematics teacher educator collaborations. The authors respond to these disparate views by suggesting ways in which we might work collectively to unpack the complexity of teaching both between mathematicians and mathematics educators, and they make that unpacking visible and collaborative with the preservice teachers that we serve.

As you engage with these chapters, consider the following questions:

- How can we be more intentional about designing professional learning collaborations that embody the features noted in these chapters?

- How might we plan for and sustain the long-term viability and productivity of a professional collaboration through shared evolution of goals and activities?

- As we prepare preservice mathematics teachers, in what ways can we explicitly model productive professional collaborations across sectors and roles?

References

Fulton, Kathleen, and Ted Britton. *STEM Teachers in Professional Learning Communities: From Good Teachers to Great Teaching*. Washington, D.C.: National Commission on Teaching and America's Future, 2011.

Grossman, Pam, Karen Hammerness, and Morva McDonald. "Redefining Teaching, Reimagining Teacher Education." *Teachers and Teaching: Theory and Practice* 15, no. 2 (2009): 273–89.

McDonald, Morva, Elham Kazemi, and Sarah Schneider Kavanagh. "Core Practices and Pedagogies of Teacher Education: A Call for a Common Language and Collective Activity." *Journal of Teacher Education* 64, no. 5 (2013): 378–86.

Tzur, Ron. "Becoming a Mathematics Teacher-Educator: Conceptualizing the Terrain through Self-Reflective Analysis." *Journal of Mathematics Teacher Education* 4, no. 4 (2001): 259–83.

Wilson, Suzanne M., and Jennifer Berne. "Teacher Learning and the Acquisition of Professional Knowledge: An Examination of Research on Contemporary Professional Development." *Review of Research in Education* 24 (1999): 173–209.

CHAPTER 17

Collaborating in a School-University Partnership:
A Focus on Preservice Teachers' Learning about Mathematics Curriculum

Gwendolyn M. Lloyd, *Pennsylvania State University, University Park*
Mary Jayne Coon-Kitt, *Pennsylvania State University, University Park*
Linda Margusity, *State College Area School District, State College, Pennsylvania*
Gail Romig, *State College Area School District, State College, Pennsylvania*
Kris Hall, *State College Area School District, State College, Pennsylvania*

Whereas many universities and schools work together in the preparation of teachers, a professional development school (PDS) is a special type of partnership focused on "preparing future educators, providing current educators with ongoing professional development, encouraging joint school–university faculty investigation of education-related issues, and promoting the learning of P–12 students" (National Association of Professional Development Schools 2008, p. 1). In PDS partnerships, school and university personnel collaborate to offer preservice teachers rich field experiences, meaningful teacher education course work connected to school sites, and authentic professional experiences as full participants in the school community. PDS teacher educators, who include both school and university faculty members, share a commitment to improving educational opportunities for children and teachers, yet bring diverse knowledge and experiences to that work. Thus, collaborative work by PDS teacher educators creates fruitful opportunities for the integration of practitioner and academic expertise (Zeichner 2010) and innovations in practice as a result.

This chapter describes a collaboration intended to enhance the learning of preservice teachers in an elementary mathematics methods course within an established PDS partnership. Preservice teachers in the methods course are "interns" engaged in full-year student-teaching internships in K–4 classrooms where a district-adopted mathematics curriculum program is used. For the past three years, methods instructors and the district's instructional coaches have collaborated to design and teach methods course activities about *mathematics curriculum*, broadly, and *selecting and adapting mathematical tasks*, specifically. The authors of this chapter include two district instructional coaches and three mathematics methods course instructors. We aim to illustrate how our collaborative activities, informed by the diverse expertise of coaches and methods instructors, have deepened opportunities for interns to inquire into the role of mathematical tasks in children's learning. In addition, we describe how this collaboration has created a context for the professional learning of ourselves and others in the PDS community.

■ Context for Our Collaboration

The context for our collaboration is a PDS partnership between the Pennsylvania State University and the State College Area School District, which surrounds the university's campus. This PDS, established in 1998, includes the nine elementary schools in the district. Pre-K–4 candidates in their junior years at Penn State can apply to the PDS program as an alternative to an on-campus teacher education program with numerous student-teaching options. Within the PDS, preservice teachers—known as interns—complete their final year of pre-K–4 preparation. Interns enroll in full-year, full-time internships in mentor teachers' classrooms and participate in four university methods courses (including mathematics methods) in the fall semester and in student-teaching seminars during spring semester. The fall methods courses and spring seminars are taught in district schools.

The teacher educators who co-teach methods courses and supervise interns make up a diverse group that includes classroom teachers, retired teachers, and university faculty members and graduate students. Methods courses are co-taught by teams representing both school- and university-based teacher educators with the intention of integrating practitioner and academic expertise (Zeichner 2010) in the design and facilitation of methods courses and the yearlong field experience.

During the 2015–2016 academic year, fifty-four interns were placed in mentor teachers' K–4 classrooms for their full-year internships. Two sections of elementary mathematics methods were taught in fall 2015, the semester of focus for this chapter. Each methods section met once per week for three hours. The four teacher educators who co-taught the course in fall 2015 included an experienced district teacher "reassigned" to the PDS, a former elementary teacher who is currently a graduate student at the university, a retired teacher and district administrator who is now the university PDS coordinator, and a senior mathematics education faculty member from the university.

Instructional Coaches and Mathematics Professional Development

Instructional coaches in the school district do not play formal roles in the teaching of PDS methods courses, yet they are valued district colleagues who provide extensive support for teachers' professional learning. During the 2015–2016 school year, five K–6 coaches were released from classrooms to work full-time with fellow teachers in reading, writing, and mathematics. The district uses a cognitive coaching model, "predicated on the assumption that behaviors change after our beliefs change" (Knight 2007, p. 10). Inquiry is a core value of the district and a key mechanism for PDS interns' learning (Cochran-Smith and Lytle 1993), and coaches use the processes of inquiry, collaboration, and reflection to empower change within four key areas: classroom environment, content and curriculum, instructional practices, and assessment.

Instructional coaches play various roles with a focus on enhancing teachers' instructional practices and increasing student engagement and learning (Campbell 2012). In our district, coaches collaborate with teachers to design and enact effective instruction, model and co-teach lessons, collect and analyze data, and engage in coaching cycles with specific goals in mind. They also serve on curriculum-writing teams and provide district-level professional development focusing on content, use of new resource materials, and creation of planning guides. Coaches provide additional after-school sessions in areas such as establishing mathematics workshops, using talk moves in classrooms, and incorporating resources to enhance students' learning of mathematics.

PDS Mathematics Methods Course

As illustrated in figure 17.1, four interconnected domains guide mathematics methods course instructors' planning of activities and assignments for interns. Course activities in each domain are guided by several "essential questions." Figure 17.2 shows the essential questions for Domain 2: *selecting and adapting mathematical tasks* (the focus of this chapter). These questions are intended to prompt and support interns' inquiry into mathematics teaching and learning (Cochran-Smith and Lytle 1993). As stated in figure 17.1, we view our work in the methods course as situated within a larger community of learners.

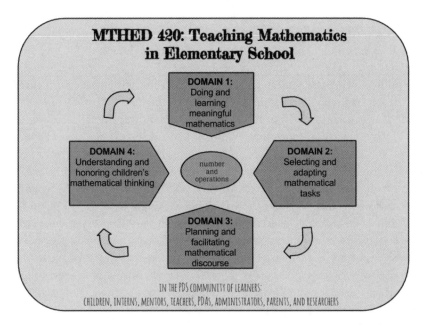

Fig. 17.1. Conceptual framework guiding the PDS mathematics methods course

2: Selecting and Adapting Mathematical Tasks *We will consider the kinds of problems and tasks that challenge students to engage in mathematical reasoning and sense-making. We will engage in cognitively demanding tasks that allow multiple entry points and a variety of solution strategies.*	**2a.** What makes problem-solving a productive activity for learning mathematics? **2b.** What are the qualities of problems and tasks that most effectively elicit students' thinking and support students' learning of mathematics? **2c.** What strategies can teachers use to adapt tasks (e.g., those found in textbooks) so that children are appropriately challenged?

Fig. 17.2. Essential questions for Domain 2 of the conceptual framework

As figure 17.2 suggests, an important goal of instruction in the methods course is to draw interns' attention to the impact of task characteristics on children's opportunities to learn (National Council of Teachers of Mathematics [NCTM] 2014; Stein, Grover, and Henningsen 1996). Many class discussions and activities are guided by Smith and Stein's (1998) mathematical task framework that offers a taxonomy of tasks based on the level of cognitive demand involved with solving them. Drawing on the notion that engagement with curricular resources can support preservice teachers' learning (Lloyd and Pitts Bannister 2011), during the semester we offer numerous opportunities for interns to solve mathematical tasks with higher and lower level cognitive demands, to classify tasks according to their levels of cognitive demand, to make reasoned adaptations to mathematics tasks, and to facilitate mathematical discussions about high-level tasks with children. When possible, we use tasks from the district-adopted curriculum program, *Math Expressions* (Fuson 2012), as the basis for these activities.

■ Collaboration between Coaches and Methods Instructors: Mathematical Tasks

Because attention to the mathematical tasks of the district-adopted curriculum program is a major focus of the work of both instructional coaches and methods co-instructors, we view Domain 2 of the methods course, *selecting and adapting mathematical tasks* (see fig. 17.1), as a fruitful area in which to collaborate. As we illustrate in the following section, our collaboration involves expanding the methods course instructional team to include district coaches for co-planning and co-teaching several in-class activities related to mathematical tasks at different points during the semester. Our collaborative activities have all focused on lessons from the district-adopted curriculum program. This ongoing collaboration between coaches and methods instructors, which began three years ago during the fall 2012 semester, has deepened interns' learning in Domain 2 and enhanced the experiences of teacher educators as well.

Coaches rotate responsibility for co-teaching with methods instructors and, across the team, participate in three to six weeks of the thirteen weeks of our methods course sessions. Over the three years of our collaboration, there have been changes in our work together in response to our reflections and learning as well as to factors such as interns' experiences, the methods course format, the makeup of the coaching or instructional team, and coaches' availability. Nonetheless, over time, our collaborative planning and teaching cycles have tended to include a similar series of activities, as shown in table 17.1. As the sequence suggests, this collaboration involves ongoing planning and decision making before, during, and after each visit by a coach to a methods class session and thus offers extended opportunities for the exchange of professional ideas and practices.

Table 17.1

Typical series of planning, teaching, and reflective activities in a collaborative cycle

Description of Activity in the Collaborative Cycle	Timing Relative to Coach Visit to Class
conversation among the methods instructors to generate ideas for lessons and activities to use in this cycle	3 weeks before
meeting of methods instructors and coaches to select lesson from district-adopted program, make plans for class activities	2 to 3 weeks before
planning by methods instructors about how to prepare interns to engage in activities with the coach	2 weeks before
coaches' preparation of materials and plans for instruction	1 to 2 weeks before
instruction in the methods class to familiarize interns with the mathematical content and focus lesson tasks	1 week before
reading of focus lesson and written reactions (in mathematics journal) by interns	during prior week
coach and methods instructors' co-facilitation of curriculum-based activities	—
discussion between methods instructors and coach, reflecting on the co-facilitated lesson	after class
planning by methods instructors about next steps with interns and next cycle of collaboration with coaches	within 1 week

One Cycle of Collaboration: An Illustration

To illustrate the nature of a collaborative cycle, this section describes in detail a visit by one coach, Kris, to the methods class during the fourth class session of the fall 2015 semester. Because interns were exploring place value concepts and children's strategies for addition and subtraction prior to Coach Kris's visit, we jointly decided to focus her visit on a third-grade lesson titled "Two Methods of Subtraction" (Fuson 2012). This lesson requires children to solve two-digit subtraction problems using two methods: *expanded method* and *ungroup first method*. We felt that the numerous two-digit subtraction tasks in this lesson could form the basis for the interns' first attempt to classify tasks by their level of cognitive demand, which they had recently read about in *Principles to Actions* (NCTM 2014). We also hoped that the tasks—many of which we considered to be lower-level tasks because of the expectation that students use specified, taught procedures—might spark curiosity by interns about alternative, more engaging tasks.

During the class session one week before Kris visited, interns completed a mathematical exploration about place value. They were then given a set of eight tasks related to multi-digit subtraction. The methods co-instructors selected four tasks from the Two Methods of Subtraction lesson (which interns had not yet seen). We viewed these as central mathematical tasks in the lesson, addressing the main objectives and mathematical ideas of the lesson, and as representative of the cognitive demand of tasks in the lesson, which we considered to be mainly low level, as they explicitly specified methods for students to use. The co-instructors also created a set of four related tasks, intended to suggest ways the lesson's tasks could be adapted into higher-level tasks. These four tasks were adapted from another curriculum program or written by Gwen, one of the methods course instructors. Each task in the collection of eight involved the expression $64 - 28$ in some way. In these tasks, students were asked write story problems (e.g., "Write a story problem that matches the equation $64 - 28 = \_\_\_$. Solve the problem and explain why your story matches $64 - 28$"), and they were invited to use and explore multiple solution strategies (e.g., "Show a third method that *you* might use to solve $64 - 28$. Explain how your method is similar to and different from the methods [in the lesson]"). Note that we revisited this set of eight tasks later in the semester when interns began to work on selecting and adapting tasks for their own classrooms.

Interns, seated in small groups and provided with base blocks, were asked to solve and discuss the tasks and classify them according to level of cognitive demand. Figure 17.3 shows several strategies used by one intern to solve $64 - 28$ in her mathematics journal. Methods instructors felt that these class activities laid the foundation for interns to consider the Two Methods of Subtraction lesson, which they were asked to read before Kris's visit. Interns were also asked to write in their mathematics journals in response to the prompts shown in the left-hand column of table 17.2.

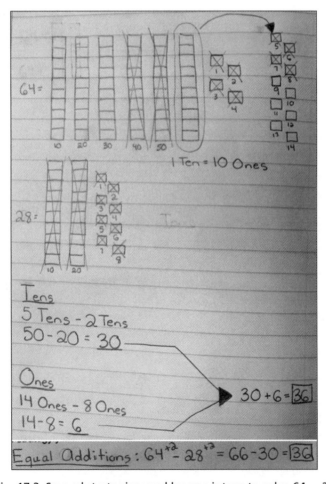

Fig. 17.3. Several strategies used by one intern to solve $64 - 28$

Table 17.2

Sample intern responses to prompts about the Two Methods of Subtraction lesson

Journal Prompt	Sample Intern Response
Describe the mathematics in the lesson. (What are the big ideas in this lesson?)	"Teen subtraction, double digit subtraction (the ungroup method)."
Describe the suggested teaching strategies. (What does the teacher do? What do students do?)	"The teacher puts the problem on the board and . . . works through it very step by step. The students follow and copy."
Describe the mathematical tasks in the lesson.	"Practice the expanded method and ungroup method. Students are expected to explain these methods."
What are some changes you might make and why?	"Let students try it their own way first. Have students work in groups first."

At the beginning of the fourth class, the methods instructors engaged interns in observing children's addition and subtraction strategies in a series of short videos (Carpenter et al. 2015). Kris joined the methods instructors in discussing the children's strategies with interns. After this discussion, we began our shared focus on the Two Methods of Subtraction lesson. Several weeks earlier, Kris and two methods instructors, Linda and MJ, had decided that an instructional strategy called *carousel brainstorming* (Lipton and Wellman 1998; McKnight 2010), as illustrated in figure 17.4, might be helpful in structuring a discussion based on interns' responses to the questions in table 17.2. This engagement strategy, used previously by the coaching team with classroom teachers, encourages participants to share ideas, agree and disagree, and extend their thinking.

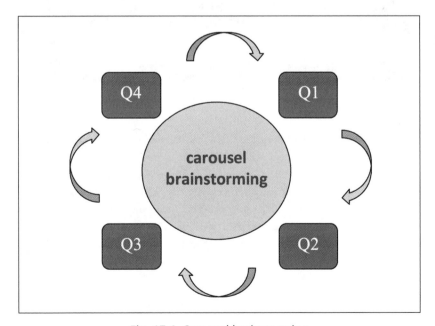

Fig. 17.4. Carousel brainstorming

Kris introduced the protocol for carousel brainstorming to interns by explaining that four large chart papers, displayed in different classroom locations, contained the four journal prompts. Interns formed small groups, and each group was assigned to one of the four questions as a starting point. When the carousel started, intern groups discussed the prompt on the chart paper, using their written journal responses (see the samples in table 17.2), and then one group member recorded the group's ideas on the chart paper. When the group arrived at the next chart, they read and discussed the previous group's notes and added new ideas and questions, as shown in figure 17.5. This process continued until each group returned to its original carousel position. As interns worked, Kris and the methods instructors monitored the time and moved among the groups, listening and making notes.

Fig. 17.5. Interns record ideas on chart paper while carousel brainstorming

Once the carousel stopped, each group was asked to review the full set of responses to their first prompt and to prepare a short summary to present to the whole class. During the summary discussion, interns added notes to their journals. Kris and the methods instructors encouraged interns to identify common threads across charts. Interns expressed tentative thoughts and questions about connections across the areas of the four prompts including, for example, how teacher actions in the lesson might affect children's experiences with particular tasks. Having discussed the level of cognitive demand of some mathematical tasks from the lesson the previous week, some interns proposed ideas or asked questions such as the following:

- Students are just supposed to follow the steps of the two subtraction methods in the lesson, but they don't really talk about why the methods work, so that could be an adaptation or a discussion that the teacher could lead.

- It would help students if there were more real-world connections for the tasks in this lesson. That might generate more strategies and discussion.

- What would you do as the teacher if a student wanted to work backward and use addition or some other strategy to solve the subtraction problems?

- Even if the purpose of a task is to provide practice, it can be done in more creative ways, like giving problems that are missing the number that is being subtracted. This would still require students to regroup and might be more challenging.

As illustrated by these examples, many of the interns' questions and ideas about tasks focused on how the lesson's tasks might be changed to honor children's unique thinking and strategies as well as how to connect place value understandings with the two methods of subtraction in the lesson. Concluding the discussion, Kris asked the interns about their experience participating in the carousel brainstorm.

After class, the methods instructors and coach discussed how carousel brainstorming seemed to have supported a rich exchange of ideas among interns. As Kris describes,

> The carousel was an avenue to share learning, extend thinking, and develop new understandings around mathematics. Interns had to describe the mathematics as well as determine best instructional practices for each lesson component. By sharing these ideas in the carousel, all voices were heard in a "silent conversation" and then shared out with the class. The power of this strategy was evident in the whole group discussion.

One goal for introducing this instructional strategy was to help interns develop ways to support children in sharing their ideas—in mathematics and other content areas as well. Later in the semester, one intern shared how she incorporated carousel brainstorming into her instruction:

> When the coaches come to methods, they provide a different perspective because we learn strategies that we can use in our classrooms regularly. I used the carousel strategy with my third graders during writing one day. Kids put their writing topics at the top of their page and their table groups passed the papers around and wrote notes/ideas/questions. It was awesome!

Because we also hoped that the experience of examining the subtraction lesson would prompt interns to begin to attend to children's engagement with mathematics in their classrooms, one of our decisions after class was to ask interns to take notes in their journals over the next week about the specific tasks comprising their students' mathematics lessons. We later used intern-collected tasks for further class explorations related to identifying the level of cognitive demand of different mathematical tasks.

Although the details go beyond the scope of this chapter, we note that our work in Domain 2 continued throughout the semester as interns progressed from initially examining and describing characteristics of tasks, to classifying tasks as providing low or high levels of cognitive demand, to eventually selecting and adapting tasks for instruction in their classrooms. Interns' reflections at the semester's end suggest that methods course activities had positioned them to continue to inquire into the role of mathematical tasks in students' learning, as these two quotes illustrate:

> After learning and practicing how to adapt mathematical tasks from our textbook [district-adopted curriculum program], I feel confident in my ability to do this in the future. It is so important to know how to adapt mathematical tasks in order to push student thinking and facilitate meaningful math discussion.

In class, I initially felt that low level tasks were "bad" and higher level tasks were preferred. However, I now understand that both low and high level tasks have a purpose and I would like to investigate this further in my classroom.

■ Professional Learning of Teacher Educators

Our primary focus in this chapter is on collaborating to support interns' learning, yet we also recognize that the collaboration between coaches and methods instructors has created a context for professional learning by ourselves and other PDS teachers and teacher educators. Consider how one methods instructor, MJ, describes professional learning in the collaboration:

> Our partnership with the coaches models for interns how collaboration between the district and the university can impact their own learning as well as the learning of their mentor teachers, coaches, and math methods co-instructors. The coaches bring instructional strategies to the class and, in turn, take away ideas for teaching mathematics that they can share with classroom teachers. Math methods co-instructors have been able to learn about more general instructional strategies that interns can connect with practices they observe in their own placement classrooms.

Gail, an instructional coach, similarly suggests that the collaboration between coaches and methods instructor offers reciprocal learning opportunities: "Coaches learn from interns and methods instructors, and interns and methods instructors learn from coaches. Everyone is learning together new ways to improve mathematics instruction for students." In particular, she describes how "the coaches' involvement in preservice teacher learning informs what they do with in-service teachers. For example, when co-planning or talking with teachers, coaches are able to use what they have learned about levels of cognitive demand from their time in the math methods course."

Unique professional learning opportunities seem to develop as we work across school and university boundaries, as described by Kris:

> Collaboration between the PDS and the district allows instructional coaches to connect the district curriculum and instruction with the interns and the university. Bringing together knowledge of the district curriculum and mathematics pedagogy helps us to develop deeper understandings of what we want for our new teachers entering the field.

Indeed, our efforts to collaborate to enhance interns' learning about mathematics curriculum have stimulated the development of new forms of expertise and new practices that integrate school and university perspectives and, ultimately, have potential to improve children's mathematical experiences.

References

Campbell, Patricia F. "Coaching and Elementary Mathematics Specialists: Findings from Research." In *Professional Collaborations in Mathematics Teaching and Learning: Seeking Success for All*, 2012 Yearbook of the National Council of Teachers of Mathematics (NCTM), edited by Jennifer M. Bay-Williams and William R. Speer, pp. 147–59. Reston, Va.: NCTM, 2012.

Carpenter, Thomas P., Elizabeth Fennema, Megan L. Franke, Linda Levi, and Susan B. Empson. *Children's Mathematics: Cognitively Guided Instruction.* 2nd ed. Portsmouth, N.H.: Heinemann, 2015.

Cochran-Smith, Marilyn, and Susan L. Lytle. *Inside/Outside: Teacher Research and Knowledge.* New York: Teachers College Press, 1993.

Fuson, Karen C. *Math Expressions.* Boston: Houghton Mifflin Harcourt Publishers, 2012.

Knight, James. *Instructional Coaching: A Partnership Approach to Improving Instruction.* Thousand Oaks, Calif.: Corwin Press, 2007.

Lipton, Laura, and Bruce Wellman. *Patterns and Practices in the Learning-Focused Classroom.* Guilford, Vt.: Pathways Publishing, 1998.

Lloyd, Gwendolyn M., and Vanessa R. Pitts Bannister. *Curriculum-Based Activities and Resources for Preservice Math Teachers.* Reston, Va.: NCTM, 2011.

McKnight, Katherine S. *The Teacher's Big Book of Graphic Organizers: 100 Reproducible Organizers That Help Kids with Reading, Writing, and the Content Areas.* New York: Jossey-Bass, 2010.

National Association for Professional Development Schools (NAPDS). "What It Means to Be a Professional Development School." 2008. http://napds.org/wp-content/uploads/2014/10/Nine-Essentials.pdf.

National Council of Teachers of Mathematics (NCTM). *Principles to Actions: Ensuring Mathematical Success for All.* Reston, Va.: NCTM, 2014.

Smith, Margaret S., and Mary Kay Stein. "Selecting and Creating Mathematical Tasks: From Research to Practice." *Mathematics Teaching in the Middle School* 3, no. 5 (1998): 344–49.

Stein, Mary Kay, Barbara W. Grover, and Marjorie Henningsen. "Building Student Capacity for Mathematical Thinking and Reasoning: An Analysis of Mathematical Tasks Used in Reform Classrooms." *Journal of Mathematics Teacher Education* 11, no. 5 (1996): 349–71.

Zeichner, Ken. "Rethinking the Connections between Campus Courses and Field Experiences in College- and University-Based Teacher Education." *Journal of Teacher Education* 61, no. 1–2 (2010): 89–99.

CHAPTER 18

Working Together to Enhance Children's Understanding of Fractions

Debra Monson, *University of St. Thomas, Minneapolis, Minnesota*
Sue Ahrendt, *University of Wisconsin–River Falls*
Kathleen Cramer, *University of Minnesota, Twin Cities*

Educational research is often highly dependent on the collaboration between university personnel and school districts. These types of collaborations can include multiple components that meet the needs of one or both of these partners. A research group from a midwestern U.S. university has successfully partnered with school districts for more than thirty years in an effort to understand student thinking, improve student achievement, and create high-quality curricula related to the teaching and learning of rational number. The partnership highlighted in this chapter is one of many in the course of this project. A group of university researchers joined with four teachers in a large urban district. This collaboration was highly focused on supporting one group of third-grade teachers' implementation of a research-based curriculum designed to improve student achievement in fraction learning while meeting state standards. This school is considered high needs, with 92 percent of the students receiving free and reduced lunch and less than 20 percent of all students meeting proficiency on state exams. The goal of this chapter is to share the components of this partnership, the lessons learned from it, and its overall benefits.

Research embedded in classrooms can provide useful insights into student thinking and give teachers much-needed information about their students (Franke and Kazemi 2001). Partnerships between universities and schools are essential for this type of educational research to occur. Erickson and colleagues (2005) highlight features that are characteristic of their collaborative approach with schools. Two of these ideas are mirrored within the features of our partnership: (*a*) the project must meet the real and existing needs of all participants, and (*b*) there must be strong agreement from both school and teacher educators on the purposes and any underlying theoretical perspectives of the project. We met with the four third-grade teachers to ensure that they were willing to carefully consider the theoretical foundations of the curriculum and to communicate our beliefs that both teachers and researchers had valuable knowledge to share during the project. Specifically, the teachers provided insight into their students, and the researchers shared their insight in content knowledge related to learning rational number. Together teachers and researchers contributed their ideas to improve the curriculum for students.

■ Partnership Goals

The partnership consisted of several goals: (*a*) to support implementation of the fraction lessons in four third-grade classrooms by providing teachers with focused professional development around student thinking and the theoretical attributes of the curriculum, (*b*) to study third-grade students' thinking as they built an understanding of rational number using this research-based curriculum, (*c*) to revise the existing lessons by considering input from classroom teachers and our study of students' thinking, and (*d*) to pilot four new lessons using the number line as a model for fractions.

The teacher participants in this research project were familiar with the curriculum, as the entire district had adopted it for all third-grade classrooms. The curriculum, though, was initially developed with fourth-grade students. This collaboration provided the research group an opportunity to assess its effectiveness with third-grade students and to identify adaptations needed for younger children. The research group in turn provided these teachers with professional development focused on student learning of rational numbers. Additionally, the state standards for third grade included the number line as a model for fractions. The standards state that students should be able to "read and write fractions with words and symbols. Recognize that fractions can be used to represent parts of a whole, parts of a set, points on a *number line,* or distances on a *number line*" (Minnesota Department of Education 2007; emphasis added). As the existing curriculum did not introduce the number line in its first module, the collaboration provided an opportunity to implement new number line lessons and study the impact on third graders' fraction learning.

Partnerships can create both practical and formal knowledge (Erickson et al. 2005). Data from this collaboration (i.e., input from teachers, samples of student work, and student interview data) were used to create a third-grade module that better meets the learning needs of third graders for the district's future use, including additional lessons to build meaning for the number line model for fractions.

■ The Curriculum, District, and University

These curricula are open-access materials and available on the project's website (http://www.cehd .umn.edu/ci/rationalnumberproject). The theoretical foundation for these curricula is based on a translation model (Cramer 2003) that suggests that mathematical ideas can be represented in five different modes: concrete, real life, verbal symbols, written symbols, and pictures. Students using these curricula experience fraction ideas from these different modes and then translate among them to develop conceptual understanding. Students using this curriculum use multiple concrete models to represent fractions, including fraction circles, paper folding strips, and counters. Students draw pictures of these models and make connections from concrete models or pictures to written symbols. They solve fraction story problems using pictures and written symbols. As students work in these different representations, they are asked to describe, justify, and explain what they are doing within these different representations.

As this research group has a long history of partnerships and staff development with this district, and as authors of the curriculum, we approached the district to ask how we could support their success as they enacted the lessons district-wide. We considered common interests so the partnership would be beneficial to all involved. We were all committed to help students meet the third-grade standards. We were interested in continually improving these lessons to support the fraction learning needs of all third graders, particularly students in this district and those with low prior achievement.

As researchers we recognized this as a way to provide the support teachers sought as we simultaneously addressed specific research questions. Answers to the following questions guided the revisions to the lessons for the district's future use:

1. Does the curriculum provide these third-grade teachers with the needed support to teach initial fraction ideas with multiple concrete models with fidelity of implementation that reflects the authors' intentions?

2. What adaptations to the curriculum do these third-grade teachers make and why? Do the adaptations support or hinder students' opportunity to learn?

3. In what ways does teaching fractions influence these third-grade teachers' own understanding of fractions and how they perceive what third graders can learn about fractions after working with this curriculum?

Adding a Number Line Component

The curriculum was missing lessons that addressed the number line model for fractions, while the state standards required third-grade students to locate and identity fractions on a number line. We took this opportunity to create new number line lessons for the district and to study their effectiveness within these four third-grade classrooms.

Additional research questions included the following:

1. How do third-grade students make sense of the number line model?

2. Do the number line lessons that focused on paper folding to number line translation support third graders in making sense of the number line model for fractions?

3. What challenges do these third-grade students have with the number line that need to be addressed in the revised lessons?

Number line lessons were developed within the same theoretical framework as the rest of the curricula. The lessons focused on the connections among context, the paper folding model, and the number line to build understanding of the number line. Students were asked to use paper folding strips, which was a familiar model, and then pictures of paper strips to model distance story problems. The teacher then projected a picture of a number line (same length) below a picture of the paper strip model and asked students how the two models both represented the context. The connections focused on how the fold lines on the paper strips are represented with tick marks on the number line and how equivalent parts on the paper strips match the equal spacing between tick marks on the number line. Comparing and contrasting the two representations was the first step in helping students learn how to construct number lines to model fractions.

The number line lessons were piloted in the partnership school only and implemented after thirteen fraction lessons that used fraction circles, chips, and paper folding as important representations for the part-whole model for fractions. As the original curricula were designed and modified based on student thinking through several iterations of teaching experiments, these number line lessons continued to be developed and modified in this iterative process. The collaboration allowed us to include our public school teacher partners in the revision of the lessons.

■ Partnership Details

The partnership began with the district adoption of the curriculum and ended with a revised curriculum for third graders. The bullet points below explain the specific steps that were included to make this partnership successful. These steps helped to keep communication open, improve the curriculum, and take advantage of the expertise of both the teachers and the university researchers. In order of how the events occurred, we completed the following tasks:

- Professional development for all third-grade teachers leading to selection of the participating teachers

- Pre-survey for the participating teachers to investigate their understanding of the curriculum and concepts contained within it

- Professional learning community (PLC) meetings to discuss key ideas in the curriculum

- Classroom observations and debriefing sessions with teachers

- Written reflection questions by teachers (done individually) after each lesson

- A post-survey completed after the entire unit that addressed student thinking, teaching strategies, and strengths and limitations of the lessons

After completing all of these steps, the researchers met, analyzed the data collected, and revised the initial lessons. These newly developed third-grade lessons were then shared with the district for future use.

■ Professional Development for Teachers

Before the implementation began, the teachers in the district were given opportunities for professional development on the implementation of the curriculum. We wanted to ensure fidelity of implementation, focusing on the authors' intended curriculum (Brown et al. 2009). Helping teachers understand and appreciate the role of translations and connections among representations, along with seeing the importance of extended time with concrete representations, was an important part of the professional development.

Half-day sessions were offered for all third-grade district teachers to examine the curriculum, discuss common student misconceptions, and explore the multiple models used in the lessons so that the curriculum would be implemented as intended. Teachers were given background information on the theoretical basis for the curriculum, the history and research behind it, sample lesson plans, and an opportunity to discuss the information included within the lessons. Videos showing students' thinking highlighted for teachers how children are able to reason about fractions when given time to develop fraction ideas using multiple representations. It is from these professional development sessions that the four teachers in this partnership were recruited for this collaboration. These teachers had all been teaching for three to five years prior to this project.

Pre-Survey

The participating teachers were given a written pre-survey that asked for information about the ways they organized their classrooms, the challenging aspects of teaching third graders about fractions, and the ways that the previous curriculum met or failed to meet the needs of their students. They responded to questions asking about their perceptions of the new curriculum lessons and staff development. This pre-survey provided us with an understanding of the context in which the partnership took place. Teachers commented that their students' most common misunderstandings involved whole number confusion. For example, many thought that $1/5$ is bigger than $1/4$ because 5 is greater than 4. They commented that their previous curriculum lacked manipulatives that would support students to build mental representations for fractions. This partnership would directly address these concerns.

Professional Learning Communities (PLCs)

Upon the teachers' decision to collaborate with the university, a university team member met with the third-grade team at their after-school PLC meetings. The professional development for teachers built on the school's current infrastructure, namely, their weekly PLC meetings. The research plan was discussed in the PLCs before the teachers taught the lessons. The teachers' voices were important elements in our research, and we wanted to make sure that message was clear and their participation would be authentic. We worked to promote communication and to value their participation.

During the implementation, one or more of our team members attended each weekly PLC meeting and discussed successes and issues of implementation. Modifications to lessons were noted, ideas for improvement were identified, and concerns about implementation were shared. For example, at the first PLC meeting after the teachers taught lessons 1–3, the teachers shared their impressions of the lessons and suggestions for improving them. First, one teacher noted that the lower performing students were more engaged in the fraction lessons than in her usual math lesson. The other teachers agreed and discussed that the reason for this was the use of the fraction circle pieces that students used. They felt that the "hands-on" nature of the lesson kept more students focused. The teachers also suggested some changes to the lessons. In lesson 2, the use of visuals of fractions in the story problems was too difficult for the students, and the teachers gave ideas for revising them and for attending to the vocabulary used in the stories. The student work originally involved pictures of circles and rectangular bars within story contexts, and we changed the activity to continue to have students use the fraction circles as they had in lesson 1 to name fractional amounts. They also proposed some practical strategies to share with other teachers. For example, one teacher decided to have a bucket for lost fraction circle pieces that students could access as needed to complete their sets. They also recommended including hints for helping students fold paper into thirds.

The teachers provided significant help at the second PLC where the discussion centered on fraction order lessons. They all agreed that third-grade children needed more time to explore with fraction circles and unit fractions before moving on to order ideas by folding strips of paper into equivalent fractional parts. We took their suggestions and created additional lessons for ordering fractions with one lesson devoted specifically to unit fractions. The teachers also provided thoughtful suggestions for rewriting the equivalence lessons so students would have more time using the fraction circles to explore simple equivalences before using the paper-folding model. In general, their suggestions helped the authors focus on pacing the ideas developed for third graders as well as the need for more time with the fraction circles manipulative before transitioning to a new model.

The PLCs strengthened relationships, built camaraderie among all participants, and gave valuable insight into the teachers' challenges and successes with the curriculum. Teacher enthusiasm for the curriculum and insights into student thinking, such as the importance of time with particular models and the importance of appropriate story problems, were evident. Researchers were able to collect information that informed modification and improvement of the lessons. The PLCs were mutually beneficial for both teachers and university researchers.

Classroom Observations and Debriefing Sessions

In addition to participating in PLCs, university researchers were invited to observe each lesson to check the level of fidelity of implementation to note the degree of alignment between the authors' intended lesson and the actual enacted lesson (Brown et al. 2007). Observers recorded lesson activities along with teacher modifications. The observation protocol focused on ideas that are central to the curriculum as noted in a table 18.1. Following each lesson, observers would debrief the teacher in person or by phone. Questions in the debriefing session were as follows:

1. What did you learn about students' thinking from today's lesson?

2. I noticed you changed ____. Why did you choose to make that change? [based on the lesson, ask about a particular adaptation to the lesson]

3. How is student A's thinking different from student B's thinking?

These responses were collected and then used to revise the lessons as necessary.

Table 18.1

Partial observation protocol shown with actual observer notes

Teacher Actions Using the Curriculum	Examples to Highlight Teacher Actions
Provide students with extended periods of time with the manipulative models so students can construct meaning for fractions, including order and equivalence ideas as well as fraction operations.	Followed the lesson plan and students used fraction circles and paper strips to order fractions on student pages. Expectation was that the students had "evidence" to support answers during group sharing.
Adjust lessons based on informal formative assessments that focus on student thinking.	Changed the fraction order tasks on student page A to include unit fractions to align with state's grade 3 goals. Also, as paper strips were difficult for students to use for some of the denominators, adapted lesson and let students use the fraction circles on the order tasks. Also changed the warm-up to order fractions using unit fractions and fractions with same denominator.
Orchestrate classroom discourse so students can share their thinking with the rest of the class, making their ideas public.	Teacher could have done a better job of getting at the big idea for lesson and helping students verbalize their thinking. Students relied on showing why a fraction was larger concretely. But the student language showing an understanding of the denominator was missing.

Written Reflections

In addition to teacher input at the PLC meetings and the discussions after each observation, teachers completed a post-lesson reflection. These post-lesson reflections were collected and reviewed. Notes were taken as to the adaptations teachers made as well as their ideas for improving the lessons. Comparisons were made across teachers' reflections to look for similar comments leading to further improvements in the lessons for third graders. The post-lesson reflection questions included the following:

1. What went well with the lesson?

2. What adaptations did you make to the lesson plan to better meet the needs of third graders?

3. What adaptations did you make on the student pages to better meet the needs of third graders?

4. To improve the lesson I suggest . . .

5. Other comments:

Post-Teaching Survey

Teachers completed a post-teaching survey that included items related to student learning and the characteristics of the most productive lessons. They were asked to comment on the strengths and weaknesses of the curriculum. Teachers were also invited to reflect on the ways that their teaching changed based on the lessons. They commented on the power of the manipulatives in the lessons and the ways that the lessons supported them in the facilitator role. When asked what surprised them about what students learned when using the curriculum, teachers commented on their students' ability to represent, order, and compare fractions, particularly among students who struggled in math class on other topics. Other feedback suggested that there be more use of context in the lessons and careful consideration of alignment to state standards. These suggestions were later used as the lessons were revised.

■ Products of the Collaboration

To document student learning, students were given the district pre- and posttests on fractions assessing state standards. A subset of students was interviewed after the lessons to better understand their thinking about fractions and fractions on the number line. The district pretest showed little prior understanding of fractions. Posttests showed 63 to 80 percent success on questions related to continuous models for fractions; 33 to 60 percent correct on items using discrete models; 61 to 88 percent on ordering items. Interviews with twelve selected students showed they were able to model fractions with circles, chips, and paper folding. They were able to order unit fractions and fractions with the same denominator based on mental representations related to the models used in instruction. Several misunderstandings were revealed on the number line tasks, which showed us that these lessons needed thoughtful revisions. These misunderstandings included issues related to the unit on the number line, making sense of the tick marks, and partitioning the number line.

In addition to increased student fraction learning, this collaboration produced both a tangible product in a set of revised curriculum lessons as well as more intangible gains, such as participants' increased understanding of the curriculum and implementation that focused on student thinking specifically around number line and fractions. Curriculum revision resulted from specific needs identified by both the teachers and researchers throughout the implementation process. The partnership, motivated by the desire to improve student achievement, nurtured deeper understandings of the way students make sense of fractions.

Researchers were inspired to rethink the role of the number line as a model for students as they learn initial fraction ideas. By examining students' thinking as they worked to make sense of the number line we came away with a better understanding of the complexities inherent in the number line model for fractions (Cramer et al. 2016). These data led to major revisions of the number line lessons. The revised lessons were then implemented the following year in another collaboration with additional third-grade teachers within the district. This opportunity to continue this partnership around implementation of the fraction curriculum was primarily due to the positive feedback the district received from the third-grade teachers who participated in the collaboration reported here.

■ What Made This Partnership Successful?

This partnership contained several aspects that made it successful. The prior successes and connections that the researchers had built in the past gave this research team the opportunity to partner with the district. A level of trust and respect among all parties existed prior to this collaboration. Because of this preexisting level of trust, teachers and researchers were willing and eager to work with one another.

The partnership enhanced the existing district focus on improving student understanding of rational number and common goals united parties in the collaboration. Both parties valued the expertise that the other group brought to the table and acknowledged that this sharing of information was crucial to the success of the implementation of the curriculum. The relationship was in no way hierarchical. Researchers appreciated teachers' crucial knowledge of their students and the environment. Teachers valued the researchers' knowledge of the theoretical underpinnings of the curriculum and reasons for the pedagogical steps embedded in the lessons. Teachers trusted the curriculum and implemented the lessons with high levels of fidelity. As partners, all areas of expertise were sincerely valued.

A preestablished PLC that was willing to focus on student thinking based on rational number was instrumental in the project's success. The current infrastructure streamlined the extra time that teachers needed to commit to this collaboration. A focus on student thinking around fractions led to productive use of this PLC time.

Since the conclusion of this research, another iteration of the number line lessons for third grade has occurred. In the second year of implementation, researchers were welcomed as co-facilitators of the number line lesson in another school within the district, leading to a revised set of number line lessons. Successful collaborations that value contributions of all partners provide a foundation for future relationships. Ultimately, these types of relationships form a basis for building connections between research and practice so that we are all better able to understand student thinking and ultimately improve student learning and achievement.

References

Brown, Stacy A., Kathleen Pitvorec, Catherine Ditto, and Catherine Randall Kelso. "Reconceiving Fidelity of Implementation: An Investigation of Elementary Whole-Number Lessons." *Journal for Research in Mathematics Education* 40, no. 4 (2009): 363–95.

Cramer, Kathleen. "Using a Translation Model for Curriculum Development and Classroom Instruction." In *Beyond Constructivism: Models and Modeling Perspectives on Mathematics Problem Solving, Learning, and Teaching*, edited by Richard Lesh and Helen M. Doerr, pp. 449–64. Mahwah, N.J.: Lawrence Erlbaum Associates, 2003.

Cramer, Kathleen, Susan Ahrendt, Debra Monson, Terry Wyberg, and Christina Miller. "Making Sense of Third-Grade Students' Misunderstandings of the Number Line." *Investigations in Mathematics Learning* 9, no. 1 (2016): 19–37.

Erickson, Gaalen, Gabriella Minnes Brandes, Ian Mitchell, and Judie Mitchell. "Collaborative Teacher Learning: Findings from Two Professional Development Projects." *Teaching and Teacher Education* 21 (2005): 787–98.

Franke, Megan. L., and Elham Kazemi. "Learning to Teach Mathematics: Focus on Student Thinking." *Theory into Practice* 40, no. 2 (2001): 102–9.

Minnesota Department of Education. *Minnesota Academic Standards: Mathematics K–12.* Roseville, Minn.: Minnesota Department of Education, 2007.

CHAPTER 19

Cross-Sector Collaboration to Improve Teaching and Learning through Focused Inquiry

Jacqueline Coomes, *Eastern Washington University, Cheney*

Barbara Alvin, *Eastern Washington University, Cheney*

Debra Olson, *Spokane Falls Community College, Spokane, Washington*

The process of solving a problem often provides a context for learning, whether that learning is formal or informal. In this chapter, we describe a professional learning project that targeted the complex and persistent issues related to students' transition from high school to college. Instructors from across educational sectors together identified the problem as how to teach students to learn and transfer skills such as critical thinking, mathematical habits of mind, deep learning, and metacognition. As a result, our project focused on improving teaching practices that help students develop these skills. We used this problem as a context for professional learning through inquiry, and we share here how this approach helped us examine our practices in relation to the problem. An important aspect of inquiry learning is sharing results of the work, which allows the system to collectively learn more about the problem and its possible solutions (Morris and Hiebert 2011; Palmisano 2013).

■ Addressing the Transition Problem through Collaborative Inquiry

In collaborative inquiry, learning occurs through a generative process and builds instructors' capacity to closely examine their teaching. The inquiry process provides tools for instructors to imagine and try possible solutions to improve student success and to gather and analyze evidence of each strategy's efficacy (Morris and Hiebert 2011). As Condon and colleagues have stated, "Learning occurs in intentional, self-directed efforts" (Condon et al. 2015, p. 7). In what follows, we highlight instructor learning through this process and illustrate how a group of instructors, working across sectors, designed their own professional learning as they studied issues affecting college readiness and success. Learning through inquiry requires that instructors identify problems, realize and question their assumptions, and examine their own roles in solving the problem. It requires developing an inquiry stance (Nelson, Slavit, and Deuel 2012).

Instructors in this project discussed the difference and relative strength of an inquiry approach over "quick fix" solutions provided by others; one described how the quick fix approach "causes dedicated and professional educators to become burned out and cynical about the possibility for thoughtful, intentional, and ongoing progress." Another instructor added, "Our understandings about how learning works will always, and should always, continue to deepen and expand," and we concluded that instructors needed to learn through their own action and reflection.

The Design of Collaborative Inquiry across Institutions

Designing collaborative inquiry across institutions takes careful planning and ongoing adaptations. The difficulties for designers and facilitators arise from the need to create conditions and support for collaborative, systematic, and ongoing inquiry. Facilitators must help instructors who work in different contexts build relationships, understand each other's challenges and constraints, and find common areas to target. The role of project leaders is to provide resources and structure to support the process; they must create protocols, find research, and structure meetings to help inquiry groups understand the process of inquiry. Figure 19.1 describes some of the roles of leaders at different points in the inquiry process and how they relate to the work of the inquiry groups, which we called cohorts.

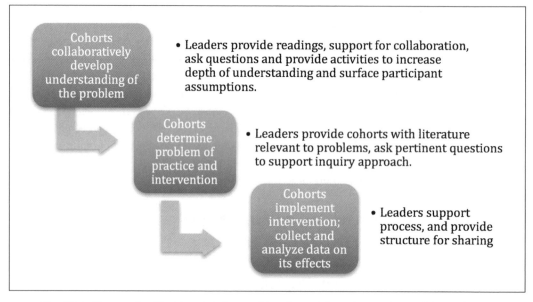

Fig. 19.1. The work of leaders is informed by the work and questions of the cohorts.

A challenge of learning through collaborative inquiry for both leaders and instructors was that it took a type of commitment that was different from other forms of professional learning. Individuals and cohorts within the project needed to commit to the process, which could be messy and unproductive. Individual instructors needed to problematize their practices and see how their teaching may affect students' success in traversing the larger system. Cohort members became interdependent during their inquiry (Wenger 1998); each instructor was expected to follow through on an iterative process designed to build shared understandings of problems, generate approaches designed to produce better results, and assess and reflect on the results (Palmisano 2013). Instructors committed to collecting and analyzing student work or observation data to determine the effectiveness of their interventions.

The inquiry process also required ways of thinking that deepened understanding of problems and that helped instructors to tune their approaches based on observations and evidence and to retest those approaches as part of an improvement cycle. As an important part of the process, they shared their story, processes, and the results of their work.

■ Creating Context for Improvement

Initially conceived by a group of higher education faculty, administrators, and high school teachers involved in the Core to College Network (2011), the goal of Successful Transitions to College was to improve students' transition to college math. Specific targets were to reduce by 4 percent the number of students from participating high schools who place into developmental courses in college and to increase by 4 percent the number of students who succeed in their first college-level class. We also wanted to create capacity for instructors from high schools, community colleges, and a university in our region to collaborate to solve problems of transitions. To this end, we established a regional learning network dedicated to working on this problem.

The Successful Transitions to College participants included mathematics and English language arts (ELA) instructors from high schools in rural, urban, and suburban districts; two community colleges; and one university in the region. Cohorts consisted of four to six instructors, with a mix of high school, community college, and university instructors of the same discipline in each cohort. All participants attended three workshops each year, and cohorts met and worked between the large meetings. Although this chapter reported on the work of math cohorts, we note that math and ELA instructors repeatedly described how much they valued each other's input.

Before the first meeting, project leaders created a website where they posted readings and discussion prompts to surface values, build collaboration, and develop understanding and ownership of the problems. The readings included articles on equity, on problems of transferring knowledge, and on teacher learning through inquiry. Instructors participated in an online discussion related to the articles. We noticed deep engagement with the readings and prompts, showing that the topics resonated with our participants' concerns. On the problem of transfer, one instructor responded to another's post that students do not apply the reasoning they have learned to situations we expect them to. He described how many students struggled to use the concepts learned in class: "It seems that they are missing even a few basic strategies for *how* they can transfer that knowledge. . . .Why would I expect them to transfer if I've never asked them to transfer?" His response indicates that he was searching for ways to help his students learn in ways that support transfer.

Instructors discussed the readings at the first meeting, helping them build relationships. At that meeting they also worked in groups to analyze the Standards for Mathematical Practice (National Governors Association Center for Best Practices and Council of Chief State School Officers [NGA Center and CCSSO] 2010) and to discuss their ideas about general and specific problems of practice they could address while working across sectors. Important ideas in these discussions included ways to develop procedural fluency, conceptual understanding, and application; and methods for teaching critical thinking, problem solving, and mathematical thinking. One group posed a question to themselves: "Standards of mathematical practice—the power of these standards is that they apply at every level and for every course, and can guide our work—how do we bring them alive in the classroom?" Another group asked if the Standards for Mathematical Practices could be the avenue for smoothing the transition among sectors. Still other groups focused on culture shifts from high school to college, including the differences in expectations. Identifying specific problems naturally led to proposing areas of improvement as a focus for their cohorts.

At the first meeting, the cohorts accepted ownership for the problems students encountered when transitioning among sectors. They examined and discussed the Common Core Standards for Mathematical Practices and ELA portraits of college-ready students (NGA Center and CCSSO 2010) to create descriptions of characteristics they sought to develop in their students. They examined ways that college instructors needed to support students to improve student success once students arrived at college. Throughout the project, instructors shared responsibility for the transition problem. At the end of the first year, a high school instructor reported, "Our collaboration has been incredibly positive and I feel that there has been a high level of positive communication and understanding between all groups involved." Protocols used to support cohorts' inquiry can be found at this book's page on NCTM's More4U website.

■ Two Key Ideas

Early in the project, two key ideas arose: Instructors from different sectors realized their assumptions about other sectors were not always correct, and cohorts who identified similar issues approached solutions in very different ways.

Examining Evidence to Understand the Problem

For their first assignment, instructors observed a class in a sector different from their own. The observations were intended to help the entire group see how students might perceive the system as they moved through the sectors; therefore, we emphasized the importance of viewing a class as a student might, naming the observation protocol the "Student Experience Visit." The observations also gave instructors practice in collecting data they could reflect on and supported the idea of implementing changes based on observable data.

We based the Student Experience Visit protocol on the values instructors discussed in the first meeting. They had identified problem solving, critical thinking, and active learning as important aspects of effective classrooms, so these were main ideas on the protocol. Instructors were asked to note, and include evidence on, the following items:

- Demands that students encountered
- Critical thinking required
- Independent learning skills required
- Collaboration skills required
- Student engagement
- Implicitly and explicitly communicated expectations

The protocol guided them to observe the context as students might and to consider the particular experiences and demands that students encountered. They were also asked to examine artifacts such as syllabi, handouts, texts, outside-of-class supports, and any other relevant evidence that could help them answer the questions. Additional areas of focus included evidence of the independent learning and collaboration skills that students displayed and the extent to which students sought to meet the expectations of the course.

Observers summarized their experiences from student perspectives. They imagined being a student in the environment they observed and described the information, prior experience, or insights into classroom expectations that would be required for them to be successful. They also described how their observations differed from their expectations and how the skills they observed differed from those expected of their own context. Instructors' reflections on their observations were essential for inquiry learning, as they allowed instructors to uncover their assumptions and helped them reflect on their own teaching.

Finding Common Ground

Leaders analyzed instructors' responses to the observation protocol and found that instructors observed practices that the group valued in all classrooms. Instructors in all sectors posed critical thinking questions, asked students to collaborate, and engaged students in whole-class discussions. Observations showed that instructors expected students to work on challenging problems, to strive to make sense of the mathematics they were learning, and to clearly describe their thinking.

A common theme in the observation comments was perseverance: Instructors noted that the students they observed were expected to persevere in solving problems together and independently and that their colleagues in other sectors helped students understand how to persevere in learning math. One university instructor commented on his observation of a high school classroom: "I observed students eager and interested in participating in the problem solving. . . . I saw students using good reasoning, communicating well, and persevering in problem solving." He noted that most students were engaged at a high level with only one small group off task, which he attributed to the teacher's expectations.

Other instructors noticed how their colleagues communicated high expectations to students. A high school instructor observed a community college instructor praise a student for the perseverance the student had shown in solving difficult homework problems. The student had expressed concern over the time it had taken him to solve the problems, and the instructor response emphasized the student's productive disposition toward understanding the mathematics.

Observing one another's classrooms encouraged instructors to question their assumptions about students' experiences in other sectors; it gave them shared experiences to support deeper collaboration and a clearer understanding of the system students must traverse. This also helped instructors to see their own classrooms in contrast to other student experiences and to see how instructors in other sectors targeted the difficult aspects of learning they all valued. Instructors became cross-sector partners in search of solutions.

■ Problems of Practice: Same Issues, Different Approaches

After discussing observation findings as a whole group, cohorts identified problems of practice to address. Project leaders designed a protocol, *Guidelines for specifying a problem of practice and defining scope of work,* to help cohorts determine a problem of practice that could be targeted with an intervention. They described how their problems addressed students' successful transition to college mathematics courses, and they planned ways to examine the effects of the intervention.

Cohorts identified areas in which they needed background information, and leaders found related research and articles for them. To get feedback and ideas from others, cohorts presented their problem statements and ideas to other cohorts. The problems of practice identified by the cohorts were similar; they targeted students' development of independent learning skills and their ability to apply prerequisite knowledge, critical thinking, and problem-solving skills. Although the problems were similar, the solutions were very different. Figure 19.2 shows the links among the project goals, the problems of practice identified by the cohorts, and the classroom-based solutions they planned to study.

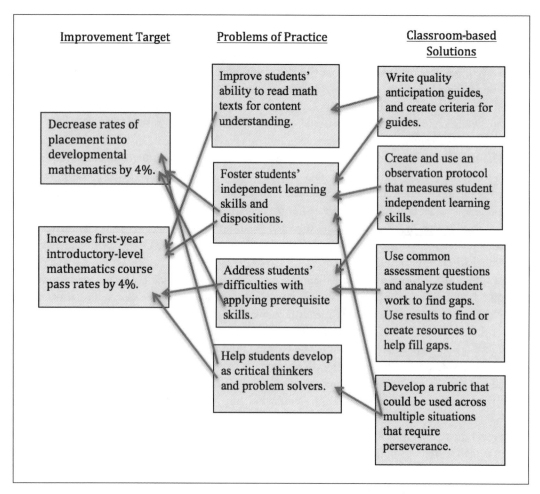

Fig. 19.2. Relationships among improvement targets, problems of practice, and interventions show different interventions for the same problem (adapted from Bryk, Gomez, and Grunow 2011)

■ The Case of an Algebra Cohort

One cohort's last presentation provides an example of how the cohorts collected data and how they implemented their intervention. The Algebra cohort included two community college, one university, and one high school instructor grouped together because of their common interest in algebra classes. Recognizing that algebra is a large hurdle to students' transition to college, this cohort identified their problem of practice as students' difficulties with independent learning and perseverance. They developed tools for assessing student work based more on processes than on answers—specifically creating a rubric to be used across multiple situations that require perseverance. They also wanted to find, develop, and use resources to create a classroom culture that fostered independent learning and perseverance.

In their first iteration of the project, the instructors each wrote challenging tasks, collaboratively wrote a rubric, and used the rubric to assess students' work on the tasks. Although they used different tasks, they each used the same rubric multiple times to show students what they valued. At the same time, the instructors incorporated strategies learned from the articles to create a classroom culture conducive to these expectations. They assessed the results of their implementation by using the rubric and gathering anecdotal evidence from students. Additional data included students' responses to a Grit Scale and a Math Perception Survey. Meeting as a cohort, they shared their results and their observations of student behavior, attitudes, performance on items, and examples of student work.

After the first iteration, the cohort met with two institutional researchers from the community college who analyzed the data the cohort had collected. Initial results were discouraging in that their measures of grit and math perception had appeared to have declined throughout the class terms. These results contradicted the instructors' observations. For example, one community college instructor noted that her initial impression was that her cultural intervention was successful. "Students are actively engaging in problem-solving tasks and working together on difficult problems, some still resisting, but improving." The other community college instructor noted, "Students seemed to like doing the grit scale and math perception survey. . . . The classroom is currently a very positive space and for many students a safe place to express ideas." However, the high school instructor noted on students' self-assessments "that students weren't very honest in their self-assessment on their Grit Scale. Not sure if this is because they are self-unaware or if they are trying to tell me what they think I want to hear."

Working with the institutional researchers, the cohort reflected on the differences between their observations and the results. The group began to wonder if students' perceptions and senses of perseverance might decline after the beginning of the term, in response to an adjustment to the expectations of the content and the course, and then rebound later in the term, albeit not so much to exceed the initial measurement. As a result of the collaboration, the cohort adjusted their second iteration and implemented their tools of measurement a third time, in the middle of the term, to determine if such a "dip" was occurring. The results of the second iteration were less clear and led to many questions from both the cohort members and the researchers. They questioned if the assessment tools measured what they intended (for example, actual perseverance vs. feelings about needing to persevere). They wondered if there were other factors they should consider and if there were other questions they should answer first. The cohort continued to plan their third iteration for the start of the next school year. They and the researchers considered alternative tools suggested by one of the project leaders, researched others, and planned a revised approach.

The Algebra cohort provided an example of a case for which the process of collaborative inquiry was essential. Collaboration with each other and, importantly, with institutional researchers allowed them to form, reflect upon, and adjust their intervention efficiently and productively. The cyclical nature of the inquiry process gave them space to learn from unexpected results and to narrow and refine their questions.

■ Discussion

The Successful Transitions Project was undertaken to address issues of students' transition from high school to college. A primary goal of the project was to develop a culture of professional learning (Wenger 1998; Wenger 2006) in which educators collaboratively applied inquiry practices to test ideas and assumptions about their teaching. Through systematically exploring the issues, cohorts identified the key problem of helping students develop higher-level thinking and learning skills. Cohorts identified specific aspects of the problem and then devised, implemented, and studied the effects of classroom practices that they expected to support higher-level thinking and learning. The large group discussions and cyclical nature of the work done by cohorts gave participants important experiences reflecting on the results of the project assignments and on the interventions they designed for their students. Instructors also deepened their understandings of the problems they identified by reading the literature, listening to one another's perspectives, and visiting classes in other sectors.

Several aspects of this project could be used by others to create similar learning opportunities for educators. The first aspect was that project leaders carefully designed activities to build respect and empathy among instructors from different sectors and different disciplines. A second aspect involved helping instructors understand the collaborative inquiry process and purposes of inquiry. While some participants had experience in inquiry learning about their teaching, developing further understanding of the process took several iterations of activities. At each large meeting, cohorts received feedback from one another and from the project leaders. Together, the first two aspects resulted in instructors from both disciplines and all sectors realizing they faced similar problems of practice. Collaboratively identifying problems of practice led cohorts to search for and test strategies to improve student attributes such as critical thinking, perseverance, deep learning, independent learning, and the ability to transfer knowledge. Instructors across sectors developed better understandings of ways to teach for and assess these complex skills.

A third aspect used to enhance the learning environment was that leaders provided guidance and support throughout the process, adapting some early versions of the structure they provided as they learned more about the challenges faced by the cohorts. However, cohorts and instructors maintained ownership for their learning. Finally, leaders provided structure for sharing among cohorts and final products.

In summary, creating and maintaining a respectful environment and helping instructors develop relationships and become open to improving their practices were necessary beginnings to helping cohorts learn through collaborative inquiry. The project leaders also needed to build on participants' varying experiences and dispositions to continually promote cohort understanding of inquiry processes and collaboration in the context of their teaching practices.

References

Bryk, Anthony S., Louis M. Gomez, and Alicia Grunow. "Getting Ideas into Action: Building Networked Improvement Communities in Education." In *Frontiers in Sociology of Education*, pp. 127–62. Dordrecht, The Netherlands: Springer Netherlands, 2011.

Condon, William, Ellen R. Iverson, Cathryn A. Manduca, Carol Rutz, and Gudrun Willett. *Faculty Development and Student Learning: Assessing the Connections.* Indianapolis: Indiana University Press, 2015.

Education First. "Featured Story: Core to College Network." 2011. http://education-first.com/impact/featured-story/core-to-college/.

Morris, Anne K., and James Hiebert. "Creating Shared Instructional Products: An Alternative Approach to Improving Teaching." *Educational Researcher* 40, no. 1 (2011): 5–14.

National Governors Association Center for Best Practices and Council of Chief State School Officers (NGA Center and CCSSO). *Common Core State Standards for Mathematics.* Washington, D.C.: NGA Center and CCSSO, 2010. http://www.corestandards.org.

Nelson, Tamara Holmlund, David Slavit, and Angie Deuel. "Two Dimensions of an Inquiry Stance toward Student-Learning Data." *Teachers College Record* 114, no. 8 (2012): 1–42.

Palmisano, Michael J. *Taking Inquiry to Scale: An Alternative to Traditional Approaches to Education Reform.* Urbana, Ill.: National Council of Teachers of English, 2013.

Wenger, Etienne. *Communities of Practice: Learning, Meaning, and Identity.* New York: Cambridge University Press, 1998.

———. "Communities of Practice: A Brief Introduction." 2006.

CHAPTER 20

Multiple Perspectives on Collaborative Teaching:
Mathematicians, Mathematics Teacher Educators, and Students

Catherine Bénéteau, *University of South Florida, Tampa*
Sarah K. Bleiler-Baxter, *Middle Tennessee State University, Murfreesboro*
Gladis Kersaint, *University of Connecticut, Storrs*
Milé Krajčevski, *University of South Florida, Tampa*
Denisse R. Thompson, *University of South Florida, Tampa*

A natural opportunity to support high-quality mathematics instruction occurs when mathematicians and mathematics teacher educators (MTEs) collaborate to plan and implement content and pedagogy courses for prospective secondary mathematics teachers. Indeed, such collaboration is in line with recommendations from the Conference Board of the Mathematical Sciences (CBMS): "It is important to encourage partnerships between mathematics faculty and mathematics education faculty" (CBMS 2012, p. 20). Through such a partnership, faculty members have the opportunity to reflect on their own practice and how that practice might need adjustment when preparing future mathematics teachers.

In this article, we share reflections from MTEs (Denisse and Gladis) and mathematicians (Catherine and Milé) who co-taught both a mathematics content and a mathematics pedagogy course as part of the Knowledge for Teaching Secondary School Project which examined the nature and process of collaborations between mathematicians and MTEs engaged in secondary mathematics teacher preparation (The Knowledge for Teaching Secondary School [KnoTSS] Project, NSF DR K-12 #0821996, with Principal Investigator Rebecca McGraw at the University of Arizona). Although we reflected throughout our collaboration, we also collected student feedback at the end of each collaboration. The perspectives of these prospective teachers (PSTs) revealed potentially problematic issues or contrasted with our perspectives as instructors. Thus, examining the PSTs' feedback caused a "disturbing" of our practice (Loughran 2006) and led us to consider missed opportunities to meet the needs of our PSTs as future mathematics teachers.

Tzur (2001) provides a four-foci model that describes teacher educators' varying levels of knowledge: learning mathematics, learning to teach mathematics, learning to teach teachers, and eventually learning to teach (or mentor) teacher educators. We use Tzur's framework to describe the focus of our reflective conversations at different points during the collaboration, in particular before and after analyzing student reflections. Although we engaged in each of the four foci, we highlight how our analysis of the PST feedback shifted our conversations from *learning to teach mathematics* to *learning to teach teachers*, thereby helping us recognize the responsibility we have to see our practice through our PSTs' eyes (Loughran 2006). We look to Loughran to help us think about how teacher educators can unpack professional knowledge with PSTs.

■ Collaboration Context and Goals

During the co-teaching experience described here, four authors (Catherine, Denisse, Gladis, and Milé) were teaching at the University of South Florida, a large metropolitan university that serves more than 47,000 students; Sarah was a doctoral student in mathematics education. The secondary mathematics education degree is a joint program comprising mathematics content courses offered by the mathematics department in the College of Arts and Sciences and mathematics-specific and general education courses offered by the College of Education. In-depth collaborations between MTEs and mathematicians have only begun within the last ten years, primarily through grant-funded collaborations led by Gladis that involved mathematicians in the planning and delivery of content-specific professional development for K–12 teachers. Both mathematicians in the collaborations described here had been involved with these grant efforts.

Each MTE/mathematician pair first co-taught a geometry course intended to address the specific content knowledge teachers need for teaching as recommended by the CBMS (2012). Then, in the following semester, each pair co-taught a high school mathematics methods course that provided PSTs the opportunity to develop concepts, skills, and pedagogical practices to support the effective teaching of mathematics (see table 20.1 for an overview of the co-teaching contexts during semesters when we collected data from PSTs). In the methods course, PSTs explored a range of mathematics content (e.g., geometry, statistics, calculus) while considering the efficacy of different instructional strategies and approaches. Among other things, they explored mathematics topics identified as challenging to students in grades 6–12, examined and evaluated the reasoning of others, considered pedagogical decisions along with their implications for teaching and learning, and discussed benefits and challenges of various ways to organize a classroom to support student learning.

Table 20.1

Overview of co-teaching contexts

Course/Semester	Instructors	Other Participants/Roles
Geometry/ Fall 2009	• Catherine (mathematician) • Denisse (MTE)	• Gladis (MTE) and Sarah (PhD student in mathematics education): Observe each class and participate in planning
Teaching Senior High School Mathematics/ Spring 2010	• Catherine (mathematician) • Denisse (MTE)	• Sarah (PhD student): Observe each class and participate in planning
Geometry/ Fall 2010	• Milé (mathematician) • Gladis (MTE)	• Sarah (PhD student): Observe each class, participate in planning, interview instructors
Teaching Senior High School Mathematics/ Spring 2011	• Milé (mathematician) • Gladis (MTE)	• Sarah (PhD student): Observe each class, participate in planning, interview instructors

Each pair conceptualized and designed both courses to be student-centered and inquiry-oriented. Teaching was planned and implemented as a joint endeavor in which both parties had equal responsibility for planning, teaching, and assessing student learning (cf. Davis 1995). Because we focus on Tzur's four-foci model of knowledge for teacher educators, we believe it important to contrast some of the differences between the mathematicians and MTEs in these collaborations, especially with regard to their formal training in learning mathematics, learning to teach mathematics, and learning to teach teachers. In particular, Catherine and Milé had spent a greater amount of time *learning advanced mathematics* (i.e., earning PhDs in the discipline); Denisse and Gladis had undergraduate degrees in mathematics with additional graduate work in mathematics. In terms of pedagogical training, Denisse and Gladis had spent a greater amount of time *learning to teach mathematics* in education programs and *learning to teach teachers* in their role as university teacher educators, and Catherine had focused on issues of pedagogy as a Project NExT fellow through the Mathematical Association of America.

■ Reflections from Co-Instructors

In this section, we provide our reflections to illustrate how, by sharing our classroom space with another instructor, we found that collaboration challenged us to consider and improve aspects of our practice to enhance instruction provided to PSTs. The comments here portray the types of reflections that instructors had *before* analyzing student data.

Reflections from the Mathematicians

Catherine and Milé both found the planning sessions with their respective MTE partner very interesting. For example, Milé noted:

> For me personally, the most interesting part of the collaboration was the joint weekly meeting when Gladis and I planned how specific material would be presented in the classroom and identified potential student questions. This provided an opportunity for me to learn what mathematics education is about, to confront some of my misconceptions about what educators do, and to offer my understanding of connections between geometry and other relevant areas of mathematics of which Gladis might not be aware. Some of this planning discussion spilled over in discussions with the students (e.g., why we cannot construct a regular heptagon with compass and straightedge, or a discussion about the intricacies of the parallel postulate), but I felt that students' expectation to be exposed to the mathematics they will teach in their classroom was not met. It was challenging to balance their expectation with providing in-depth knowledge of Euclidean geometry.

The collaboration also affected the teaching that occurred in the classroom. Catherine remarked:

> I felt that the collaborative experience was a starting point for changing the way I teach in all my courses. At the beginning of the geometry course, I spent more time at the front of the room than later in the semester. Watching the way Denisse wandered around the room interacting with students gave me practical insight into how a more student-centered classroom might look. That collaboration prompted me to become involved in the development and implementation of guided inquiry activities in calculus following the 'Process Oriented Guided Inquiry Learning' or POGIL™ model. Learning how to manage all the output that comes from students when you run this kind of classroom is difficult and involves more thinking on the spot about how to react to students, as compared to a well-planned lecture.

Both mathematicians felt that instructor conversations about assessments led to important developments; some assumptions had to be made explicit to be understood and perhaps needed to be justified. For example, Catherine tended to give frequent short quizzes and weekly homework, and she had to reflect on this practice and justify its worth to Denisse. As another example, Milé tended to give much more partial credit than Gladis when they graded student-generated proofs; when Gladis questioned this practice, Milé had to think carefully about it and be intentional about how he applied credit to students' work. Milé noted:

> One positive aspect of this collaboration was the opportunity to re-examine my evaluation practices. I was perplexed by the overall lack of preparation of the majority of my students to study a university-level curriculum. This resulted in vague evaluation criteria based on whether students showed *satisfactory*, *minimal*, or *no proficiency*. After tactfully questioning my assessment practice (based on other collaborations prior to our fall 2010 co-teaching of geometry) and pointing to its apparent inadequacy, Gladis created a rubric for scoring proofs. Even though I was hesitant to accept what I perceived as yet another bureaucratic hurdle, questioning every single criterion of this rubric and seeing it as an attempt to canonize proof writing, I realized that it can also be seen as a tool which enables students to clearly identify weak points in their mathematical exposition. The rubric was simple enough to be adjusted and modified for evaluating specific problems when needed and,

more importantly, demonstrated to future teachers how to use such an instrument in their classroom.

In yet another case, Denisse suggested asking assessment questions that included examples of students' reasoning, such as in figure 20.1, and asking PSTs to evaluate the correctness of such reasoning. After experiencing the effectiveness of this approach, Catherine changed exams in other mathematics courses because she learned this was an effective approach for getting students to apply their mathematical knowledge (see Bénéteau, Bleiler, and Thompson 2014 for more details).

As a teacher, you gave a test question related to the triangle inequality theorem. Below are the question and two sample responses. Critique each response. Is it correct? If so, why? If not, why not?

Question: Can 6, 3, and 3 be the side lengths of a triangle?

Pat: Yes, because two sides have the same length, the triangle is an isosceles triangle.

Terry: I compared the lengths of the sides. Because the two smaller sides sum to equal the larger side, the lengths can form a triangle.

Fig. 20.1. Example of an assessment task that requires critiquing the reasoning of others

Overall, both Catherine and Milé found the discussions in each of the three areas of planning, teaching, and assessing had a stimulating and lasting impact on their classroom teaching. In particular, their thinking about teaching was most influenced when their collaborator challenged their ideas or offered alternative approaches to teaching or assessing. In this way, the collaboration provided an opportunity for mathematicians to reflect on *learning to teach mathematics* (Tzur 2001) and to consider how the pedagogical approaches implemented in their co-taught courses could transfer to other mathematics courses that they teach.

Reflections from Mathematics Teacher Educators

Although both Denisse and Gladis had formal training in mathematics, they felt a tacit need to establish mathematical competence to support their work with mathematicians. Denisse noted:

> My research focuses on teaching and learning mathematics and mathematics curriculum at grades 6–12, not advancing new mathematical knowledge. I recognize that my mathematician colleague knows much more mathematics than I do, and this initially made me a bit nervous. It was critical that she view me as a legitimate instructor for a content course at the university level, and not just at the K–12 level.

The MTEs also believed it was important that PSTs see them teaching content to affirm their roles as content specialists.

Teaching the mathematics courses, particularly the geometry course, highlighted difficulties associated with reconciling the use of an inquiry instructional approach with a need to cover a certain amount of content. As noted by Denisse:

> . . . [co-teaching] highlighted some of the challenges faced when making this inquiry-based instructional approach a reality, particularly in a college-level mathematics course

that doesn't meet daily. Also, when students seem to have weak mathematical backgrounds and you realize they will be responsible for preparing the next generation of students, there is a natural desire to want to give them more.

Further, the MTEs often heard from mathematician colleagues that many of the prospective teachers not only are weak in content knowledge but also do not work hard. Co-teaching the content course gave them better insight into these views and a common basis for discussing how to address the issue with their colleagues. For example, Gladis shares how she viewed her role supporting Milé's effort to consider alternative instructional practices to ensure success for all students:

> I believe our co-planning and co-teaching experiences challenged assumptions Milé made about students and what they did or did not know. I recall when he asserted that these students were somehow "different" or "brighter" than other geometry students he had taught. He was often surprised by the nature of the discussion when students challenged presented ideas or generated valid proofs using approaches he had not expected. It gave us an opportunity to discuss how the structure of the learning environment, class discussions, and assessment tasks provided students opportunities to reveal what and how they know the subject matter. I had to be explicit about and provide rationales for each and every instructional decision, particularly for impromptu reactions to classroom occurrences. At times, this was a challenge.

The reflections by both mathematicians and MTEs represent an awareness of the various perspectives that underlie their practices, in particular with a focus on Tzur's category of *learning to teach mathematics*.

■ Reflections from PSTs

To gain insights about how PSTs perceived our roles as co-instructors, Sarah, who observed and collected data during classes and planning sessions, had the PSTs complete an open-ended questionnaire about the benefits or disadvantages of being students in co-taught courses. Although Sarah did not ask PSTs to reflect specifically on planning, teaching, and assessing, their responses suggested they noticed important issues with respect to these components of co-teaching. In what follows, we summarize our co-teaching with respect to these three components in an effort to examine our practices in light of the PSTs' perspectives on our practice.

Planning

Each semester, the co-teaching pairs met weekly to reflect on the activities of the prior week (e.g., points of confusion/clarification) and to prepare for the coming week. We used these planning meetings to consider how to address the content and the inquiry-focus, develop assessment tasks, and discuss assignments and grading. During the planning sessions, both collaborative teams created PowerPoint (PP) slides for their lesson. In the Catherine/Denisse collaboration, the accompanying notes on the slides often included both a mathematical and a pedagogical objective for the day's lesson, possible timing, and anticipated pedagogical strategies to be used. To ensure true co-teaching, notes also specified who would lead that class segment, with the non-lead instructor providing additional classroom support. PP slides were meant to be outlines of the lesson, rather than a detailed exposition, to allow for student inquiry and instructor improvisation if necessary;

they also served as a starting point to review a lesson and prepare for the subsequent lesson. Figure 20.2 contains a sample slide and notes from the Catherine/Denisse geometry class. Although both Catherine and Milé were initially resistant to the use of PP slides, they acknowledged that the slides were useful as a communication tool for planning, as a mechanism to control the timing and flow of the class, and as a means to keep the class focused and on track.

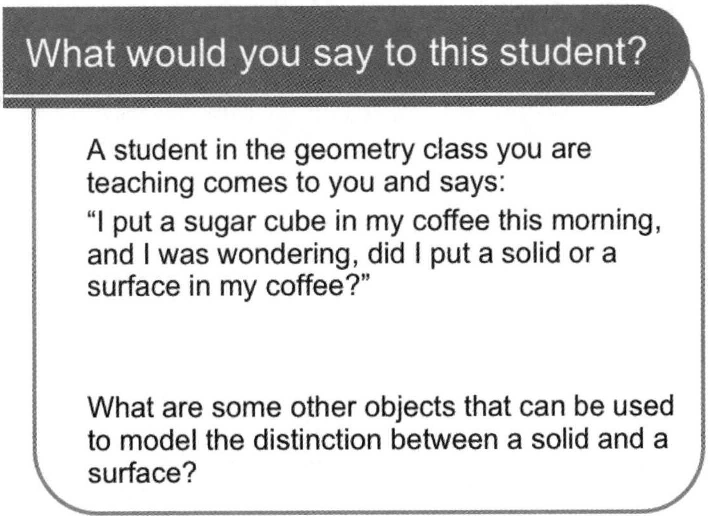

What would you say to this student?

A student in the geometry class you are teaching comes to you and says:

"I put a sugar cube in my coffee this morning, and I was wondering, did I put a solid or a surface in my coffee?"

What are some other objects that can be used to model the distinction between a solid and a surface?

Lead: Catherine   Timing: 11:10 – 11:20.

Some relevant points: Make the point that the words we use in English and the words we use in mathematics sometimes have slightly different meanings, or sometimes we are less precise in English than we need to be in mathematics. (For example, in English, the words *surface* and *solid* may be interchangeable.)

A point to be made: Use the cube from the relational solid kit to show that the cube in this context, as opposed to the sugar cube from our first example, is really a surface, it's the outside that we might pass our finger along. One way to see this is that we can unfold the cube into its two-dimensional net. Think about the analogy of an orange and its peel.

A note about dimensions: This is a tricky one: In a high school text, we might see a definition of a 3-dimensional object as an object which separates space into two regions. This is exactly our definition of a surface. Mathematicians may see a surface as a 2-dimensional object and a solid as a 3-dimensional object.

Fig. 20.2. An example of a PP slide and notes used by Denisse and Catherine

---

As explicated in the PP slides in figure 20.2, Catherine planned to lead a discussion about the use of the word *surface* and help students distinguish *surface* from *solid* as related to a three-dimensional figure. Denisse suggested using the cube from a relational solid manipulative kit to help students make this distinction, particularly because the solid could be covered by its plastic net. This is just one example of how the mathematician and mathematics teacher educator brought their respective expertise to bear in planning for classroom instruction.

Although PSTs did not witness our planning efforts, they frequently commented on their perceptions of how we planned. For instance, students in the Gladis/Milé geometry course had strong perceptions about the roles each instructor took in planning. One student commented:

> I feel like Dr. Kersaint [Gladis] planned all the lessons and technology, yet Dr. Krajčevski [Milé] actually taught so it was kind of not so good. Dr. Krajčevski then had to teach using technology or whatever else Dr. Kersaint planned when it is obvious he's much more comfortable on the whiteboard and we all learned better that way.

Interestingly, Milé was often the creator of the PP slides and technology demonstrations. For example, figure 20.3 illustrates Milé's use of a PP presentation as an instructional tool to present a task to students. After reviewing the task, which initially consisted of *only* the questions on the slide, Gladis *added* the image to support students' thinking. Prior to these planning efforts, Milé had not considered how the use of particular images may support or hinder students' learning. Gladis encouraged the use of PP as a means to focus each class session on intended goals and ensure both instructors were clear about planned activities. However, the instructors had different views about the use of technology. Milé noted:

> At that time, I felt that the subject of technology in the teaching of geometry was overemphasized by my collaborator. In a course where the most challenging objects to sketch on the whiteboard were triangles, parallelograms, and circles, which can easily be sketched by freehand drawing, the use of technology disrupted the "natural flow" of the discussion about important concepts because of time constraints.

In contrast, Gladis felt that the use of interactive geometry software, even when used as just a demonstration tool, enabled the illustration of multiple examples to support discussion about various topics and not limit students' visualization about the concepts being discussed. Despite having a different point of view, Milé attempted to use the technology because he perceived the need to prepare secondary teachers to be able to teach and learn with technology. Perhaps students sensed Milé's mixed feelings about whether the technology was an asset, and they thought he could not have planned such activities.

Circles
(review)

- How can we determine if a given point belongs to a given circle?
- Is the center of a circle part of the circle?
- Circle versus disc, how they differ?
- Can two circles with non-congruent radii be congruent?
- What is the relationship between a radius and a diameter in a circle?

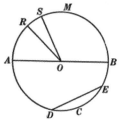

Milé: Should we see how students will react to the following: If every diameter has two radii, do we have twice more radii in a circle than diameters? The definition of a chord is simple enough to be given here (so that all three significant segments—radius, diameter, and chord—are present).

Engage the class in a discussion. Examples: Is every diameter a chord? Can noncongruent circles have congruent chords?

Gladis Note: I have included a picture. It will appear when you click.

Fig. 20.3. Example of a PP slide from a planning session by Milé/Gladis

Additionally, students asserted that planning was not done in a way where the instructors synchronized their perspectives to have complete agreement during class discussions, in responses provided to students, or in how information was shared. Students felt a tension when co-instructors had different approaches or opinions for addressing content or responding to student queries. They perceived such interactions as meaning the instructors did not have the same expectations for learning. For example, one student in the Gladis/Milé class reflected:

> I would say they didn't seem to agree on some of the content taught. Their standpoints were not consistent or the same. I feel like when teaching a class collaboratively, they should have made sure they were on the same page.

The PSTs seemed to find in-class negotiations problematic, for example, when instructors offered alternative approaches to explain the same mathematical content or when instructors used differing levels of precision when answering student questions. Milé remarked:

> It was puzzling to me how Gladis could, without difficulty, decipher the true meaning of a student question and provide a satisfactory answer to a student in contrast to my tendency to be as precise as possible and answer exactly what a student is asking. As an illustration, a casual remark by a student like ". . . so, the line goes forever in both directions" would get two answers: (*a*) "Yes, it does" and (*b*) "It depends on what you mean by goes on forever." Reflecting on this episode, I've realized that my spontaneous response to this question was an outgrowth of my mathematical training. The notion or definition of "goes forever" does not belong to the formalized mathematical structure of geometry, so I was simply asking for a formal definition of this concept, believing this is the only way to make sense out of

this question or of an answer that will follow. In a later conversation, Gladis explained that she was aware of this; by providing the student with an affirmative answer, the process of sense-making for this student is not interrupted. In addition, it does not detract from the focus on the day's lesson by taking the class in a different direction.

We were trying to be responsive to student thinking and classroom discussion and avoided following a script. However, some students interpreted this openness to different ideas as a lack of planning (i.e., had the instructors planned well, they would fully agree during class).

Teaching

When we planned for class, there was no intention to have the mathematician focus on content and the MTE focus on pedagogy; rather, we expected both instructors to address content or pedagogical connections based on ideas and concepts discussed as part of course planning. For instance, in one discussion in the methods course around geometry, Catherine discussed the van Hiele model of geometric thought (Crowley 1987); then Denisse had the students engage with a mathematics problem (see fig. 20.4) that crossed boundaries with mathematics and pedagogy. Students solved and discussed the problem to assess their own mathematical knowledge. They then crossed into pedagogical issues as they considered potential misconceptions students in their classrooms might have, which they shared via a document camera, and discussed how they would attempt to address those misconceptions. Catherine followed up by helping students analyze potential misconceptions and place them at a particular van Hiele level. For instance, a student who identifies the quadrilateral as a parallelogram because "it looks like one" is likely at the *visualization* stage; a student who begins to check properties, such as the slope of opposite sides, and then makes the same conclusion is moving toward *analysis*. A student who checks slopes to recognize that opposite sides are parallel and checks the lengths of segments to note they are all congruent before concluding the figure is a rhombus is likely at the *informal deduction* level, not extending work far enough to deduce that adjacent sides are perpendicular as well so that the figure is actually a square, thereby being classified at the *deductive* level (Crowley 1987).

PROBLEM

- Plot quadrilateral TOPS with coordinates
  T = (0, 3), O = (-3, -1), P = (1, -4), and
  S = (4,0). Identify the quadrilateral with as specific
  a name as possible. Justify your classification.

- Determine at least two misconceptions or partial
  solutions (be specific) that you expect students to
  write as well as a complete successful solution.

Fig. 20.4. Sample problem used to discuss van Hiele model of geometric thought (adapted from Beckmann, Thompson, and Rubenstein 2010, p. 83)

However, in spite of this intent to share roles equally, regardless of the course, the PSTs tended to identify the mathematician as the *content* teacher and the mathematics educator as the *teaching strategies* teacher. One PST wrote, "Dr. Bénéteau did most of the real math teaching while Dr. Thompson would introduce teaching strategies." PSTs seemed to partition the instructors into preconceived roles and made assumptions that there were clear and distinct knowledge bases and boundaries for each instructor based on their titles/roles. When reflecting on the mathematician, PSTs would repeatedly explain how they learned more "math" from that person; when reflecting on the MTE, PSTs would reflect on the MTE's attention to students' learning and on teaching the content. This was not necessarily a negative from the PSTs' point of view. As one PST commented, "We learn how to be accurate mathematicians from Dr. Bénéteau and how to communicate our good ideas from Dr. Thompson. What's the point of only having half those skills?"

In both collaborations, PSTs noticed the mathematicians and MTEs had different types of interactions with students. For example, although both provided instruction, students, particularly in the geometry course, perceived the mathematician as being at the front of the room "teaching" the material while the MTE interacted more when students worked in groups. "It just seemed Dr. Bénéteau did more work at the board and Dr. Thompson did more work with the groups." At times, they perceived the MTE as a mediator between the mathematician and the students: "Dr. Kersaint could occasionally help clarify if there seemed to be a misunderstanding between the class and Dr. Krajčevski."

The PSTs noticed more collaborative and interactive activities were used as part of instruction than would be the case in a typical mathematics course. As they reflected on their experiences, they commented on the bridging between the disciplines, the linking of theory and practice, and that much of what they learned could be applied when they taught in the future.

Assessing

When planning how to evaluate PSTs in the geometry and high school methods courses in both collaborations, the instructors had to negotiate the types of tasks they would assign to PSTs, the kinds of questions to ask on homework, quizzes, and exams, as well as how to grade the various assignments. Each pair agreed to discuss their grading criteria, be involved in grading, and not tell PSTs who graded what. It was not uncommon for each of us to grade half of an assignment or to alternate the grading of assignments.

Across both collaborations, PSTs felt there were differences in expectations related to grading from the instructors. At times, some PSTs claimed that one of the graders was much tougher than the other. For instance, in the Catherine/Denisse collaboration, PSTs commented "Too many conflicting ideas, not knowing what the expectations are because there are two different graders." At other times, PSTs assumed the instructors had different roles in grading. For instance, in the Gladis/Milé methods course, some students asserted that Milé should not be grading their assignments because, as a mathematician, he was not qualified to grade in a methods course: "I do not think that Dr. Krajčevski should be grading our work regarding methods besides the comments on math material."

Overall, PSTs' comments suggested that they were most concerned with what they perceived as conflict among the co-instructors with respect to assessment. We hypothesize this could be for two reasons: (1) PSTs were particularly concerned with their grades and therefore they had a strong desire for one clear and consistent assessment criterion from their co-instructors, rather than valuing feedback from two potential perspectives (cf. Patterson, Syverud, and

Seabrooks-Blackmore 2008; Robinson and Schaible 1995); or (2) as is evidenced by our instructor reflections in the previous section, we found our own practices in the category of assessment were the most malleable during this collaboration, and therefore, since we were growing the most in this area, PSTs recognized this as problematic for their own experience as learners.

■ Four-Foci Model of Teacher Educator Development and Implications

Referring back to Tzur's (2001) four-foci model of teacher educator development, we highlight our engagement in individual and collective reflection as we considered our joint roles in improving our classroom practice. Prior to collecting and analyzing data from PSTs, our collaborative conversations tended to lie in the domain of *learning to teach mathematics*. In particular, we spent much of our time reflecting on what constitutes effective mathematics instruction and on negotiating our individual perspectives on effective mathematics instruction with our collaborator. With respect to *learning to teach mathematics*, the mathematicians felt that they benefitted from the collaboration by learning new assessment strategies and by considering instructional strategies for more actively engaging students in mathematical thinking. The MTEs felt that they benefitted from the collaboration by gaining perspective of the content-knowledge needs of the PSTs and the realities of teaching an inquiry-based content course in the limited time constraints of a college course.

However, when we read and analyzed PSTs' comments on our collaborative instruction, we were surprised by their perception of disagreement or conflict. PSTs were often uncomfortable when they perceived disagreements or differences between their co-instructors. Yet from the instructor perspective, the process of examining differences of opinion or approaches in addressing mathematics content and teaching was intellectually stimulating and an opportunity for learning. For us, what PSTs perceived as conflict was simply academic discourse that served as the catalyst for improving our practice.

In our analysis of student reflections, we noticed our collaborative conversations transitioned from a focus on *learning to teach mathematics* to a focus on *learning to teach teachers*. Examining PSTs' comments changed the nature of our reflections from our roles as course instructors (i.e., "What are specific changes to my teaching practices?") to our roles as teacher educators (i.e., "How are my/our teaching practices influencing the development of prospective teachers?" "What understandings about teaching are being developed by these experiences?"). In particular, considering the perspectives of PSTs in this endeavor brought to our attention the need to help future teachers make sense of what they were experiencing. This is a central tenet of Tzur's model in which he asserts the need to "intentionally orient educators' reflection on the relationship between their activities to foster learning experiences in others and on the effects of those activities" (p. 276). Our co-teaching experiences provided a stimulating venue to engage in discussions surrounding *learning to teach mathematics* and *learning to teach teachers*, with the latter category of discussions emerging from the collection and analysis of PSTs' reflection data.

Implications for Teacher Education

Tzur's model provides a framework for us, as mathematicians and MTEs, to think about stages in our own growth in learning about our teaching. In addition, the perspectives of PSTs provided insights into further ways to enhance our teaching as teacher educators. Their perspectives suggested we missed opportunities to help them unpack the complexity of teaching, as recommended by

Loughran (2006). For instance, when instructors had differing views during instruction or two different responses to a PST's question (as in the earlier comment about a line that "goes forever"), we could have stepped out of our role as instructor and shared the reason why we responded as we did, helping the future teachers consider the pedagogical implications of our individual decisions. In other words, we could have unpacked our professional knowledge or beliefs as a way to help the future teachers think about teaching. As Loughran notes:

> Without serious attention to teachers' professional knowledge, despite the best intentions and efforts of all involved, learning to teach may then still be misinterpreted, or unwittingly perceived, as largely comprising technical competency and the accumulation of teaching procedures. Therefore, if such interpretations are to be challenged, teacher educators need to push the boundaries of their own practice in making their professional knowledge clear and explicit for their students of teaching. (p. 46)

Thus, we could have made "unpacking of the professional knowledge of teaching . . . an integral aspect of teaching about teaching" (Loughran 2006, p. 46) within the context of both the mathematics course and the pedagogy course. We could have thought aloud with PSTs about why we made certain decisions in teaching and perhaps why we changed course in the midst of a lesson. That is, "seeing ourselves through [our] students' eyes" (p. 61) made it clear that we needed to explain our instructional decisions more than we initially considered. We needed to explain why we disagreed and what was to be learned from these disagreements.

In addition to using collaboration as a means to enhance our learning to teach mathematics (Tzur 2001), we could have used it as an opportunity to help PSTs in their learning to teach mathematics, and thus focus on our role as teacher educators rather than primarily as teachers of mathematics. In particular, we would have liked to aid PSTs in the realization that teaching mathematics, particularly when attempting to use inquiry, is complex. Planning only goes so far—the enactment of a lesson can take on a life of its own as teachers and students interact with each other, and the planned lesson may result in the enacted lesson taking an unintended path. "When teaching is unpacked by teachers, . . . then the constant undercurrent of choices, decisions, competing concerns, dilemmas and tensions are made clear for all to see" (Loughran 2006, p. 30). Unpacking our instructional decisions would have potentially been beneficial for us as well as for the future teachers.

References

Beckmann, Charlene E., Denisse R. Thompson, and Rita N. Rubenstein. *Teaching and Learning High School Mathematics.* Hoboken, N.J.: John Wiley & Sons, 2010.

Bénéteau, Catherine, Sarah K. Bleiler, and Denisse R. Thompson. "Promoting Mathematical Reasoning through Critiquing Student Work." In *Annual Perspectives in Mathematics Education: Using Research to Improve Instruction*, edited by Karen Karp, pp. 151–60. Reston, Va.: National Council of Teachers of Mathematics, 2014.

Conference Board of the Mathematical Sciences (CBMS). *The Mathematical Education of Teachers II.* Washington, D.C.: American Mathematical Society in cooperation with the Mathematics Association of America, 2012.

Crowley, Mary L. "The van Hiele Model of the Development of Geometric Thought." In *Learning and Teaching Geometry, K–12*, edited by Mary Montgomery Lindquist and Albert P. Shulte, pp. 1–16. Reston, Va.: National Council of Teachers of Mathematics, 1987.

Davis, James R. *Interdisciplinary Courses and Team Teaching: New Arrangements for Learning.* Phoenix, Ariz.: Oryx Press, 1995.

Loughran, John. *Developing a Pedagogy of Teacher Education: Understanding Teaching and Learning about Teaching.* New York: Routledge, 2006.

Patterson, Karen. B., Susan M. Syverud, and Janice Seabrooks-Blackmore. "A Call for Collaboration: Not Jack of All Trades." *Kappa Delta Pi Record* 45, no. 1 (2008): 16–21.

Robinson, Betty, and Robert M. Schaible. "Collaborative Teaching: Reaping the Benefits." *College Teaching* 43, no. 2 (1995): 57–59.

Tzur, Ron. "Becoming a Mathematics Teacher-Educator: Conceptualizing the Terrain through Self-Reflective Analysis." *Journal of Mathematics Teacher Education* 4, no. 4 (2001): 259–83.

PART V

Enhancing Preservice Mathematics Teachers' Development

Introduction

Hal Melnick, *Bank Street College of Education, New York, New York*

Cochran-Smith and colleagues (2016) suggest that future preservice teacher education emphasize collaboration, sharing, thinking and studying education together. The four chapters in this section present examples of a new paradigm for educating new mathematics teachers. Each of the four chapters highlight university faculty and school district personnel studying methods that offer beneficial collaboration between preservice teachers (PSTs; teachers engaged in internship or residency in schools) and veteran teachers (ISTs; teachers who are considered mentors, in-service teachers, or cooperating teachers). Each reading provides promising examples where new teacher learning has moved away from authoritarian, absorption-based programs. Instead, PSTs are taken to be reflective collaborators, co-constructing knowledge about teaching and about how one learns to teach well, and providing learning opportunities for in-service teachers to grow in tandem.

In the first chapter of this section, **Using Improvement Science to Transform Internship Experiences through Co-Teaching Strategies**, authors Sears, Brosman, Gainsburg, Oloff-Lewis, Stone, Spencer, Riggs, Bigetti, Cayton, Grady, Clarke, and Andreasen emphasize the centrality of co-planning and examine the possibility of preservice teacher education using different co-teaching strategies. They identify six different models for co-teaching as structures to shift the role and enactment of preservice teaching. By administering the research methodology of improvement science, the authors (a group of mathematics education faculty from eleven universities across the United States) set out to study how the notion of internship experiences of preservice teachers can be improved. This form of research is designed to offer more immediate and applicable results than traditional research methodology. This study establishes a case for giving preservice and in-service teachers a structure to collaborate using various forms of co-teaching methods. The authors describe what might be needed to lay the foundation for a new view of preservice teacher education: one that emphasizes a mutual-learning, democratic process where neophyte teachers are acclimated into professional learning environments from the very start of their career. It also offers universities some creative thoughts on redesigning preservice teacher education programs of study.

In **Beyond Division of Labor: Transforming Student Teaching**, Wieman provides a dramatic descriptive case study. His honest portrayal of his experience can shake up the traditional role and responsibilities of the classic IST, PST, and the fieldwork professor. He suggests that these earth-moving shifts in roles and responsibilities offer definite risks but provide enormous promise as well. Wieman reports that after one cycle of co-planning together with his preservice teacher and the cooperating teacher, he (who was the college supervising professor) agreed to teach a math lesson. This lesson served the dual function of modeling cognitively demanding teaching for the preservice teacher and also building trust with the cooperating teacher. While the first lesson Wieman teaches is stellar, things do not go well in the second lesson. Keeping their focus on the idea of learning through honest reflection, collaboration, and communication, the PST, cooperating teacher, and Wieman reflect on their next steps. The learning opportunity provided by the presumed "failed" lesson has a profound effect on both the cooperating teacher and the preservice teacher. As preservice teacher education programs move forward in design, this repositioning of roles offers much to consider.

The next chapter, **Cycles of Collective Planning, Enactment, and Reflection in Elementary Teacher Education**, by Hallman-Thrasher, describes a study where preservice teachers participating in an integrated field experience and mathematics methods course co-plan cognitively demanding lessons. Unique in this design is that the cooperating teachers adjust their teaching schedules to allow triads of PSTs to teach the same lesson repeatedly to different small groups of students. The lessons are videotaped for reflection and analysis by the teaching triad and reviewed with the college professors' input as needed. Each time the lesson is taught, the PSTs are asked to analyze the nature and scope of their questions, the responses of their young students, and the nature of interaction between children and mathematics. This design offers the opportunity for "learning teachers" to work toward improving their ability to engage children deeply in mathematical discourse. By planning lessons, sharing observations, questioning one another, and enacting teaching of children, the PSTs have repeated opportunities to test their skills in a non-hierarchical peer teaching setting in schools. Using an array of carefully crafted external rubrics (e.g., Hufferd-Ackles, Fuson, and Sherin 2004), this design affords PSTs with firsthand experience with standards-based instructional design and self-evaluation. The authors posit that by asking PSTs to teach three cycles of the same lesson, repeatedly analyze their videotapes, and collectively use shared rubrics to assess mathematics discourse, these PSTs are positioned with tools for self-improvement throughout their careers.

In the final chapter, **Fostering Collaboration and the Co-Construction of Knowledge: A Multidimensional Perspective**, Quebec Fuentes and Spice include a comprehensive PST and IST literature review. This chapter breaks apart the delineated role definitions of the PST and IST. The work reported here is set in the larger context of the National Council of Teachers of Mathematics's (NCTM) *Principles to Actions* (2014), which endorses continuous professional growth in a climate of collaboration. The authors propose a professional development program that enlarges the neophyte teacher's education experience. At its core, ISTs and undergraduate PSTs (middle and secondary mathematics education majors) engage in ongoing collaboration, planning, and teaching in addition to the supervised field component of the PSTs' program of study. Together, PSTs and ISTs solve mathematics problems and analyze cases of mathematics lessons. The chapter describes how the partners aimed to co-construct a growth agenda and shared goals for their participation, examining what factors supported (or interfered with) productive collaborations and how knowledge about teaching could be co-constructed to promote growth and change in both the PST and the IST. The authors provide insight into how preservice teachers and in-service teachers can work collaboratively in a democratic process.

Overall, the chapters in this section can benefit university faculty/researchers involved in teacher education, in-service mathematics teachers who serve as cooperating teachers, preservice teachers selecting programs for teacher education, and administrators who wish to maximize professional learning for their staff who have student teachers in their classrooms. Each chapter presents the need for trust and describes how trust grows out of skillful co-planning, co-teaching, and co-constructing lessons. Conversely, they also describe what prevents collaboration or undermines trusting relationships in schools—and the disheartening results when collaboration fails. These chapters reaffirm the potentialities of learning by doing, learning by teaching, and the powerful learning that comes from reflection while being an active teaching novice or a facilitator of a preservice teacher's growth.

Some questions to consider as you read the chapters in this section:

- How can a repositioning of roles serve as a potent growth opportunity for preservice teachers, in-service teachers, and college faculty alike?

- How can different models for co-teaching influence the training of neophyte teachers as they perform the role of classroom interns?

- How can cyclical planning, teaching, reflecting, and reteaching support new teacher growth?

- How does deep reflection and video observation of one's own teaching affect a new teacher's sense of competence and confidence?

- If new teachers are expected to engage children deeply in mathematical discourse, how do we educate them to embrace that practice at the start of their careers and work toward improvement?

- How can knowledge about teaching be co-constructed so that both the PST and the IST can grow and change?

References

Cochran-Smith, Marilyn, Ana Maria M. Villegas, Linda Whalen Abrams, Laura C. Chávez Moreno, Tammy Mills, and Rebecca Stern. "Research on Teacher Preparation: Charting the Landscape of a Sprawling Field." In *Handbook of Research on Teaching*, 5th ed., edited by Drew H. Gitomer and Courtney A. Bell, pp. 439–547. Washington, D.C.: American Education Research Association, 2016.

Hufferd-Ackles, Kimberly, Karen Fuson, and Miriam Sherin. "Describing Levels and Components of a Math-Talk Community." *Journal for Research in Mathematics Education* 35, no. 2 (2004): 81–116.

National Council of Teachers of Mathematics (NCTM). *Principles to Actions: Ensuring Mathematical Success for All*. Reston, Va.: NCTM, 2014.

CHAPTER 21

Using Improvement Science to Transform Internship Experiences through Co-Teaching Strategies

Ruthmae Sears, *University of South Florida, Tampa*

Patricia Brosnan, *Ohio State University, Columbus*

Julie Gainsburg, *California State University, Northridge*

Jennifer Oloff-Lewis, *California State University, Chico*

Jami Stone, *Black Hills State University, Spearfish, South Dakota*

Catherine Spencer, *California State University, San Bernardino*

Laurie Riggs, *Cal Poly Pomona*

Stephanie Biagetti, *California State University, Sacramento*

Charity Cayton, *East Carolina University, Greenville, North Carolina*

Maureen Grady, *East Carolina University, Greenville, North Carolina*

Pier Junor Clarke, *Georgia State University, Atlanta*

Janet Andreasen, *University of Central Florida, Orlando*

Traditional methods of educational research can be impracticably slow. A year or more might elapse before posttests show that the intervention has produce results or failed to. In other fields, such as medicine and engineering, waiting a year for results is indefensible because of the urgency of the considerations, such as whether a patient will survive surgery or whether a bridge might fall, and time is a critical factor in obtaining research results. Educators also need quicker results. Improvement science offers an attractive alternative, because it is designed to study practices rapidly, make appropriate changes immediately, and continue the cycle of improvement (Bryk et al. 2015). In this chapter, we describe our use of improvement science to transform internship experiences for secondary mathematics education student teachers with co-teaching strategies.

■ What Is Improvement Science?

Improvement science focuses on essential goals for practice and uses evidence to determine positive movement toward those goals. Improvement science employs *process measures*, to monitor whether the change idea is performing as intended, and *balancing measures*, to monitor adverse implications (Bryk et al. 2015). When evidence shows that the practice is generating undesirable outcomes, inquiry is conducted to determine the cause of these outcomes; appropriate changes are then made to achieve better outcomes for all. Improvement science is guided by three practical questions: "1. What specifically are we trying to accomplish? 2. What change might we introduce and why? 3. How will we know that a change is actually an improvement?" (Bryk et al. 2015, p. 114).

Improvement science studies involve multiple sites in order to enable an examination of how the suggested change works differently in different contexts. To inform a broad community, it is insufficient to identify ideas under controlled situations only; rather, it is vital to support the sustainability and viability of ideas across multiple, real-life contexts.

Improvement science relies on teams dedicated to common improvements. These teams are referred to as network improvement communities (NIC). Members of a NIC share information, work in parallel, and connect to external factors and larger problems (Bryk et al. 2015). The educators in our NIC convened around a desire to improve the internship experience in our teacher education programs.

■ Plan-Do-Study-Act (PDSA) Cycle

The process of inquiry in improvement science, described by Bryk and colleagues (2015), is the *plan-do-study-act* (*PDSA*) cycle. Because it is cyclical, it can answer questions that arise as the inquiry develops. During the *plan* phase, the team identifies the change needed, hypothesizes potential strategies, and considers means to measure the nature and magnitude of the change. During the *do* phase, individuals enact the change strategy and collect data on how the strategy was executed. For the *study* phase, data are analyzed, the team compares what occurred to what was predicted, and ideas are extracted for the next cycle. Finally, in the *act* phase, decisions are made about how to proceed based on what was learned. Initial ideas may be abandoned, adjusted, or adopted.

■ Our Journey in Improvement Science

Our NIC, the authors of this paper, consisted of mathematics education faculty from eleven universities across the United States. We come from mathematics teacher programs of different sizes, with varying student populations and different program structures. Despite the variety in our programs, we shared a common interest in improving internship experiences (otherwise known as student teaching, in which interns spend an extended, supervised period of time in classrooms and assume instructional responsibilities), because internship experiences are crucial to effective teacher preparation (National Council for Accreditation of Teacher Education [NCATE] 2010). According to Darling-Hammond (2006), the experiential component of teacher education has traditionally been somewhat haphazard and disconnected from theoretical teachings. Our NIC shared a number of problems with internship experiences across our programs. These included philosophical differences between school and university personnel regarding teaching and learning, a lack of professional learning opportunities to help mentor teachers to implement new standards and curriculum materials, and difficulties in recruiting and retaining mathematics teachers for high-needs schools. Also, mentor teachers are often unsure how to mentor (Anderson 2007), many interns feel unprepared to teach mathematics (Ingersoll 2012), and university faculty are sometimes ineffective change agents (Veal and Rikard 1998). Once these problems were identified, we discussed possible causes, namely, insufficiencies in communication between school and university personnel (Zeichner 2010), goal setting, professional learning opportunities, and leadership for new ideas for internship experiences.

We subsequently reviewed the literature to learn how we might improve the quality of internship experiences. We identified co-teaching as a promising change mechanism based on its success in special education, where it has been shown to strengthen partnerships between university personnel and teachers, motivate ongoing professional development, and improve student learning (Friend et al. 2010). Because high quality co-teaching requires high quality co-planning, we decided to emphasize co-planning in our investigation as well. Aware that the structure of internship experiences varies widely across institutions, we looked to improvement science as a means to effectively implement and study co-teaching across our programs.

■ Co-Planning and Co-Teaching Strategies

Co-planning and co-teaching increase interns' and mentors' opportunities to learn from each other, and they can alleviate mentor teachers' and administrators' concern about putting interns completely in charge of a class of students (Brosnan et al. 2014). Co-planning begins with building relationships and trust between mentors and interns. At first, the mentor takes the lead in planning and conducts "teach alouds" to reveal the many and varied decisions teachers must consider when planning for instruction. Over time, interns gain confidence in the process and make greater contributions to instructional planning (Brosnan et al. 2014).

Co-teaching is a pedagogical practice that fosters collaboration and communication between teachers, who share a common space in the delivery of instruction and assessing learning (Bacharach, Heck, and Dahlberg 2010). Co-teaching began in special education, where general and special education teachers shared instructional efforts (Friend et al. 2010). Subsequently, educators began to apply the same practices in general teacher-preparation programs (Bacharach et al. 2010). Co-teaching is a paradigm shift from the traditional internship experience to one in which mentor and intern share responsibility for planning and instruction. Mentor teachers encourage mutual respect for and acknowledgment of the interns as co-teachers from the first day of the internship (Brosnan et al. 2014). Introducing the intern as a co-teacher helps students see the intern as an advantage—an extra teacher in the room to help them learn.

Interns and mentor teachers can both benefit from co-teaching strategies, which provide real-time instructional support, classroom management support, and opportunities for collaboration. For our pilot, we employed six co-teaching strategies adapted from the special education literature: *one teach, one observe*; *one teach, one assist*; *station teaching*; *parallel teaching*; *team teaching*; and *alternative teaching* (Friend et al. 2010; Murawski and Spencer 2011). These are summarized in fig. 21.1.

Approach	Class Set-up	Quick Definition	Benefits	Notes
One Teach, One Observe	Whole Class	One of the teachers is in the front of the class leading instruction. **The other is gathering specific information.**	It provides an extra set of eyes in the classroom; provides data about instruction or student learning; easy to implement.	It can easily develop into a habit; **generally effective if the lead teacher and observer agree in advance what is to be observed.**
One Teach, One Assist	Whole Class	One teacher works with the whole class, while the other teacher assists individual students or groups of students. Assistant may also provide assistance with classroom management and a "voice" to articulate student concerns	Provides assistance to individuals throughout the lesson; easy to implement – does not require a lot of planning.	It can easily become a habit, and may cause one teacher to always feel like assistant. Hence **changing roles is essential.**
Station Teaching	Regrouping	Students are divided into three or more small groups to go to stations or centers. Students rotate through multiple stations. Teachers can facilitate individual stations or circulate among all stations	Smaller groups are better for instruction, assessment, and class management; allows for differentiation, movement, and hands-on activity	**Teachers need to be willing to use their space differently.** Both teachers need to plan for their group. Classroom management and transition needs to be structured, and independent station needs to be well planned and self-sufficient.
Parallel Teaching	Regrouping	Both take half the class in order to reduce student-teacher ratio. **Groups may be doing the same or different content in the same or different ways.**	Smaller groups are better for instruction, assessment, and classroom management. It allows teachers to have their own groups.	Teachers need to be willing to use their space differently. **Both teachers need to co-plan for their group;** classroom management and organization needs to be negotiated. Do not switch the groups during a lesson
Team Teaching	Whole Class	Both teachers are in front of the class, working together to provide instruction. This may take the form of debates, modeling information, compare/contrast, or role-playing.	Demonstrates parity and collaboration between teachers; good for modeling; fun for role-playing	**Takes planning and willingness to "share the stage".** Both teachers need to feel comfortable in front of the class, which means no one is walking around or individualizing at that time.
Alternative Teaching	Whole Class	One teacher works with a large group of students, while the other teacher works with a smaller group providing re-teaching, pre-teaching, or enrichment as needed.	Good for smaller and more specific group work; good for addressing IEP/504 goals	**Need to be sure NOT to always pull the same kids or it becomes a "class inside a class" and can create stigmatizing, especially if small group is "strugglers". Be sure to consider space, noise levels learning gaps, and means to re-assimilate the small group members back into the larger group.**

Fig. 21.1. Various co-teaching models adapted from Murawski and Spencer (2011, p. 97)

■ How Our Team Used Improvement Science to Implement and Study Co-Teaching

Following the process of improvement science, our NIC identified the change to be tested (namely, the adoption of co-teaching strategies during internship experiences), developed instrumentation, and determined the data collection protocol for our multiple sites. We collected detailed notes about the PDSA cycle activities, administered surveys, and analyzed the data (Bryk et al. 2015). After a few institutions piloted co-teaching, we reflected on patterns in the data and made recommendations for changes in the subsequent cycle. Here, we discuss this first PDSA cycle in greater detail.

■ Plan Phase

Faculty members from eleven institutions met during the summers of 2014 and 2015, and they engaged in online meetings throughout the academic year to discuss the benefits of co-teaching and its potential to transform internship experiences. We hypothesized that *one teach, one observe* would be the most widely used co-teaching strategy and that few interns and mentors would be aware of other co-teaching strategies. These faculty members worked in subgroups to draft professional development modules and develop instrumentation to measure the extent and nature of co-teaching implementation and its impact. Descriptions of these instruments (Pre-Survey, Professional Development Survey, Just-in-Time Survey, and Exit Survey) are described below:

- **Pre-Survey**—On this survey, mentors and interns rate their knowledge about and ability to implement the Common Core Content Standards and Standards for Mathematical Practice (National Governors Association Center for Best Practices and Council of Chief State School Officers [NGA Center and CCSSO] 2010), as well as their knowledge of strategies to teach diverse learners, co-teaching, and various assessment practices. The survey is administered before the professional development and internship experiences.

- **Professional Development Survey**—This survey is administered at the end of the professional development experience. Mentors and interns are asked to describe the extent to which they found the professional development experience to be effective and to have enhanced their understanding of co-planning and co-teaching.

- **Just-in-Time Survey**—This survey, ideally administered at least twice during the internship, asks mentors and interns to describe their co-teaching experiences as the semester progresses. They are also asked to describe instructional norms and to rate the quality of communication, frequency of co-planning, and perceived benefits of co-teaching. A section for optional comments is included.

- **Exit Survey**—This survey, administered at the end of the internship, comprises open-ended questions about participants' experiences with co-teaching, interactions with collaborators, and the impact of the professional development experience.

Do Phase

During the *do* phase of Cycle 1, team members from four institutions and their affiliated schools agreed to implement co-teaching with a subset of their mathematics interns and collect data. The faculty at these institutions sent emails to interns and mentor teachers asking them to complete the various surveys. These faculty members also observed and took field notes in classrooms where interns were co-teaching, and they interviewed mentors and interns about their co-teaching and the impact on classroom climate. Considering the variation in length and timing of internship experiences across institutions, we agreed to collect data throughout the academic year, allowing faculty members to identify the best time to collect the data at their institution. Our maximum sample for a single survey was five mentor teachers and ten interns.

Study Phase

We conducted thematic analysis of data from the surveys and classroom observations from the four institutions. We reflected on participants' knowledge about co-teaching, the frequency and nature of co-teaching strategies used, and the challenges that hindered the extent to which co-teaching could be adopted during internship. Process measures were largely gleaned from the surveys and balancing measures mainly from team members' observational and interview data. At face-to-face meetings in 2015 and 2016, our team identified emergent themes across institutions and issues that appeared unique to a particular institution. These themes and institution specific issues would shape our next PDSA cycle.

Act Phase

After observing that our data collection process could be cumbersome, we revised our surveys. The tenure-line faculty members on our team were not always able to supervise interns, so we recognized the need to educate non-tenure-line university field supervisors about co-teaching. Additionally, we considered how to disseminate the professional development modules to a practitioner audience to further support the implementation of co-teaching strategies. Finally, recognizing that it was highly unlikely that teachers would implement co-teaching strategies if they had not first engaged in high quality co-planning, we made plans to emphasize and to provide more training in both co-planning and co-teaching strategies. Based on these lessons, we revised our initial PDSA cycle for the second cycle, scheduled for 2016–2017.

■ Lessons Learned from Cycle 1

During our first PDSA cycle, we learned about the extent to which various co-teaching strategies were used on the four campuses, the implications of adopting co-teaching during internship experiences, the challenges of having too many surveys, the importance of carefully co-planning lessons, and the need for significant professional development. Here, we elaborate on the lessons we learned and on our modifications for future PDSA cycles.

Classroom observations by team members revealed that most of the co-taught lessons used the *one teach, one assist*, or *one teach, one observe* strategies; about half of the pairs (mentors and interns) also tried *station teaching. Team teaching, parallel teaching,* and *alternative teaching* were rarely observed. For the next cycle, we would like to see mentors and interns try these other co-teaching strategies. This would enable us to examine the effectiveness of the range of co-teaching strategies in different contexts. We also noticed some variation in co-planning and co-teaching across contexts. For instance, in one urban context, the mentor teachers used co-planning and co-teaching to assist only with formative assessment, while in other contexts they were used for all instructional activities.

Personal correspondence with mentor teachers and Just-in-Time Surveys provided evidence that mentors saw co-teaching as having a positive impact on student learning. Mentor teachers perceived that co-teaching increased opportunities for personalized instruction and improved instructional quality. For instance, one mentor teacher noted via email correspondence, "I think it's great thing to have two adults in the room. It allows me a lot more flexibility when I work with kids" (teacher A, email 2015). Similarly, another teacher wrote, "But with two . . . you have so much more capabilities of getting to each student. So there is hardly a day that goes by that every student hasn't had contact with at least one of the teachers." (teacher B, email 2015).

On the Just-in-Time Survey, the mentor teachers ($n=5$) generally agreed that co-teaching was beneficial and that it fostered student-centered instruction. Similarly, the interns' survey responses ($n=10$) indicated that the co-teaching experience supported their learning to teach. The faculty's observations and interviews provided a triangulated view of the merit of implementing co-teaching during internship experiences. Faculty members noted that students in co-teaching classrooms appeared to receive more individual attention and more consistent instruction, and they were less distracted by classroom management issues than in classrooms where interns had not co-taught with their mentors.

While *process measures* (derived from our small sample's responses to the Just-in-Time Survey) showed participants' appreciation for co-teaching, the *balancing measures* (derived from observation and interview data) revealed that our surveys were overly burdensome for participants. In fact, none of the interns or mentor teachers completed the Professional Development Survey, and no mentor teacher completed the Exit Survey. We learned that, given the many responsibilities of mentors and interns, completing multiple surveys is too time-consuming, especially if there is no monetary reward.

Additionally, the data we did collect from the interns' Just-in-Time and Exit Surveys made clear that careful planning is critical to successful implementation of co-teaching. One intern described the value of co-planning with her mentor:

> Overall, I would say that it [co-planning] was a very beneficial experience. I appreciated having the support of my CT [mentor] for classroom management and for figuring out how to scaffold my lessons. She is great at developing scaffolded notes for them and has many of her own resources to use. Also, she was very generous in letting me use all of the materials she has developed over the years, including notes for students, assignments, quizzes, and tests. [intern A, exit survey 2015]

Other interns described the importance of talking through the lesson with their mentors and the value of the feedback that they received on lesson plans. Mentor teachers also described benefits that they derived from co-planning and co-teaching with the interns. In one instance, two interns and their mentor teachers co-planned and subsequently co-taught a *station teaching* activity. One of the mentor teachers reported that she had never really seen great value in *station teaching* until she experienced the planning and implementation of this activity with the interns. Overall, we found that an environment that was supportive, respectful, and well planned provided benefits for interns and mentors alike.

Despite the recognized value of co-planning and co-teaching, both mentors and interns expressed concerns about finding time to co-plan, which limited the number of co-taught lessons. In addition, faculty members' classroom observations and their personal communications with mentors and interns indicated that sometimes the communication process during co-planning was perceived as cumbersome and problematic. Due to limited time for lesson planning, interns and mentors found it difficult to plan multiple lessons together that incorporated co-teaching.

Finally, we noticed a need to improve the nature and frequency of co-teaching and co-planning professional development experiences. Sites varied widely in the kinds and duration of professional development experiences they provided for participants. Across the campuses, the total time allocated to training varied from thirty minutes to a full day. We concluded that careful thought needs to be given to professional development if co-teaching is to be implemented effectively.

■ Plans for Cycle 2

Due to our findings from our *study* and our *act* phases, we revised our surveys, enhanced the professional development experiences, and acknowledged the need to meet more frequently to analyze data across institutions in order to take full advantage of the improvement science model. For our next PDSA cycle, we seek to have seven institutions engage in the data collection process to expand our data sources. To reduce the data collection burden on mentors and interns, we have abandoned the Pre-Survey and reduced the number of questions on the Just-in-Time Survey. Additionally, we sought to improve professional development in both co-planning and co-teaching by using a voiced-over PowerPoint presentation and creating online video clips of various co-planning and co-teaching strategies in action. These modules can now be used during initial training or as refresher guides during the academic semester. In our next PDSA cycle, we plan to send monthly newsletters to all NIC members that will encourage greater use of co-planning and all six co-teaching strategies. We surmise that calling frequent attention to co-planning and co-teaching strategies in formal and informal communications with mentors and interns will increase the prevalence of these strategies being used during internships.

■ Conclusion

We chose to use improvement science to transform internships via co-planning and co-teaching strategies because improvement science uses content knowledge as well as organization knowledge to adapt an idea to fit various contexts. Based on our process measures, we concluded that mentor teachers and interns generally viewed co-planning and co-teaching strategies favorably. However, our balancing measures showed that we needed to reduce the data collection burden on participants and provide more consistent and ongoing professional development for both co-planning and co-teaching. As we continue to engage in the iterative process of PDSA cycles, we will continuously seek to identify factors that increase the sustainability and effectiveness of co-planning and co-teaching in various settings. Improvement science afforded us an opportunity to acknowledge variation among the internship experiences at multiple institutions while seeking to achieve a common goal.

References

Anderson, Derek. "The Role of Cooperating Teachers' Power in Student Teaching." *Education* 128, no. 2 (2007): 307–23.

Bacharach, Nancy, Teresa Washut Heck, and Kathryn Dahlberg. "Changing the Face of Student Teaching through Co-Teaching." *Action in Teacher Education* 32, no. 1 (2010): 3–14.

Brosnan, Patricia, Marguerethe Jaede, Erica Brownstein, and Sandra A. Stroot. "Co-Planning and Co-Teaching in an Urban Context." Paper presented at the Annual Meeting of the American Educational Research Association, Philadelphia, Pennsylvania, April 3–7, 2014.

Bryk, Anthony S., Louis M. Gomez, Alicia Grunow, and Paul G. LeMahieu. *Learning to Improve: How America's Schools Can Get Better at Getting Better.* Cambridge, Mass.: Harvard Education Press, 2015.

Darling-Hammond, Linda. "Constructing 21st-Century Teacher Education." *Journal of Teacher Education* 57, no. 3 (2006): 300–14.

Friend, Marilyn, Lynne Cook, Deanna Hurley-Chamberlain, and Cynthia Shamberger. "Co-teaching: An Illustration of the Complexity of Collaboration in Special Education." *Journal of Educational and Psychological Consultation* 20, no. 1 (2010): 9–27.

Murawski, Wendy W., and Sally Spencer. *Collaborate, Communicate, and Differentiate!: How to Increase Student Learning in Today's Diverse Schools.* Corwin Press, Thousand Oaks, Calif.: 2011.

National Council for Accreditation of Teacher Education (NCATE). "Transforming Teacher Education through Clinical Practice: A National Strategy to Prepare Effective Teachers." *Report of the Blue Ribbon Panel on Clinical Preparation and Partnerships for Improved Student Learning.* Washington, D.C.: NCATE, 2010.

National Governors Association Center for Best Practices and Council of Chief State School Officers (NGA Center and CCSSO). *Common Core State Standards for Mathematics.* Washington, D.C.: NGA Center and CCSSO, 2010. http://www.corestandards.org.

Veal, Mary Lou, and Linda Rikard. "Cooperating Teachers' Perspectives on the Student Teaching Triad." *Journal of Teacher Education* 49, no. 2 (1998): 108–20.

Zeichner, Ken. "Rethinking the Connections between Campus Courses and Field Experiences in College- and University-Based Teacher Education." *Journal of Teacher Education* 61, no. 1–2 (2010): 89–99.

CHAPTER 22

Beyond Division of Labor:
Transforming Student Teaching

Rob Wieman, *Rowan University, Glassboro, New Jersey*

In the United States, student teaching remains a staple of traditional teacher education programs and is widely viewed as essential to effective teacher preparation (Darling-Hammond and Cobb 1995; National Research Council 2010). However, student teaching is also plagued by incoherence; student teachers often hear one set of messages from university-based teacher educators and a different set of messages from school-based cooperating teachers (Clarke, Triggs, and Nielsen 2014). Mathematics teacher educators may see mathematics as a set of connected ideas that are best learned through intellectual struggle (see, for example, Hiebert et al. 1997). Practicing teachers, on the other hand, may see mathematics as a set of skills, resulting in teaching that places more stress on demonstration and practice (Philipp 2007). They also may be more responsive to contextual contraints, such as behavioral issues, pacing guides, and shared assessments (Lemov 2010).

Researchers have found that, in the context of student teaching, cooperating teachers and university-based supervisors engage in a division of labor that mirrors the discontinuities described above (Clarke, Triggs, and Nielsen 2014). University supervisors evaluate student teachers on a set of assignments aligned with theory taught in university methods courses and required for certification. Cooperating teachers, on the other hand, oversee the day-to-day work of student teachers consistent with local constraints and norms. They support student teachers in responding to pressing demands that are not addressed by supervisors or methods classes.

This division of labor enables cooperating teachers and university supervisors to work together. Within their respective areas of influence and expertise they operate with relative freedom while avoiding the conflict that might result from having to agree on specific, common criteria for successful student teaching. Unfortunately, this division of labor also perpetuates the disconnect between teacher educators and teachers. Student teachers often find themselves in the stressful and confusing position of making sense of conflicting messages (Clarke, Triggs, and Nielsen 2014).

A range of writers have shown how shared responsibility for student learning can improve classroom instruction (Morris and Hiebert 2015; Bambrick-Santoyo 2010; Saunders, Goldenberg, and Gallimore 2009). Sharing responsibility for student learning could also introduce coherence to student teaching. As university supervisors, cooperating teachers, and student teachers work together to define goals, plan lessons, and evaluate teaching based on student learning, they could create opportunities to develop shared knowledge of students, content and pedagogy and to forge agreement on deeper issues of teaching and learning. On a large scale, such changes would involve changing the structure and requirements of student teaching. In the meantime, how might university supervisors, cooperating teachers, and student teachers work together to share responsibility for student learning and with what results?

A chance to answer this question arose when Allison (a cooperating teacher) unexpectedly invited Rob (a university-based supervisor and author of this article) to teach a mini-lesson. This led to a daylong collaboration that placed student learning at the center of a new relationship between Allison, Rob, and Jen (the student teacher; Allison and Jen are pseudonyms). This created powerful learning opportunities for each of them, and it clarified connections between university courses and classroom teaching.

■ Context

During the last semester of her teacher certification program, Jen did her student teaching at a local high school in Allison's classroom. Each day Allison and Jen discussed planning, instruction, students, and other aspects of teaching and learning. As the university supervisor, Rob observed and evaluated Jen's performance five times and oversaw her completion of university assignments.

During their first meeting, Jen, Rob, and Allison structured their work together. At the beginning of the semester, Allison would teach a lesson first period, Jen would teach the same lesson third period, and then they would debrief and plan for the next day during a prep period. When Rob observed, they followed the schedule outlined in figure 22.1.

Period	Class	Responsibilities
1	Algebra 1	Allison teach; Jen, Rob observe
2	Honors Algebra 1	Allison and Rob confer at start of period 2; Jen, Rob revise lesson
3	Algebra 1	Jen teach revised lesson; Rob, Allison observe
4	Planning	All three debrief

Fig. 22.1. Observation schedule

This structure allowed for some collaboration. However, Rob and Allison still maintained a clear division of labor during Rob's first two visits. Rob set goals for Jen based on his observations and the university rubric. Allison deferred to Rob when it came to setting the agenda for their discussions and deciding what to concentrate on when evaluating Jen.

When Rob arrived for his third observation, Allison commented that her students were more reserved when he came to observe. Allison asked Rob to lead a five-minute mini-lesson on the slope of vertical and horizontal lines. She thought that if her students saw Rob teach, they would become more comfortable with him, and thus behave more "typically" when he observed. This would provide Rob with a more representative window into Jen's teaching.

■ Research Questions

Rob decided to lead this mini-lesson. As he did, he hoped to use this experience to think about several important questions:

- How might a supervisor leading a class discussion change the relationship between supervisor, student teacher, and cooperating teacher?

- What learning opportunities for Rob, Jen, and Allison would arise from Rob leading a discussion among Allison and Jen's students?

- Which features of the practicum setting and professional relationships support such collaboration? Which features act as barriers?

- What are the risks and rewards of such collaborations?

■ The Case

As the day unfolded, Rob took extensive notes, which became the basis of an extended field memo. He then shared the memo with Jen and Allison, who added details and clarified questions that Rob had. In addition, three years after this incident, Jen shared her recollections of the day and her reactions to an early draft of this paper. This documentation of the events became the basis for the descriptive case that follows.

Rob began the mini-lesson by drawing a vertical line and a horizontal line on the board. He asked what the slope of each line was. The ensuing discussion lasted for the rest of the period. Rob used moves specifically designed to encourage participation, elicit student thinking, focus it on important mathematical ideas, and provide opportunities for explanation and justification. For instance, he —

- elicited a variety of answers to his initial question before asking for explanation;

- asked students to turn and talk about important and controversial statements; and

- asked students if they agreed or disagreed with a peer's statement.

These moves allowed Rob to surface important student misconceptions, and they provided opportunities for students to make sense of why a vertical line has an undefined slope, why a horizontal line has a slope of zero, and how these two ideas are connected to rates of change and division. Jen and Allison were excited to see students participating and reasoning and interested in how Rob's moves supported them in doing so. Jen specifically commented on how the lesson provided an example of the kind of discourse that she had learned about in her college courses but had rarely seen or tried to enact. They were eager to see how the third-period class might engage in such a conversation, and they asked Rob to lead the discussion again.

This next discussion was quite different. As in the first lesson, Rob began by asking students what the slope of a vertical and horizontal line was. Several students demonstrated misconceptions about slope that had not arisen during the first lesson. Rob had trouble focusing the conversation, and students were unsure of what he was asking, resulting in frustration and confusion. Rob, Allison, and Jen were surprised and disappointed, as they had anticipated another "model" performance from an expert.

However, this "failure" also proved to be an opportunity. It showed that even an expert does not magically know how to teach all children at all times and that teaching inevitably involves false starts and unexpected outcomes. While many teachers and teacher educators say mistakes are doorways to learning, few feel good when they are not successful and will sometimes abandon their efforts to improve in the face of initial failure. This second lesson provided a clear and concrete opportunity to persist in the face of disappointment and to recast unexpected teaching outcomes as learning opportunities. Given the complexity of teaching and how much effective teachers need to know and be able to do, lessons that do not go according to plan are inevitable, and the ability to learn from them is essential.

Allison, Rob, and Jen decided that planning and enacting a revised discussion, based on their analysis of the two lessons, would allow them to directly address the complexity of teaching and learning and would show Jen an example of learning from teaching. They adjusted the schedule, and they worked together to plan a revised lesson on the same topic that Jen would lead later in the day.

They began by making sense of an important student misconception. During the second lesson students had agreed that the following two statements were equivalent:

$$12 \div 0 = ? \qquad \text{and} \qquad ? \times 0 = 12$$

Students then said, "Nothing times 0 equals 12. Nothing is the same as zero, so the question mark must be zero."

This misconception led Rob, Jen, and Allison to clarify three specific models of division, which they then planned to elicit from students and represent on the board at the beginning of the discussion (see fig. 22.2).

12 ÷ 4 = 3 means:		
3 groups of 4 fit into 12	If I split 12 into four groups, three are in each group	4 x 3 = 12

Fig. 22.2. Planned representation for the board

They then planned specific questions that would focus student attention on the meaning of $4 \div 0$ and that would help students use the meaning of division (written on the board) to reason about the impossibility of dividing by zero. When Jen led the discussion, she was able to focus student attention on the meaning of division. Students argued that $4 \div 0$ cannot equal zero, since $4 \div 0 = 0$ is the same as saying that $0 \times 0 = 4$, which is clearly false. Students' exit tickets also demonstrated this reasoning. It was powerful to see how, with the support of the plan Jen, Allison, and Rob had created together, Jen was able to succeed where Rob had so recently struggled.

■ Findings

How might leading a discussion change the relationship between supervisor, student teacher, and cooperating teacher?

In asking Rob to teach the class, Allison repositioned him as a teaching colleague, engaging in a public display of practice that others might critique and learn from. By accepting her invitation, Rob granted Allison a role in setting the agenda for their shared work together. Finally, in planning with Jen and having her teach a revised lesson, Rob and Allison repositioned her as a colleague with a shared responsibility to educate children.

This repositioning also redefined Rob, Allison, and Jen as learners and as co-creators. Rather than acting as experts with all the answers, Allison and Rob worked with Jen to learn how to plan and enact a better lesson, and they modeled for her a process of continued professional learning undertaken with colleagues. Allison, in particular, appreciated this change of roles, affirming over the course of the next few weeks how she valued Rob's willingness to acknowledge and share the difficulties and dilemmas of teaching, rather than acting as an outside expert.

What learning opportunities for Rob, Jen, and Allison resulted from Rob leading a discussion?

This collaboration, and more specifically the second lesson, which did not go according to expectations, provided opportunities to learn about student thinking and planning. Interestingly, Jen, Rob, and Allison learned different things from this experience. Rob and Allison learned about students conflating "nothing" with "zero," and how the equivalent multiplication fact interpretation of division could help them reason about that misconception.

For Jen, "The biggest benefit I got from the day was seeing the power of planning questions." In addition, Jen's learning evolved over time. On the day of the lesson she commented on how the planning had resulted in a successful lesson. Later, she commented on her evolving appreciation of the experience.

> Now that I have completed 3 years teaching high school math ... I think ... allowing everyone to be a learner is an important concept for all student teachers, cooperating teachers and university supervisors. ... While the experience at the time felt scary, uneasy, unpredictable and not completely successful, I would not go back and change anything from that day.

Which features of the practicum setting and professional relationships support such collaboration? Which features act as barriers?

There were three major conditions that allowed the collaborators to move out of their traditional roles: flexibility, trust, and a shared challenge.

Each of the actors involved had to exhibit flexibility. Rob shed his official role as evaluator, stepped into the role of colleague, and rearranged his schedule to stay for the day. Allison changed her lesson plans in response to an unanticipated discussion. Finally, Jen planned and taught a whole new lesson.

Clearly, in order for student teachers, university-based supervisors, and cooperating teachers to work together in this way, they must trust one another. Allison had to trust that Rob was able to teach competently. Rob had to trust that his modeling of fallibility would not result in him losing the respect and trust of Allison and Jen. Finally, Jen needed to trust that whatever happened, Rob and Allison would support her and not evaluate her negatively. When student teachers are in a learning process, it is helpful to suspend judgment and study what does and does not get the results they intend. Teaching a whole new lesson without observing it first was a new leap for Jen and one that would inevitably raise to the surface issues to be discussed, but not judged.

The final factor that gave this collaboration so much of its power was the shared challenge of creating an effective lesson. All three collaborators were invested in the success of the lesson. They worked together on the challenging task of creating a plan, based on their shared understanding of the mathematics and student thinking, that would enable Jen to support student learning. Collaborative planning required that everyone's ideas were listened to, respected, and challenged or questioned in the service of creating a lesson designed to meet the needs of a wide range of students.

What are the risks and rewards of such collaborations?

This case demonstrates that collaborations between university supervisors and cooperating teachers entail concrete risks and promise rewards that may not be evident at first.

Risks—For each of the actors involved, this collaboration involved concrete risks. A successful lesson that was considerably different from those that Allison generally taught could disempower Allison, casting Rob as the expert, someone uniquely positioned to model effective instruction. An unsuccessful lesson could undermine Rob's position as an expert and evaluator and result in student confusion and frustration that Allison and Jen would have to confront in future lessons. Finally, as a student teacher, Jen risked teaching ineffectively in front of those charged with evaluating her. Usually, this risk was alleviated by planning the lesson well in advance. Jen heightened that risk considerably by planning a new lesson with challenging content that invited student misconceptions and teaching it shortly after it was planned. However, since all three planned it together, all three would take some responsibility for its success or failure.

Institutional pressures made it difficult for Jen, Rob, and Allison to take these risks. Allison was held responsible for student achievement and for following strict pacing guides, making it risky to allow for collaborations that result in changed plans. By spending the day with Jen, Rob diverted time from other activities that are the basis for his professional advancement. Finally, Jen's teaching was evaluated on an ambitious rubric from the university that left little room for unsuccessful lessons. For instance, just to meet expectations on two of the forty-five domains of the rubric, Jen needed to do the following:

- Provide, **at least three times a week**, practice and/or application in critical/creative thinking, problem solving, and decision making while working on the formulation and/or testing of hypotheses, accommodating various points of view without subject matter distortion, and bringing enthusiasm and relevance to the discipline.

- Apply learning theory to accommodate differences in student intelligence, perception, cognitive style, and achievement levels. Modify instructional methods, materials, and the environment to deliver developmentally appropriate instruction. Provide documentation illustrating the use of multiple sources of data to set appropriate challenge-level learning outcomes for **a small group of students** and the results of its use for the class.

Given the complexity of these standards and the difficulty of meeting them, student teachers are considerably less likely to plan lessons on observation days that may surface misconceptions or to include open-ended questions that require planning for a wide variety of possible student responses. For their part, university supervisors need to provide documentation of all of the criteria on their final evaluations. Ambitious lessons that result in less than stellar performances, even as they may provide the learning opportunities described above, make the task of documenting success much more difficult for supervisors. All of these issues make it much more likely that observed lessons be treated as performances that show expertise rather than as opportunities to learn.

Uncertain rewards—Although the risks of the collaboration described above are concrete and immediate, the rewards are less tangible and difficult to measure.

One benefit of this collaboration might be greater coherence between what student teachers learn in their university courses and what they experience in their student teaching. Allison and Rob together provided a chance for Jen to experience the questioning and detailed lesson planning that she had learned about in her teacher education program. Similarly, collaborations between supervisors, cooperating teachers, and student teachers can help them all to learn how to learn from practice. They can demonstrate how teaching is a complex endeavor, not a formulaic act that can be easily measured by checking off items on a rubric. By analyzing the relationship between planning and enactment—and between what teachers anticipate and what actually happens—teachers, supervisors, and student teachers can all learn more about teaching, learning, and learning how to teach throughout one's career. However, there is no simple measure to determine if collaborations achieve these ends, nor is there an easy way to empirically determine which factors had the most important effects on this process.

■ Conclusions

This change in roles for student teachers, co-operating teachers, and university-based supervisors connects to larger discussions about how to improve teaching on a broad scale. Given the complexity of teaching, and the continued lack of a shared professional knowledge base, many have argued that positive change requires transforming schools and other educational institutions into learning organizations (see Bryk et al. 2015). Education researchers have proposed that this approach could transform the relationship between teachers and academics (Hiebert, Gallimore and Stigler 2002). Instead of teachers being positioned as consumers of knowledge generated by expert researchers, teachers and researchers would together define problems of practice and test possible improvements through activities like collaborative lesson design and revision.

Such an approach could alleviate some of the risks to collaboration described in this chapter. For instance, redefining student teaching as a collaborative learning experience could provide space for university supervisors to teach lessons, not as outside experts whose authority might compromise that of the cooperating teacher, but as part of a team investigating how specific practices or lesson plans might be improved. Collaborations such as the one described above might become seen as models that teachers could use in their own work with colleagues, developing their own capacity to work with others to improve instruction.

Many schools and districts have already set up structures for collaboration in response to the push for professional learning. Advocates for collaboration in the context of student teaching could point out the proliferation of mandated professional learning plans and the growth of professional learning communities as evidence of the growing push for collaboration. Making such collaboration part of student teaching could prepare student teachers for these structures and activities, and it could provide teachers and university supervisors with opportunities to develop their own skills in these areas. Allowing school personnel who are already charged with overseeing such collaborations (e.g., assistant principals, department chairs) to serve as university-based supervisors could introduce further coherence into student teaching; student teachers and cooperating teachers would be working with the same person in the context of professional learning.

■ Continued Challenges

In addition to the barriers described above, there are other difficulties in moving to more collaborative relationships among student teachers, cooperating teachers, and university supervisors. One of the most salient is the tremendous disparity in the qualifications and skills of both cooperating teachers and university supervisors. University supervisors represent a wide range of experience, from college professors with relatively little classroom experience but strong knowledge of research, to retired teachers with many years in mathematics classrooms, to retired administrators with many years of evaluating teachers but minimal experience in mathematics. Cooperating teachers range in levels of experience, in beliefs about teaching and learning, and in familiarity with a variety of pedagogical approaches. Designing collaboration models based on this diversity of backgrounds would be difficult.

A continuing dilemma is in the role of evaluation and its effect on learning. On the one hand, those who certify teachers have a responsibility to evaluate their performance to ensure a necessary level of competence. On the other hand, evaluation brings with it high stakes, and it discourages the kind of risk taking that often is the key to learning. Indeed, the learning that is described above was the result of a lesson that was not effective. As described, high standards for effective lessons on student teaching evaluations might, ironically, limit student-teacher learning. These pressures are exacerbated by the current push for external evaluations, such as edTPA, that seek to limit subjective professional judgment and substitute it with valid and reliable measures.

■ Moving Forward

The challenges described above are difficult and not easily surmounted. To help do so, advocates for this collaborative approach to student teaching could push for a more realistic set of evaluation criteria that do not hold novice teachers accountable to unrealistic levels of mastery. They could also push for evaluation to include collaboration and risk taking, so that when student teachers teach lessons that were not effective, they are judged by their ability to work with others to make sense of those lessons, to learn from them, and to improve them. They could also work to develop and coordinate professional development opportunities for cooperating teachers, university supervisors, and student teachers. Sustained professional development for cooperating teachers, in which they collaborated with university personnel to improve their own practice, could provide a model for the kind of collaboration that both could engage in with student teachers and align professional development efforts with student teaching.

References

Bambrick-Santoyo, Paul. *Driven by Data*. San Francisco: Jossey-Bass, 2010.

Bryk, Anthony S., Louis M. Gomez, Alicia Grunow, and Paul G. LeMahieu. *Learning to Improve: How America's Schools Can Get Better at Getting Better*. Cambridge, Mass.: Harvard Education Press, 2015.

Clarke, Anthony, Valerie Triggs, and Wendy Nielsen. "Cooperating Teacher Participation in Teacher Education: A Review of the Literature." *Review of Educational Research* 84, no. 2 (2014): 163–202.

Darling-Hammond, Linda, and Velma L. Cobb. *Teacher Preparation and Professional Development in APEC Members: A Comparative Study*. Washington, D.C.: U.S. Department of Education, 1995.

Hiebert, James, Thomas P. Carpenter, Elizabeth Fennema, Karen C. Fuson, Diana Wearne, Hanlie Murray, Alwyn Olivier, and Piet Human. *Making Sense: Teaching and Learning Mathematics with Understanding*. Portsmouth, N.H.: Heinemann, 1997.

Hiebert, James, Ronald Gallimore, and James W. Stigler. "A Knowledge Base for the Teaching Profession: What Would It Look Like and How Can We Get One?" *Educational Researcher* 31, no. 5 (2002): 3–15.

Lemov, Doug. *Teach Like a Champion: 49 Techniques That Put Students on the Path to College*. San Francisco: Jossey-Bass, 2010.

Morris, Anne K., and James Hiebert. "Openness and Measurement: Two Principles for Improving Education Practice and Shared Instructional Products." *Mathematics Teacher Educator* 3, no. 2 (2015): 130–45.

National Research Council (NRC). *Preparing Teachers: Building Evidence for Sound Policy*. Report by the Committee on the Study of Teacher Preparation Programs in the United States. Washington, D.C.: National Academies Press, 2010.

Philipp, Randolph A. "Mathematics Teachers' Beliefs and Affect." In *Second Handbook of Research on Mathematics Teaching and Learning*, edited by Frank K. Lester, pp. 257–318. Charlotte, N.C.: Information Age Publishing, 2007.

Saunders, William M., Claude N. Goldenberg, and Ronald Gallimore. "Increasing Achievement by Focusing Grade Level Teams on Improving Classroom Learning: A Prospective, Quasi-Experimental Study of Title I Schools." *American Educational Research Journal* 46, no. 4 (2009): 1006–33.

CHAPTER 23

Cycles of Collective Planning, Enactment, and Reflection in Elementary Teacher Education

Allyson Hallman-Thrasher, *Ohio University, Athens*

A key goal of mathematics instruction is supporting students to understand how to construct, defend, and question mathematical arguments. The National Council of Teachers of Mathematics (NCTM 2000, 2014) has called on teachers to make facilitating meaningful mathematical discourse a priority, and "construct viable arguments and critique the reasoning of others" has been identified as a mathematical practice in which all students should engage (National Governors Association and Council of Chief State School Officers [NGA and CCSSO Center] 2010, p. 6). Amid calls to increase attention to discourse in mathematics, teachers struggle to move discussions beyond an Initiation-Response-Evaluation sequence (Boaler and Brodie 2004; Walshaw and Anthony 2008) where the teacher *initiates* a (procedural) question, a student *responds* (usually a short answer), and the teacher *evaluates* for correctness (Mehan 1979).

Difficulties arise for teachers who attempt to facilitate discussions that are based on their students' thinking and grounded in mathematical reasoning, including the following: establishing norms for discussion and developing students' autonomy (Nathan and Knuth 2003; Yackel and Cobb 1996); providing enough help without sacrificing content (Smith and Stein 2011); balancing mathematical challenge with accessibility (Stein et al. 2009; Williams and Baxter 1996); and maintaining integrity to student thinking and the discipline of mathematics (Ball 1993; Engle and Conant 2002; Sherin 2002). One challenge of interest is facilitating discussions while maintaining the cognitive demand of tasks (e.g., requiring students to develop their own strategies and not simply imitate the teacher's strategy). This is essential to ensure that students grapple with challenging mathematics (Stein et al. 2008) and that mathematical discussions do not become sharing sessions with no mathematical point (Smith and Stein 2011).

Facilitating mathematics discussions is a *high-leverage practice,* a practice that is essential for novices to know and be able to carry out and that has large payoffs for student learning (Ball et al. 2009). The complex practice of facilitating mathematics discussions accessible to novices can be decomposed into a manageable grain-size that can be "articulated, studied, and rehearsed" (Sleep and Boerst 2012, p. 1039). Teacher educators can scaffold novices' learning through *approximations of practice* by which novices engage in activities of teaching in ways that approach, but not exactly replicate, the work of teaching. In this chapter, I describe how engaging preservice elementary teachers (PSTs) in cyclical collaborative approximations of practice supported their learning to facilitate productive mathematics discussions.

■ Project

As part of an integrated field experience embedded in their first of two mathematics teaching methods courses, eight PSTs engaged in work aimed at improving their ability to facilitate mathematics discussions. They worked in teams of three, rotating roles of two teachers and one video recorder to enact high-demand, problem-solving tasks with pairs of elementary children. They enacted the same task for three weeks (with different children each week) to understand children's approaches and ways of thinking and, in turn, to refine their responses to the children's thinking over time.

PSTs completed weekly cycles of planning, co-enacting high-demand tasks, and collaboratively reflecting on enactment video (Kazemi et al. 2010). Rather than using traditional lesson planning, I provided PSTs with three to four student solutions for each task and asked them to create a hypothetical student-teacher dialogue to follow each (fig. 23.1; modified from Crespo, Oslund, and Parks 2011). With my feedback (as their methods course instructor) on these dialogues, each PST planned questions and hints for different scenarios (e.g., a child needs help getting started or has a specific common misconception). Each week, they revised plans to include new ways to respond to children's thinking, and they composed written analyses of their sessions working with children that included responses to group members' analyses. Extensive rubrics for assessing math-talk (Hufferd-Ackles, Fuson, and Sherin 2004), problem solving (Jacobs and Ambrose 2003), and student thinking guided the PSTs' reflections (appendixes A–C). (Printable versions of the rubrics in appendixes A–C are available at this book's page on NCTM's More4U website.) The PSTs were invited to examine the quality of (and who was responsible for) creating representations, providing ideas, asking questions, constructing explanations, and validating ideas, but they were not expected to assess each element of every rubric every week. I asked PSTs to consider what aspects highlighted in the rubrics they noticed in analyzing their work with children. It was the PSTs' responsibility to determine what they attended to in their analyses each week and to set the course for their own improvement.

Task: Place 12 pennies in 3 piles with no two piles having the same number of pennies	
Dialogue 1	**Rationale for Teacher Moves**
S: Student randomly puts 12 pennies into 3 piles until she finds 6, 4, 2. Then she moves a penny from the 4 pile to the 2 pile and has 6, 3, 3. "That's not right." She move the pennies back to 6, 4, 2 and moves one from the 6 pile to the 4 pile. "I keep making them with the same number." **T:**	
Dialogue 2	**Rationale for Teacher Moves**
S: Student finds 6-5-1, and 6-4-2, and 5-4-3 by rearranging one penny at a time, and then gets stuck. **T:**	
Dialogue 3	**Rationale for Teacher Moves**
S: Student has found 5 of the solutions (6-5-1, 6-4-2, 5-4-3, 7-4-1, and 7-3-2) and after several more attempts claims these are the only solutions. **T:**	

Fig. 23.1. Twelve Pennies task dialogue assignment

Our methods class aimed to develop awareness of children's mathematical thinking, how it differs from adult thinking, and how it might affect teaching. In class, we worked on problem-solving tasks and discussed strategies and children's typical approaches so PSTs could experience problem-solving tasks as learners themselves. I (the instructor) modeled talk moves (revoicing, questioning, applying another's strategy) that PSTs were to use with children, and PSTs reflected (in writing and discussion) on transcripts and video of mathematics discussions. For eight weeks of the course, one of two weekly class sessions met at a local K–5 elementary school. The diverse school (570 students; 39 percent African American, 8 percent Asian, 5 percent Hispanic, 4 percent multiracial, 43 percent white) had a longstanding partnership with the elementary teacher education program and this methods course. The school's teachers chose twenty "academically average" fifth graders to participate. Though the teachers did not select tasks, observe, or provide feedback, they had helped craft the experience as a pull-out program (to allow teachers to work with smaller groups on remediation and enrichment in the classroom) that focused on problem solving and concepts not currently covered in class (in order to provide PSTs with freedom from the need to cover particular instructional objectives in each session). Direct instruction was discouraged. PSTs were to use the techniques discussed and practiced in our methods class to help children articulate their thinking, solve tasks, and connect to the mathematical concepts embedded in the tasks.

■ Changes in PSTs' Discussion Practices

To illustrate PSTs' changes during the field experience, I share examples of one group's enactments of the Twelve Pennies task (fig. 23.1). This was a productive task to use because it could be easily modeled and it helped to make the children's thinking accessible to novices unfamiliar with exploring children's mathematical thinking. It also had multiple solutions—seven ways to arrange the pennies—and aspects needing further clarification (e.g., Can a pile have no pennies? Is 9-2-1 a distinct solution from 1-2-9?), which provided obvious points to discuss with children. Students were most often easily able to find some solutions and were satisfied, so teachers had to press children to find all solutions and address the task's subtle underlying concept, articulating how they knew all solutions had been found by having a systematic way of generating solutions that accounted for all possible combinations. One group's (Casey, Nadia, and Kate) enactment cycles of this task illustrate changes in the PSTs' practice for facilitating discussions.

Initial Task Planning and Enactment

Planning for the task varied. In the dialogues, Casey's questions were too vague to be helpful ("Can these numbers be arranged any other way?"), whereas Nadia's led students directly to the solution. Unable to hypothesize children's approaches, Nadia and Casey assumed little intervention would be needed to help children develop insight. Kate also prompted with her own strategy at the end of her dialogue but used multiple questions to understand children's thinking first (for dialogues, see appendix D). I advised Casey and Nadia to consider what might happen next and to tailor questions to the specifics of children's work: What if a child does not answer questions in the way that you want? What if it takes more than one or two questions to help a child find more solutions? I noted that Kate's questions for eliciting thinking were effective but suggested that she consider how to help children organize their solutions without directly asking them to do so.

In their task plan, the three teachers constructed possible correct and incorrect student responses and how they would respond to each (see appendix E). Casey's only changes from her task dialogue were a generic eliciting strategy question and a prompt to use manipulatives. Though Nadia retained some of her directive responses that suggested strategies, she increased her attention to the specifics of solutions, asking why certain strategies were used and how to ensure that all solutions were found. Kate made most of her questions that had hinted at an organized list strategy more subtle, and she included questions that addressed how all solutions were found.

In the first task enactment, the children's work closely mirrored the solutions and conversations the PSTs had hypothesized in the task plans and task dialogues. Each child had generated some, but not all, solutions (some systematically and some not) and had made permutations of the same solution. Nadia and Kate stepped each child through an organized reconstruction of their list and then asked them to explain their solutions:

C3:	I did 3 circles and put pennies in them and guessed and checked.
Kate:	OK.
Nadia:	OK. But at some point that stopped working right? We kept getting the same thing? So what'd we do?
C3:	So we, well, we knew 10 could be that without getting an even number, so we put in 9, and then we added each number to each circle.
Nadia:	So we started at 10, and we knew . . . well, we started at 12, we knew we couldn't do that and we went to 11. We knew we couldn't have that many in one pile. We went to 10 and it would have been 10-1-1, which wouldn't have worked, so then we started with 9. And we just worked our way down from there.

Kate:	[*to C2*] OK. Do you want to explain kind of what you did?
C2:	Well . . . I . . .
Kate:	You did the same thing at first, right? You did the circles and guess and check.
C2:	But then, I didn't really like that.
Kate:	And then you said, "Wait a second, I have an idea."
C2:	Yeah, so I erased. Well, I did. I did 9 plus 1 and then I did, I took one away from here and added it here [*pointing to 9 + 2 + 1, took one from 9 and added it to 2 to get 8 + 3 + 1*]. And just kept going down the line. And after that . . .
Kate:	And you can see that pattern, right? That you removed one and you added one. Right?
C2:	And then after that I used the ones I had down here. I added those. And I kept going back to . . . And then I saw and then I would go like 6 and 6.
Kate:	You kept the first number the same and thought of all the options, right?
C2:	Yeah.
Kate:	Then there's some of them that are repeating, right? But you explained how that worked, right? [*C2 nods.*]
Casey:	You guys understand it?
C2 and C3:	Mm-hmm.

Typical of many PSTs initially, this group asked small questions that walked children through the teachers' own thinking. Follow-up questions reduced tasks to recalling basic facts without children understanding how or why those actions solved the task. PSTs answered questions to elicit thinking themselves or asked them in a way that made the answer obvious. Earlier, Casey had suggested children work together, but no one picked up on it and Casey did not follow up. Her only other intervention was a cursory check for understanding that failed to assess what the children actually understood. The children worked in parallel with no accountability for listening to or understanding one another. Rather than encourage student-to-student talk, the PSTs revoiced (usually in a more sophisticated form) what one child said or did to the other.

Reflections and Revisions for the Second Enactment

Over their three weeks of work on the Twelve Pennies task, the group attended to the *source of ideas* of the Math-Talk rubric (appendix A), and *explaining mathematical thinking* and *eliciting a strategy* from the Math-Talk and Problem-Solving (appendix B) rubrics. They recognized that it was "very frustrating to help the [children] realize that they could use organized lists or charts to solve the problems without explicitly telling them to" (Casey reflection) and that "I need to work on not trying to lead them on with obvious hints" (Kate reflection). Nadia, concerned with the *responsibility for learning* dimension of the Math-Talk rubric, wanted to ensure they, the PSTs, and the children had the answer "right." The PSTs also noticed that without developing student-to-student interaction, their discussions would remain at lower levels across all four dimensions of the Math-Talk rubric, and they realized that their actions limited student collaboration. In the first enactment, each child had generated a solution the other was missing, providing a natural opportunity for collaboration. I advised, "Your job is to not be content with just finding a few solutions—how do you know you found them all? When [children] compare answers, they will see they've missed some and then you can suggest perhaps they missed others." Casey hypothesized the group should establish collaboration as an expectation early: "I think if we start out by saying 'work together to solve this problem,' it [working together] will be an automatic response" throughout the session (Casey reflection).

With these reflections and feedback, the PSTs revised their task plan (appendix F), attending carefully to the quality of their *questioning* to help the children generate solutions such as "What's the largest amount of pennies you have in a pile? What's the smallest?" (Casey, Nadia) or "Can a single pile have 12 pennies? 11, 10, 9, 8? Why or why not?" (Kate). In an effort to shift the *source of ideas* to the students, they hinted less directly about using an organized list to justify that all solutions had been found: "But let's think about how we can make a way that ensures we don't miss any other options. You can base it off of similar traits you recognize from your already discovered solutions" (Kate).

In the second enactment, Nadia and Casey worked on *exploring incorrect strategies* of the Problem-Solving rubric and pressing for complete explanations. In this excerpt, Nadia worked with C1 generating solutions, while Casey worked with C6:

Nadia:	Let's look at these two. . . . Is there any method to what you're doing right now?

C1:	Um, really just looking for how many ways I can make 10. . . . Go down here and I would go down this way [*points to 5-4-3-2 column in fig. 23.2*].

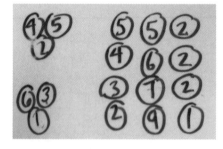

Fig. 23.2. C1's diagram

Nadia:	What do you mean go down that way?

C1:	If you did 5 plus 5 equals 2, OK so then I would do 4. I'd be going down this way [*pointing to second column, where she has 5-5-2, 4-6-2*], so I'd be doing 6 and then this would be 7 like that . . . I could do 3-7-2. I could do 2-1-9, something like that.

. . .

C1:	I think I have a solution. It could be, I thought it would 36 but I might be wrong with that.
Nadia:	Why did you think it would be 36?
C1:	Because if there's 3 groups and there's 12. . . . Yeah, so there's 12 pennies in each one . . . it would equal 36. But that's just a guess.
Nadia:	A guess? Well, let's keep going and see how many you can find.

Nadia elicited student thinking, questioned to clarify, and encouraged testing hypotheses rather than validating them for her child.

Casey's interventions built on student work rather than redirecting it as her group had previously:

Casey:	Why did you start with 9?
C6:	I just thought the first time to do 11 plus 1. Then I just I thought I can subtract 2 [from the 11] and try to make 3 piles out of it.
Casey:	So you knew that 11 didn't work because 11 plus 1 is 12 but you only had 2 numbers or 2 piles. Why didn't you do 10 + 1 + 1?
C6:	Because one [pile] cannot have two [of the same number].
Casey:	Good, so you just went down to 9. So what would your next step be?
. . .	

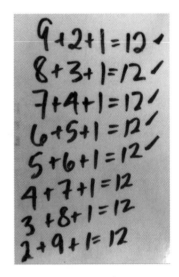

Fig. 23.3. C6's diagram

Casey:	OK, let's stop right there. Don't erase it; you're doing a really good job. Explain to me this top one [9 + 2 + 1 = 12 in fig. 23.3]
C6:	First I put 9 + 2 + 1 = 12. With the other ones down here, I started to do 9 and I subtracted 1 from 9 and added 1 to this one [*took 1 from 9 and gave it to the 2 to get 8 + 3 + 1 = 12*]. So what I did to the first number I did to the second.

Though each PST and child worked one-on-one, more attempts were made to support their collaboration. Casey pressed them to explain ideas to one another three times before one child explained an idea taken up by the other: "Another thing that I did is I found two numbers that equal 10 and I used them. So like 5 plus 5 but you couldn't do that one. 6 plus 4." When the other child said "7 plus 3 is another makes 10," Casey asked him to use that idea to generate another solution.

Reflections and Revisions for the Third Enactment

The second enactment exemplified a dilemma from the Problem-Solving rubric, *timing assistance*, or "knowing exactly when to jump in" (Kate reflection). Casey found it "incredibly frustrating watching silently as the students worked the problems completely wrong . . . but I wanted them to find out the flaws in their attempts." Similarly, Nadia wondered if "the wait time is taking too long" (Nadia reflection); however, Kate stated (and I concurred):

as the one not teaching this week I can tell you that it was not a ridiculous amount of time you were giving them to respond. You let her talk it out and figure out on her own that it didn't work—and that is important to her fully understanding the problem. You supported her and didn't shut her down which will help her in the long run. (Kate reflection)

I also suggested that PSTs encourage student collaboration earlier in the activity, as each child was using a strategy that would have filled in a gap for the other, and the group "determined" (Casey reflection) to make it a priority for their third enactment. Kate noted that although their "questions were deeper and more thought-provoking" they "did not ever really encourage the kids to question each other (or us) very often" (Kate reflection).

In this enactment they observed new correct and incorrect approaches: overgeneralized solutions (12 × 3), using coins besides pennies (interpreting the task as ways to make 12 cents), use of actual pennies to construct piles, lists of number sentences, making 10s addition facts, and systematic removal of repeated solutions. Casey added questions about using manipulatives and looking for patterns that she had used to effectively manage these strategies: "You have two solutions with 6; are there any others with 6 in a pile? What about 5 and 7?" Other revisions for the third enactment were minor, in part because the major revisions created for the second enactment had helped them successfully navigate these diverse strategies.

In the third enactment, PSTs emphasized *extending thinking* and student collaboration to achieve higher levels on the Math-Talk rubric. Requiring that one student serve as the scribe established the need for students to collaborate at the session's beginning. As a result, PSTs noted that children "fixed each other's mistakes the whole time" (Kate reflection) without teacher prompting. The children also debated a justification:

Casey:	Why did you just erase that one [*10-1-1*]?
C5:	It can't be 10. One of the numbers can't be 10.
Kate:	Why?
C5:	Because, umm . . .
C7:	[*to C5*] Because it is a two-digit number.
C5:	[*to C7*] No!
Casey:	It is a two-digit number.
C5:	[*to C7*] It *is* a two-digit number but it's because 10 would have to have two ones.

The PSTs posed an extension, Fifteen Pennies, to see if the children could extend the strategy of choosing the highest possible number for any pile and working down. When the children suggested 13, 14, and 12 as maximum pile sizes, Kate questioned to help them articulate a justification and specifically directed them to explain their ideas to each other, not her.

Supporting Teachers' Growth in Facilitating Discussions

The approximation of practice described here incorporated a type of assisted performance (Mewborn and Stinson 2007), collaborative teaching cycles, and systematic collective reflection with a common tool. These structures created opportunities for teacher learning that would otherwise have been missed. Typically, elementary teachers have to wait a full year to repeat a task with new children, but the structure of the collaborative teaching cycles in this experience allowed PSTs to gain three "years" of practice, enacting a task in just three weeks. Repeating the same tasks with different children within the collaborative teaching cycles provided teachers with opportunities to refine enactments of specific tasks and, more generally, to refine strategies for facilitating mathematics discussions that could be generalized to *any* task. They could hypothesize responses to children's thinking, test their responses, and revise subsequent enactments. Task dialogues helped them to envision a starting point for their work, and reflecting and revising their plans each week helped them to expand that vision. As Casey described, "My ability to anticipate and respond to students' solutions, provide and elicit good explanations, ask questions and give hints, and lead discussions changed drastically." Teaching collaboratively with a group meant their goals for improvement were less likely to be derailed, because when one PST faltered, another could step in. When Nadia's child found the missing final solution and Nadia did not pose a follow-up question, Kate stepped in asking, "How did you figure that out?" and Nadia immediately followed up with her own question.

Weekly collective reflection helped PSTs notice aspects of their enactments they may have otherwise missed. For example, when Nadia saw a child "explaining an answer I said 'right' on the tape but I had to rewind the video a couple of times to understand what he meant," it helped *Casey* be more aware and critical of her own actions:

> Nadia's concern about not fully understanding a student's reasoning is valid. I think we assume they understand how they solved the problem and that we do too. But sometimes we don't know why they solved a problem a certain way or how they even got to the answer! I am guilty of hearing an explanation and just nodding my head or saying "Good job!" when I don't even know what is going on. I didn't notice that I did that until Nadia pointed it out. (Casey reflection)

Having a common tool (e.g., the set of rubrics) for analyzing discussions gave preservice teachers a consistent language and framework for thinking about their interactions with children. Casey struggled with "making the underlying mathematical concepts evident" (Problem-Solving rubric): "I felt like asking for the student to look for a pattern was way too obvious." The common tools provided a common image of a good mathematics discussion for PSTs to measure themselves against, and PSTs developed self-assessment skills in choosing which aspects of the rubrics to attend to each week. Returning to the same skills over time with clear guidelines from a common set of tools for assessing improvement supported learning to facilitate discussions. Over the semester, Kate recognized the need to carefully attend to student work: "Very rarely did their depictions truly show their thinking. Unless you had been watching them the whole time, you would have no way of understanding how they got from the start of their picture to the end of their solution" (Kate reflection).

■ Conclusion

Preservice teachers can make progress in facilitating discussions focused on student thinking in a relatively short time with intensive support and structures that foster peer collaboration and reflection. Repeating the enactment cycles provided opportunities to hypothesize, test, and revise each week. These immediate opportunities for improvement increased success at a complex teaching skill that engages students in mathematical practices (NGA Center and CCSSO 2010) and supports conceptual understanding of mathematics (NCTM 2014). Collaboration helped PSTs to notice and meaningfully respond to their interactions with children. Teaching collaboratively helped to maintain the focus on children's thinking *and* the mathematical concepts of task. Reflecting collaboratively supported the PSTs' developing awareness of the impact of their teacher moves. Using a common tool for reflection enabled the PSTs to assess themselves to identify and decide how to remediate missteps. The rubrics for reflection directed the PSTs' attention to concrete elements of the discussions and student thinking and provided a clear framework for how to evaluate their effectiveness.

PSTs empowered with these skills will be better able to elicit and use student thinking as a lever for instruction, and they are more likely to carry this practice into their teaching careers. The collaborative teaching and reflecting cycles in this project equipped the PSTs with skills to monitor their own teaching with an eye toward evaluating the impact of their teacher moves. Their self-assessment and collaborative reflection supported the PSTs in learning to elicit and respond to student thinking by using each teaching cycle to analyze children's strategies and explanations and to revise and test the PSTs' responses. The ability of PSTs to self-assess their mathematics discussions can then sustain their improvement long after leaving their teacher education program. Though the work described here was aimed at preparing preservice teachers, practicing teachers can also learn from using high-demand tasks, considering mathematics from the child's perspective as part of lesson planning, and engaging in systematic self-assessment with peers.

References

Ball, Deborah. "With an Eye on the Mathematical Horizon: Dilemmas of Teaching Elementary School Mathematics." *Elementary School Journal* 93, no. 4 (1993): 373–97.

Ball, Deborah, Laurie Sleep, Timothy Boerst, and Hyman Bass. "Combining the Development of Practice and the Practice of Development in Teacher Education." *Elementary School Journal 109* (2009): 458–76.

Boaler, Jo, and Karen Brodie. "The Importance, Nature, and Impact of Teacher Questions." In *Proceedings of the 26th Conference of the Psychology of Mathematics Education* (North America), vol. 2, edited by D. E. McDougall and J. A. Ross, pp. 773–81. Toronto: OISE/UT, 2004.

Crespo, Sandra., Joy A. Oslund, and Amy N. Parks. "Imagining Mathematics Teaching Practice: Prospective Teachers Generate Representations of a Class Discussion." *ZDM: The International Journal on Mathematics Education,* 43, no. 1 (2011): 119–131.

Engle, Randi. A., and Faith R. Conant. "Guiding Principles for Fostering Productive Disciplinary Engagement: Explaining an Emergent Argument in a Community of Learners Classroom." *Cognition and Instruction* 20, no. 4 (2002): 399–483.

Hufferd-Ackles, Kimberly, Karen Fuson, and Miriam Sherin. "Describing Levels and Components of a Math-Talk Community." *Journal for Research in Mathematics Education* 35, no. 2 (2004): 81–116.

Jacobs, Victoria R., and Rebecca C. Ambrose. "Individual Interviews as a Window into Teachers' Practice: A Framework for Understanding Teacher-Student Interactions during Mathematical Problem Solving." Paper presented at the annual meeting of the American Educational Research Association, Chicago, April 2003.

Kazemi, Elham, Heather Beasley, Angela Chan, Megan Franke, Hala Ghousseini, and Magdalene Lampert. "Learning Ambitious Teaching through Cycles of Investigation and Enactment." Presentation at the National Council of Teachers of Mathematics Research Pre-session Conference, San Diego, Calif., April 2010.

Mehan, Hugh. "'What Time Is It, Denise?' Asking Known Information Questions in Classroom Discourse." *Theory into Practice* 18, no. 4 (1979): 285–94.

Mewborn, Denise S., and David W. Stinson. "Learning to Teach as Assisted Performance." *Teachers College Record* 109, no. 6 (2007): 1457–87.

Nathan, Mitchell J., and Eric J. Knuth. "A Study of Whole Classroom Mathematical Discourse and Teacher Change." *Cognition and Instruction* 21, no. 2 (2003): 175–207.

National Council of Teachers of Mathematics (NCTM). *Principles and Standards for School Mathematics*. Reston, Va.: NCTM, 2000.

———. *Principles to Actions: Ensuring Mathematical Success for All*. Reston, Va.: NCTM, 2014.

National Governors Association and Council of Chief State School Officers (NGA Center and CCSSO). *Common Core State Standards for Mathematics*. Washington, D.C.: NGA Center and CCSSO, 2010. http://www.corestandards.org.

Sherin, Miriam G. "A Balancing Act: Developing a Discourse Community in a Mathematics Classroom." *Journal of Mathematics Teacher Education* 5, no. 3 (2002): 205–33.

Sleep, Laurie, and Timothy Boerst. "Preparing Beginning Teachers to Elicit and Interpret Students' Mathematical Thinking." *Teaching and Teacher Education* 28, no. 7 (2012): 1038–48.

Stein, Mary Kay, Randi Engle, Margaret Smith, and Elizabeth Hughes. "Orchestrating Productive Mathematical Discussions: Five Practices for Helping Teachers Move Beyond Show and Tell." *Mathematical Thinking and Learning* 10, no. 4 (2008): 313–40.

Stein, Mary Kay, and Margaret Schwan Smith. *5 Practices for Orchestrating Productive Mathematics Discussions*. Reston, Va.: National Council of Teachers of Mathematics, 2011.

Stein, Mary Kay, Margaret S. Smith, Marjorie Henningsen, and Edward A. Silver. *Implementing Standards-Based Mathematics Instruction: A Casebook for Professional Development*. 2nd ed. New York: Teachers College Press, 2009.

Walshaw, Margaret, and Glenda Anthony. "The Role of Pedagogy in Classroom Discourse: A Review of Recent Research into Mathematics." *Review of Educational Research* 78, no. 3 (2008): 516–51.

Williams, Steven, R., and Juliet A. Baxter. "Dilemmas of Discourse-Oriented Teaching in One Middle School Mathematics Classroom." *Elementary School Journal* 97, no. 1 (1996): 21–38.

Yackel, Erna, and Paul Cobb. "Sociomathematical Norms, Argumentation, and Autonomy in Mathematics." *Journal of Research in Mathematics Education* 27, no. 4 (1996): 458–77.

Appendix A

Rubrics to Guide Reflections: Math-Talk (Hufferd-Ackles et al. 2004)

Level 0: Traditional teacher-directed classroom with brief answer responses from students			
A. Questioning	**B. Explaining mathematical thinking**	**C. Source of mathematical ideas**	**D. Responsibility for learning**
Teacher is the only questioner. Short frequent questions function to keep students listening and paying attention to the teacher.	*No or minimal teacher elicitation of student thinking, strategies, or explanations; teacher expects answer-focused responses. Teacher may tell answers.*	*Teacher is physically at the board, usually chalk in hand, telling and showing students how to do math.*	*Teacher repeats student responses (originally directed to her) for the class. Teacher responds to students' answers by verifying the correct answer or showing the correct method.*
Students give short answers and respond to the teacher only. No student-to-student math talk.	No student thinking or strategy-focused explanation of work. Only answers are given.	Students respond to math presented by the teacher. They do not offer their own math ideas.	Students are passive listeners; they attempt to imitate the teacher and do not take responsibility for the learning of their peers or themselves.
Level 1: Teacher beginning to pursue student mathematical thinking. Teacher plays central role in the math-talk community.			
A. Questioning	**B. Explaining mathematical thinking**	**C. Source of mathematical ideas**	**D. Responsibility for learning**
Teacher questions begin to focus on student thinking and focus less on answers. Teacher begins to ask follow-up questions about student methods and answers. Teacher is still the only questioner.	*Teacher probes student thinking somewhat. One or two strategies may be elicited. Teacher may fill in explanations herself.*	*Teacher is still the main source of ideas, though she elicits some student ideas. Teacher does some probing to access student ideas.*	*Teacher begins to set up structures to facilitate students listening to and helping other students. The teacher alone gives feedback.*
As a student answers a question, other students listen passively or wait for their turn.	Students give information about their math thinking usually as it is probed by the teacher (minimal volunteering of thoughts). They provide brief descriptions of their thinking.	Some student ideas are raised in discussions but are not explored.	Students become more engaged by repeating what other students say or by helping another student at the teacher's request. This helping mostly involves students showing how *they* solved a problem.

Rubrics to Guide Reflections: Math-Talk (Hufferd-Ackles et al. 2004) *continued*

Level 2: Teacher modeling and helping students build new roles. Some co-teaching and co-learning begins as student-to-student talk increases. Teacher physically begins to move to side or back of the room.

A. Questioning	B. Explaining mathematical thinking	C. Source of mathematical ideas	D. Responsibility for learning
Teacher continues to ask probing questions and also asks more open questions. She also facilitates student-to-student talk—e.g., by asking students to be prepared to ask questions about other students' work.	*Teacher probes more deeply to learn about student thinking and supports detailed descriptions from students. Teacher open to and elicits multiple strategies.*	*Teacher follows up on explanations and builds on them by asking students to compare and contrast them. Teacher is comfortable using student errors as opportunities for learning.*	*Teacher encourages student responsibility for understanding the mathematical ideas of others. Teacher asks other students questions about student work and whether they agree or disagree and why.*
Students ask questions of one another's work on the board, often at the prompting of the teacher. Students listen to one another so they do not repeat questions.	Students usually give information as it is probed by the teacher with some volunteering of thoughts. They begin to stake a position and articulate more information in response to probes. They explain steps in their thinking by providing *fuller descriptions* and *begin to defend* their answers and methods. Other students listen supportively.	Students exhibit confidence about their ideas and share their own thinking and strategies even if they are different from others. Student ideas sometimes guide the direction of the math lesson.	Students begin to listen to understand one another. When the teacher requests, they explain other students' ideas in their own words. Helping involves clarifying *other* students' ideas for themselves and others. Students imitate and model teacher's probing in pair work and in whole-class discussions.

Rubrics to Guide Reflections: Math-Talk (Hufferd-Ackles et al. 2004) *continued*

	Level 3: Teacher as co-teacher and co-learner. Teacher monitors all that occurs, still fully engaged. Teacher is ready to assist, but now in more peripheral and monitoring role (coach and assistant).		
A. Questioning	**B. Explaining mathematical thinking**	**C. Source of mathematical ideas**	**D. Responsibility for learning**
Teacher expects students to ask one another questions about their work. The teacher's questions still may guide the discourse.	*Teacher follows along closely to student descriptions of their thinking, encouraging students to make their explanations more complete; may ask probing questions to make explanations more complete. Teacher stimulates students to think more deeply about strategies.*	*Teacher allows for interruptions from students during her explanations; she lets students explain and "own" new strategies. (Teacher is still engaged and deciding what is important to continue exploring.) Teacher uses student ideas and methods as the basis for lessons or mini-extensions.*	*The teacher expects students to be responsible for co-evaluation of everyone's work and thinking. She supports students as they help one another sort out misconceptions. She helps and/or follows up when needed.*
Student-to-student talk is student-initiated, not dependent on the teacher. Students ask questions and listen to responses. Many questions are "Why?" questions that require justification from the person answering. Students repeat their own or other's questions until satisfied with answers.	Students describe more complete strategies; they defend and justify their answers with little prompting from the teacher. Students realize that they will be asked questions from other students when they finish, so they are motivated and careful to be thorough. Other students support with active listening.	Students interject their ideas as the teacher or other students are teaching, confident that their ideas are valued. Students spontaneously compare and contrast and build on ideas. Student ideas form part of the content of many math lessons.	Students listen to understand, then initiate clarifying other students' work and ideas for themselves and for others during whole-class discussions as well as in small group and pair work. Students assist each other in understanding and correcting errors.

■ Appendix B

Rubrics to Guide Reflections: Problem-Solving Interactions (Jacobs and Ambrose 2003)

Supporting the child during problem solving	Level 1: Works toward answer	Level 2: Watches the child	Level 3: Begins probing child's strategy	Level 4: Probes child's strategy and facilitates mathematical connections
Ensuring problem comprehension	Rarely even addresses problem comprehension	May repeat problem	May repeat, explain, embellish, and personalize problem	Explores child's understanding of problem before using Level 3 tactics
Adjusting the problem	Rarely adjusts problems	Rare but may change numbers or context	May change numbers or context	May change problem type, numbers, or context
Exploring partial or incorrect strategies	Rarely probes except when answer is wrong	May do minimal probing with general questions	Tries to probe but may not get a complete explanation	Elicits details of strategy and links to the story and encourages reflection
Encouraging other possible strategies	May tell the child how to solve the problem	Generally moves on without encouraging other strategies	May suggest that a child should solve the problem another way	May provide general or specific suggestions based on what the child has done
Timing assistance	Too short wait time	Sufficient or too long wait time	Sufficient wait time	Sufficient wait time
Handling miscounts	Unacceptable to leave wrong answers	Miscounts not always corrected	Miscounts not always corrected	Miscounts not always corrected

Rubrics to Guide Reflections: Problem-Solving Interactions (Jacobs and Ambrose 2003) *continued*

		Level 1: Works toward answer	Level 2: Watches the child	Level 3: Begins probing child's strategy	Level 4: Probes child's strategy and facilitates mathematical connections
Eliciting a strategy explanation	Clarifying the child's strategy	Rarely requests strategy explanation	Generally requests explanation but accepts any response	Requests explanation but may get unclear or unused strategies	Requests explanation of child's actual strategy (and sometimes rationale)
	Pushing the child to be articulate	Rarely requests strategy explanation	Accepts any articulation	May accept unclear articulation or provide a clearer explanation	Pushes for child to clearly articulate his/her strategy and thinking
Extending the child's thinking	Encouraging flexibility in strategy use	Rarely asks for a second strategy	Rarely asks for a second strategy	May ask for a second strategy but limited requests for strategy comparisons	May encourage more sophisticated or efficient strategies and prompt strategy comparisons
	Linking to symbolic notation	Rarely requests links to symbolic notation	Rarely requests links to symbolic notation	Rarely requests links to symbolic notation	May elicit reflection on multiple representations
	Generating new problems	Rarely links problems	Rarely links problems	Rare but may provide a follow-up problem	May link subsequent problems conceptually

■ Appendix C

Rubrics to Guide Reflections: Analyzing Student Thinking

	Beginning	Intermediate	Advanced
Reveals multiple strategies	Student attempts at least one strategy to solve problem. Problem may not be solved correctly.	Student attempts at least one strategy to solve problem. Problem is solved correctly—or is nearly correct. Student may have attempted to explore a second strategy or may have used a second strategy very similar to the first.	Student attempts at least two solution strategies. Problem is solved correctly or student tried to reconcile different answers. Solution strategies show different ways of thinking. Solution strategies advance a new mathematical idea.
Uses drawings, number sentences, writing or diagrams to show thinking	Student work shows answer, but does not reveal student thinking.	Student works one representation to show thinking about problem. Representation chosen may be correct but may not show how the student solved the problem.	Student work uses more than one representation to show thinking. At least one representation shows how student solved the problem. One representation may be unique.
Reveals understanding of significant mathematics concepts	Student work may be incorrect, may reveal confused thinking, or may be correct, but may not reveal understanding of major concepts.	Student work reveals an understanding of some concepts related to operations, place value or arithmetic.	Student work reveals an understanding of multiple mathematical concepts. Student work may go beyond previous class discussions.
Uses tools to solve problem (could be N/A if student did not need tools)	Tools may be used ineffectively or incorrectly. Inappropriate tools may be chosen.	Tools chosen helped student solve the problem. Tools may be the same ones always used.	New tools may have been explored. Tools chosen seem particularly appropriate for problem. If not needed, tools are not used.

■ Appendix D

Casey, Nadia, and Kate's Dialogue for Prompt 3 of 12 Pennies Task

Dialogue prompt 3: Student has found 5 of the solutions (6-5-1, 6-4-2, 5-4-3, 7-4-1, 7-3-2) and after several more attempts claims these are the only solutions.

Casey's dialogue	Casey's rationale
T: Why do you think there aren't any more? S: Because I put all the numbers where they could go. T: Let's look at your answers together. Can you change any of your answers around to get a different combination?	Student thinks they have found all of the answers and that there are only five ways to arrange the pennies. Because the student thinks they have found all the answers, I thought it would be a good idea to encourage them to look at the answers they already had and see if they could get another answer from the ones they already had.

Nadia's dialogue	Nadia's rationale
T: How about you make a list to try and organize your thoughts and so we can see how you got your answers so far. Once the list is made I would point out that the first pile in all his answers so far start with 7, 6, and 5. T: Are there any possible answers where the first pile starts with a number higher than these?	Making a clear organized list is the goal of this problem. By the student making a list it will help them sort out their thoughts and maybe recognize a pattern. With my second hint hopefully the student will be able to recognize that there is an answer with the first pile of 8 pennies and another answer with the first pile of 9 pennies. Then he should be able to see with his list that it is easy to double check our work if we start with the highest number possible in the first pile and work down from there. Making a list is the best hint for when a student gets stuck on this because this is a lot of work to do in your head.

Casey, Nadia, and Kate's Dialogue for Prompt 3 of 12 Pennies Task *continued*

Kate's dialogue	Kate's rationale
T: How do you know for sure that those are the only solutions?	← Gets student to consider why they think there are no more solutions. Asking this direct question will make them think deeper for an "explanation" of their decision. If it was a wrong decision, they would more clearly see their faulty reasoning after trying to explain it.
S: Well, nothing else I was trying worked when I was moving them around. It always broke the rule about not having two piles of the same size.	
T: How were you choosing the solutions you found?	← Once more, explanations of their thinking will help them see their mistakes more clearly *on their own*—which is important.
S: I started with one stack and just moved a penny or two at a time into other piles until it worked.	
T: Ok. That is a good strategy—I like that you are using manipulatives to find your answers! However, do you think there is a way to use this plan and make sure that it is organized so that you don't miss any of the answers? Maybe you can start with one number in the first pile and keep it the same, while moving pennies between the other two piles until you can't find any other options?	← Tries to get students to lean toward organizing their work, which would in turn cause deeper thinking to be done. ← Gives a small hint to help them go in the right direction (only if they really need it).

■ Appendix E

Excerpts of Casey, Nadia, and Kate's Task Plans for Responses to Hypothesized Incorrect Solutions

Incorrect Solutions

—Incomplete list of solutions

—Moves only one penny at a time

—Can only generate a few solutions and gives up or thinks that is all the solutions

—Keeps making permutations of the same solution

Casey's planned responses	Nadia's planned responses	Kate's planned responses
—Why do you think there aren't any more solutions? —See if you can change any of your answers around to get a different combination. —How did you get these first three answers? —Can these numbers be arranged any other way? —Here's 12 unifix cubes. If you think it would help you solve the problem, you can use the cubes to represent the 12 pennies and arrange them into piles.	—Why do you say these are the only solutions? What is your reasoning? —What do you notice about the amount of pennies in your first pile? —How about you make a list to try and organize your thoughts and so we can see how you got your answers so far. —After the student sees that so far in his answers the first pile begins with a 7, 6, or 5, I would ask him if there is a way to rearrange them so that the first pile starts with a number larger than these. —Why don't you try using some of the manipulatives? —Can you make a list for me so that we can see what answers you already have? —Why do you keep only moving one penny at a time? Can you explain your reasoning on that for me? —How can we be sure we have all the possible answers? —I noticed you moved one penny at a time. Are there any possible answers you could get by moving two pennies at a time? What about moving three pennies?	—How do you know for sure that those are the only solutions? —Do you think there is a way to use this plan and make sure that it is organized so that you don't miss any of the answers? —Maybe you can start with one number in the first pile and keep it the same, while moving pennies between the other two piles until you can't find any other options? —What do you notice has to be true about the other two piles when your first pile has 6 in it? —Do you think there are more options than just those three? —Reminding the student what their previous solutions were so that they can notice what they were doing right, as well as making them think harder about any options they missed when they didn't have that exact way to reason about it fresh in their minds. (This leads nicely into making an organized list rather than random guess and check)

■ 304 ■

■ Appendix F

Task Plan Revisions

(*Note:* Strike-through text means that this text was revised by one of the PSTs.)

	Enactment 2 Task Plan Revisions	Enactment 3 Task Plan Revisions
Casey	Can you organize your list? What is the maximum number of pennies you could have in a pile? There are 7 possible ways to arrange the pennies: 9-2-1, 8-3-1, 7-2-3, 7-4-1, 6-4-2, 6-5-1, and 5-4-3. How would the problem change if we had a different number of pennies?	What numbers add to 12? How can you organize your list? You have two solutions with 6. Are there any others with 6 in a pile what about 5 and 7? Here are 12 pennies. See if using these fake pennies will help you solve the problem. How would the problem change if we had ~~a different number of~~ 15 pennies?
Nadia	What numbers add to 12? What's the largest amount of pennies you have in a pile? What's the smallest? Can you have a pile with more pennies? Can you have a pile with fewer pennies? What if we had 14 pennies instead of 12?	~~Do you think making a list would help?~~ How would you make the list if we had 14 pennies instead of 12?
Kate	If there are ____ many in the first pile, how many pennies must be in the other two piles combined? I see the highest amount you put in one pile is 7. Can you have piles that have more than 7? Can a single pile have 12 pennies? 11, 10, 9, 8? Why or why not? Do you think there are more options than what you have now? How can you narrow down some of your options? Are there amounts that just won't work to have in one pile? OK, so you have a list of some solutions that you know work for this problem. Do you see what makes them fit the requirements? I know this is going to sound tricky, but let's think about how we can make a way that ensures we don't miss any other options. You can base it off of similar traits you recognize from your already discovered solutions.	Are there any more solutions to be made with 6 in the first pile?

CHAPTER 24

Fostering Collaboration and the Co-Construction of Knowledge:
A Multidimensional Perspective

Sarah Quebec Fuentes, *Texas Christian University, Fort Worth*
Loren Spice, *Texas Christian University, Fort Worth*

The current climate surrounding teacher evaluation has resulted in less teacher-led collaboration; more top-down, mandated collaboration; and more competition between teachers (Network for Public Education [NPE] 2016). In response to these findings, the NPE (2016) recommends that "teacher collaboration . . . be a teacher-led cooperative process that focuses on their students' and their own professional learning" (p. 17). Similarly, one of the Guiding Principles of the National Council of Teachers of Mathematics' (NCTM 2014) *Principles to Actions*, professionalism, endorses continuous professional growth in a climate of collaboration. In this chapter, we describe a professional development (PD) program designed to foster collaborative partnerships between preservice teachers (PSTs) and in-service teachers (ISTs).

■ The Preservice/In-Service Teacher Relationship

Our program offers a broad picture of the possibilities for interaction between PSTs and ISTs; historically and in the literature, however, most such interaction takes place during field placements and student teaching as part of teacher education programs. Student teaching has been a culminating experience for PSTs for nearly a century (Veal and Rikard 1998), and it has been characterized as a vital part of PST development (Butler and Cuenca 2012). The IST is often positioned as a mentor for the PST, but this role is realized in different ways. For instance, an authoritarian point of view (Butler and Cuenca 2012; Davies 2005) "often conjures up an image of an older, wiser person passing on wisdom and guidance to a younger, less experienced person" (Feiman-Nemser 1998, p. 69). This emphasizes the unidirectional flow of learning. In contrast, Jeruchim and Shapiro (1992) highlight the potential for bidirectional learning in their definition of mentoring: "At its best, a close, intense, mutually beneficial relationship . . . built on both the mentor's and protégé's needs. Both give and both receive" (p. 23).

Kwan and Lopez-Real (2005) reviewed the literature and identified ten mentor roles ranging from authoritarian (e.g., assessor) to collaborative (e.g., equal partner). They found that mentors' perceptions of their roles varied, with the practical *provider of feedback* receiving the highest percentage of responses. The vast majority (80 percent) of mentors said that their experience had not changed their perspective. Most of the remaining 20 percent moved from seeing the PST as playing a purely dependent role to realizing that both the PST and IST have the opportunity to develop professionally. Although the focus of student teaching tends to be on the learning of the mentee (Valencia et al. 2009), there is potential for the IST, or mentor, to learn as well (e.g., Rickard and Veal 1998).

Several reasons have been given why this potential is not always realized. ISTs are provided little support or training and guidance about expectations and possibilities (Butler and Cuenca 2012; Valencia et al. 2009), and they are often forced to rely solely on their experiences as student teachers (Valencia et al. 2009). The failure to explore nontraditional roles minimizes the potential for both parties to learn from the experience. Feiman-Nemser (2001) found that some mentors focused on "'fixing' novices' problems rather than treating them as occasions for joint problem solving or shared inquiry" (p. 1032). The norms of schools also contribute to a lack of collaboration (Feiman-Nemser 1998; NCTM 2014). As Feiman-Nemser (2001) states:

> The social organization of schooling and the culture of teaching also make it difficult for mentors and novices to work together in productive ways. . . . For the most part teaching is a highly personal, often private activity, . . . [so] teachers have little experience with the core activities of mentoring—observing and talking with other teachers about teaching and learning. (p. 1033)

Collaborative inquiry into the practice of teaching is often missing from student teaching.

Feiman-Nemser (2001) calls for new models in which the IST and PST learn together. Similarly, Veal and Rickard (1998) recommend a more collaborative supervision model involving shared power and decision making and offering the potential of professional development for everyone. Critical to this collaborative model are equal communication among members; development of a common language; respect for others' unique contributions; joint structuring of the student teaching experience; and identification of individual strengths, weaknesses, goals, and action plans. These features align closely with those of communities of practice (Clausen, Aquino, and Wideman 2009; Sim 2010), "groups of people who share a concern, set of problems, or a passion about a topic, and who deepen their knowledge and expertise in this area by interacting on an ongoing basis" (Wenger, McDermott, and Snyder 2002, p. 4).

Our PD program promotes learning grounded in practice through reflection and collaboration between high school mathematics teachers and undergraduate middle-secondary mathematics education majors. The concept of communities of practice guided the formation of three preservice/in-service partnerships focused on establishing and developing shared goals and the co-construction of knowledge. The separation of the program from the official student teaching arrangement avoided some factors that can contribute to an authoritarian view of the collaborative relationship, such as the assignment of a grade (Bullough and Draper 2004). Below, we describe the PD program and the resulting three partnerships. To close, we discuss the features of partnerships that are important for fostering collaboration and the co-construction of knowledge.

■ Professional Development Program

We designed our semester-long program to foster a bottom-up approach to collaboration, supporting participants in finding their own motivation to participate and even creating their own definition of the most suitable approach to collaboration. Before the partnership semester, we interviewed each PST who expressed interest in participating in the program, gathering information about backgrounds and expectations. We then worked with the head of the mathematics department at the cooperating high school, who combined the information we had gathered with her knowledge of the teachers in her department to suggest suitable candidate ISTs for collaboration. We contacted these candidates to ask if they were interested in participating in the program.

Once all participants were recruited, we had another round of individual interviews. For the ISTs, we gathered information about their backgrounds, expectations, and desired areas for professional growth. For the PSTs, we focused on their preferences for the classes with which they would work and their (self-diagnosed) strengths and areas of potential development.

We used this information to assign partners and to plan a needs-based workshop at the beginning of the semester. The workshop consisted of two full-day sessions, and it served two important purposes. First, it allowed the partners to meet for the first time and gave them an intensive introduction to working together. Second, by combining problem-solving sessions with case studies focused on collaboration (e.g., Du 2009), it encouraged them to think directly and indirectly about the nature of collaboration and to define the collaborations that they intended to co-create. In particular, joint problem-solving sessions developed communication between partners; and the reading and discussion of the case studies highlighted potential collaborative activities (e.g., co-planning and collecting and analyzing data to inform instructional decisions), factors that lead to productive collaborations (e.g., establishment of a shared goal and communication), and factors that do not lead to productive collaborations (e.g., lack of trust). On the second day of the workshop, ISTs and PSTs met in pairs and used what they learned about productive collaborations to discover shared goals and make initial plans for collaborative activities in the pursuit of these shared goals. While flexibility was emphasized throughout the program, and partners were encouraged to make any changes needed to improve their collaboration, we emphasized the significance of this initial planning by having each pair record their proposed ideas and strategies on a form, of which they and we kept a copy.

We offered considerable latitude, but we expected that partners would spend five hours per week, for roughly twelve weeks, on joint collaborative activities, such as inquiry into practice, lesson planning, co-teaching, and lesson debriefing. Forbes and Billet (2012) describe five co-teaching models, three of which apply to the setup of our program. In the *lead and support* model, one partner teaches the lesson while the other observes or circulates the classroom helping students. *Alternative teaching* occurs when partners work with different subsets of students based on their identified needs. Partners *team teach* when they deliver a lesson together. For all models, collaboration outside of lesson implementation is critical (Forbes and Billet 2012).

Starting the collaboration a few weeks into the semester allowed the PSTs to enter their partner ISTs' classrooms late enough that some basic classroom culture had been established, but early enough that it was still sufficiently flexible to accommodate a new member. The collaboration also had enough time to develop so that the PSTs could become a fully integrated part of the culture. Near the end of the semester, once partners had had a chance to establish clearly defined roles and practices, we observed each pair for one full class session.

In addition to these joint activities, PSTs and ISTs engaged in individual weekly reflective activities. PSTs wrote and submitted journal entries documenting their experiences, and ISTs filled out weekly surveys on which they answered a mix of Likert-style and open-ended questions about the development of their collaboration on both the small (what specific activities were performed) and large scale (what they and their partners had learned from one another, and whether and how their goals and perceptions had changed).

Roughly halfway through the semester, we held a two-hour follow-up end-of-day workshop at the cooperating high school. The pairs delivered brief presentations on the nature and development of their collaborations and their progress toward their shared goal(s), and they then engaged in an extended targeted lesson-planning session.

Finally, we closed with a third round of individual interviews. Participants reflected on their collaboration, the roles they had played in it, and whether and how it had changed their ideas about the teaching and learning of mathematics. Throughout, the program components that promoted participant reflection (e.g., interviews, journals, and surveys) also served as data-gathering tools for us to examine the development and nature of the collaborations. More information about the pre-program interview questions, the form for the IST-PST collaborative plan, and the IST weekly survey can be found at this book's page on NCTM's More4U website.

■ The Partnerships

Guided by the literature and two prior iterations of the program, we focused our data analysis on two areas: development of a shared goal (Clausen at al. 2009) and co-construction of knowledge. Examination of previous partnerships revealed that a shared goal was critical to the formation of a genuine collaboration (Quebec Fuentes and Spice 2015; Spice and Quebec Fuentes 2014). The program was designed to ensure the realization of at least two basic *given goals*: (1) the IST has a partner (not assistant) to provide support in the classroom, and (2) the PST gains practical experience. We expected the *shared goal* to extend further and to center on an aspect of the teaching and learning of mathematics. We also wanted to adhere to Jeruchim and Shapiro's (1992) definition of the mentor relationship, which involves the co-construction of knowledge, and to explicitly avoid a more authoritarian model. Therefore, we examined the data related to each partnership for evidence of the creation of a shared goal, what and how each partner learned during the experience, and the factors that contributed to the various outcomes.

Through this multi-case study, a partnership matrix emerged with the axes representing the co-construction of knowledge and the establishment of a shared goal (fig. 24.1). *Shared beyond given* indicates that the partners collaboratively established a professional development goal in addition to the two aforementioned given goals. *Shared but given* means that the partners agreed on the two given goals but did not consider any other goals. *No shared* describes a situation in which the partners may have had individual goals but did not decide on any common goals. The three pairs fell in different locations in the matrix. A description of each partnership follows.

		Goal(s)		
		Shared beyond Given	Shared but Given	No Shared
Direction of Learning between Pair	Bidirectional	Ian and Laura		
	Unidirectional		Jane and Maureen	
	Isolated or None			Kathy and Nora

Fig. 24.1. The axes of the partnership matrix represent the establishment of a shared goal and the co-construction of knowledge.

Kathy and Nora

Nora majored in psychology as an undergraduate and received her alternative certification a year after graduation. (All names are pseudonyms.) At the time of the PD program, Kathy was a senior middle school mathematics major, and Nora was beginning her third year of teaching at the partner school. Nora also had additional out-of-classroom responsibilities. She missed the crucial second day of the opening workshop, in which the participants were supposed to discuss a plan and shared goal for their partnership. In response to an open-ended prompt on the second weekly IST survey about the development of the collaboration, Nora responded, "We are still not completely focused on what we are hoping to achieve by collaborating."

Initially, Kathy and Nora used a prep period at the end of each week to discuss plans for the following week. During the fourth week, Kathy taught a lesson in which she inadvertently conveyed incorrect information to the students, and this proved a turning point in her relationship with Nora. Afterward, Nora did not trust Kathy, but she also did not communicate her concerns. The prep period became just a work session. This transition in the nature of the partnership was evidenced in the reduction of Kathy's tasks to stamping homework, helping students, grading, and distributing materials. In fact, Nora described Kathy as an assistant. The change also emerged in Kathy's journals, with the pronoun *we* (e.g., "During this time we work together to figure out what we will be going over next week" [week 2]) giving way to *I* (e.g., "I distributed . . . . I . . . stamped . . . I picked up" [week 11]). Several times throughout the semester, Nora's obligations required her to leave Kathy in charge of a class. Kathy enjoyed these opportunities, stating, "I liked it . . . those are some of the days that I did the most." It is particularly notable that she said this of the days on which her partner was absent.

In the post-interview, Nora said, "There was no defined relationship. I wasn't even sure what we were doing a lot of times. . . . But, I guess we never had a defined goal of what *she* wanted out of it" (emphasis added). Kathy and Nora did not even jointly pursue the two given goals, much less create their own shared goal(s). Further, they stated, separately and explicitly, that they had not learned from each other. Nora attributed this to Kathy not asking many questions or giving her much feedback. Kathy believed that she gained practical classroom experience, especially with respect to student thinking about mathematics content, but that this occurred in isolation and on her own initiative.

Jane and Maureen

At the time of the PD program, Jane was a senior mathematics major and education minor, and Maureen was in her third year of teaching. During the initial workshop, Jane and Maureen outlined their shared goals, including exposure to the reality of the classroom for Jane (given goal 2) and effective co-teaching. Their plan to pursue these goals included communication in general and developing lessons together in particular.

Jane taught some of Maureen's classes, beginning in the second week. The model that they followed was that Jane observed as Maureen taught a class, and then she taught it herself. Maureen thus felt confident that Jane "is going to do like I would do," but she worried that "it limited her to just mimic me all the time."

The classroom observation indicated that Jane and Maureen had not made the classroom into a shared collaborative space. Although Maureen was present while Jane was teaching, she did not interact with Jane or with the students. Indeed, in the post-interview, Jane said, "When I teach, [Maureen] just sits and gets a chance to plan" and "while [Maureen's] teaching, I'll make a worksheet." Maureen agreed that she and Jane had never found a means for sharing power in the classroom. She felt that "communication back and forth may have been easier if we were peer-to-peer, but I guess she felt like . . . I was in charge." She added later that her role was "mentor-ish, but I wanted it to be peer. . . . I feel like she wanted me to tell her what to do." By contrast, Jane said, "I think that we're both equals. . . . It wasn't just that I was the assistant in the classroom and she was the teacher."

Ian and Laura

At the time of the PD program, Ian was a junior mathematics major and education minor, and Laura, who had previously been an engineer, was beginning her second year of teaching after having earned her alternative certification. The shared goal that they discovered during the initial workshop was to research various methods of teaching and explore them from both the theoretical perspective of Ian's education classes and the practical perspective of Laura's classroom. Their plan was to research and discuss these instructional approaches, try them in the classroom, and evaluate their implementation.

Their enthusiasm led them to begin immediately—Ian titled his first weekly journal entry "jumping [in] head first"—and also to establish an equal footing in the classroom. Although the research was not as productive as they had hoped, they settled on four instructional approaches that they wanted to explore: direct instruction, discovery-based approaches, cooperative learning, and technology. For example, Ian was concerned about student overreliance on technology, but Laura was comfortable with technology in her classroom and was enthusiastic about continuing to use it. These differing attitudes on a fundamental aspect of the classroom culture were a constant source of discussions, and even disagreement; but Ian and Laura's acceptance and exploration of this conflict seemed to have deepened their collaboration.

Both Ian and Laura were enthusiastic about the success of their collaboration and planned to continue working together outside the formal program. The depth of their collaboration was evident; they spoke comfortably of each other's likes, dislikes, and preferences, and they used an inclusive language that demonstrated that the classroom was a shared space. Laura said, "It was very easy for us to give feedback to one another. . . . We were comfortable with each other, . . . [and] we were able to discuss freely." Ian agreed, saying, "We had an amazing collaboration. . . . She would . . . give very specific feedback, . . . [and] I would do very much the same thing to her." They emphasized that the collaboration had also served the *students* well; Ian pointed out that they "built lesson[s] in a way that the students get two perspectives." When Laura spoke of their collaboration, she used the word *we* much more frequently than *I*, and even referred to "*our* students" (emphasis added).

■ Learning from the Partnerships

The three partnerships demonstrated disparate outcomes. The two less successful collaborations indicated possible challenges to establishing preservice/in-service partnerships. Kathy and Nora's lack of any shared goals and learning from each other is attributed to several factors. First, Kathy and Nora did not participate in the opportunity (on the second day of the initial workshop) to begin by defining a shared goal. Second, their tenuous collaboration further deteriorated after an unaddressed conflict that resulted in the loss of trust. Both of these issues could have been remedied through communication. Last, though Nora strove to be a better mathematics teacher—she frequently read books related to teaching and was pursuing her master's degree in mathematics education—she did not view the PD program in its entirety as a means of supporting her professional growth in collaboration with Kathy.

Like Nora, Maureen did not view the PD program as an opportunity for her to learn, even though she did support Jane in gaining practical classroom experience. Jane and Maureen's partnership mirrored a more traditional and hierarchical preservice/in-service relationship (i.e., student teacher–cooperative teacher) (Veal and Rikard 1998). Although their proposed shared goal was effective co-teaching and, on the surface, their strategy appeared to reflect the *lead and support* model, Jane and Maureen's approach lacked collaborative planning and implementation, so the shared goal effectively shifted to the two given goals (classroom support for Maureen and experience for Jane).

In contrast, Ian and Laura established and pursued a shared goal, resulting in the co-construction of knowledge. Ian and Laura conducted joint inquiry into different practices, which involved researching literature, co-planning lessons, implementing a *team teaching* model, and debriefing. Although they sometimes had differing perspectives, Ian and Laura communicated about their conflict, which gave both partners an opportunity to learn.

■ Conclusion

All three partnerships provide a window into the factors that are critical for building collaborations that result in professional growth (Clausen 2009; Sim 2010):

- **Shared goals** — The collaboration focuses on establishing, pursuing, and reflecting on progress toward shared goals.

- **Communication** — Shared goals cannot be discovered or achieved without frank and free communication.

- **Conflict** — Communication can lead to conflict, which, if embraced, leads to learning.

- **Trust** — None of the above is possible without the participants' implicit trust in one another.

In the program, we supported the partners in establishing these critical components during the opening workshop; however, we limited our later role to observing how the partnerships developed over time. Combining this observation with intervention at potentially hazardous turning points, as indicated in the weekly data-gathering tools by the loss or absence of any of the aforementioned critical factors, could result in stronger long-term collaborations.

The general structure of the PD program can be applied to various settings in which teacher educators may be involved and collaboration is an essential element (e.g., professional development schools). First, as recommended by Veal and Rickard (1998) and implemented in our program, all parties involved should engage in the planning of the joint experience. Learning about productive collaborations and considering common professional goals foster this process. Second, program participants need to have opportunities to regularly reflect on the development of their collaborations and progress toward shared goals. The tools of reflection take on several purposes: that is, to support self-reflection, communication between collaborators, and assessment of partnerships by program leaders. Last, based on their evaluation, program leaders need to be prepared to intervene and guide participants in repairing or reconstructing the aspects of the relationship (e.g., shared goal, communication, conflict, or trust) that have broken down or not been established.

Our approach to successful collaborative co-construction of knowledge could also be applied in a student teaching environment. In addition to fostering the four critical components through the general structure, this approach would require ISTs, PSTs, and supervisors to reframe their perspectives on student teaching and professional development. Some of the formal structures of student teaching often lead to a hierarchical view of the IST-PST relationship. Teachers also often perceive PD as a short-term, mandated activity rather than a long-term experience in which they have an active role in collaboration with their peers (NCTM 2014). However, the intensive on-site interaction of our program (or the student teaching experience) encourages the creation and pursuit of shared goals. In any setting, fostering preservice/in-service partnerships centered on shared goals and the co-construction of knowledge expands ISTs' perspectives on professional development (NCTM 2014) and starts PSTs on a trajectory of career-long growth through systematic reflection on practice in collaboration with peers (Darling-Hammond 2006).

References

Bullough, Robert V., and Roni Jo Draper. "Making Sense of a Failed Triad: Mentors, University Supervisors, and Positioning Theory." *Journal of Teacher Education* 55, no. 5 (2004): 407–20.

Butler, Brandon M., and Alexander Cuenca. "Conceptualizing the Roles of Mentor Teachers during Student Teaching." *Action in Teacher Education* 34, no. 4 (2012): 296–308.

Clausin, Kurt W., Anna-Marie Aquino, and Ron Wideman. "Bridging the Real and Ideal: A Comparison between Learning Community Characteristics and a School-Based Case Study." *Teaching and Teacher Education* 25, no. 3 (2009): 444–52.

Darling-Hammond, Linda. "Constructing 21st-Century Teacher Education." *Journal of Teacher Education* 57, no. 3 (2006); 300–13.

Davies, Bethan. "Communities of Practice: Legitimacy Not Choice." *Journal of Sociolinguistics* 9, no. 4 (2005): 557–81.

Du, Fengning. "Building Action Research Teams: A Case of Struggles and Successes." *Journal of Cases in Educational Leadership* 12, no. 2 (2009): 8–18.

Feiman-Nemser, Sharon. "Teachers as Teacher Educators." *European Journal of Teacher Education* 21, no. 1 (1998): 63–74.

———. "From Preparation to Practice: Designing a Continuum to Strengthen and Sustain Teaching." *Teachers College Record* 103, no. 6 (2001): 1013–55.

Forbes, Leslie, and Stacy Billet. "Successful Co-teaching in the Science Classroom." *Science Scope* 36, no. 1 (2012): 61–64.

Jeruchim, Joan, and Pat Shapiro. *Women, Mentors, and Success*. New York: Fawcett Columbine, 1992.

Kwan, Tammy, and Francis Lopez-Real. "Mentors' Perceptions of Their Roles in Mentoring Student Teachers." *Asia-Pacific Journal of Teacher Education* 33, no. 3 (2005): 275–87.

National Council of Teachers of Mathematics (NCTM). *Principles to Actions: Ensuring Mathematical Success for All*. Reston, Va.: NCTM, 2014.

Network for Public Education (NPE). *Teachers Talk Back: Educators on the Impact of Teacher Evaluation*. Kew Gardens, N.Y.: NPE, 2016. http://networkforpubliceducation.org/wp-content/uploads /2016/04/NPETeacherEvalReport.pdf.

Quebec Fuentes, Sarah, and Loren Spice. "Challenges Encountered in Building a University–High School Collaboration: A Case Study." *The Professional Educator* 39, no. 1 (2015).

Sim, Cheryl. "Sustaining Productive Collaboration between Faculties and Schools." *Australian Journal of Teacher Education* 25, no. 5 (2010): 18–28.

Spice, Loren, and Sarah Quebec Fuentes. "Building a University-High School Collaboration." In *Sound Instruction Series Volume 3: Collaboration in Education*, edited by Melody D'Ambrosio Deprez, pp. 83–88. Stuyvesant Falls, N.Y.: Rapid Intellect Group, 2014.

Valencia, Sheila W., Susan D. Martin, Nancy A. Place, and Pam Grossman. "Complex Interactions in Student Teaching: Lost Opportunities for Learning." *Journal of Teacher Education* 60, no. 3 (2009): 304–22.

Veal, Mary Lou, and Linda Rikard. "Cooperating Teachers' Perspectives on the Student Teaching Triad." *Journal of Teacher Education* 49, no. 2 (1998): 108–19.

Wenger, Etienne, Richard McDermott, and William M. Snyder. *Cultivating Communities of Practice: A Guide to Managing Knowledge*. Boston: Harvard Business School Press, 2002.

Reflections and Commentary

This volume highlights the progress we are making in mathematics education at a time when it can feel as though our efforts are running into one obstacle after another. From the days of the "math wars" to today, the mathematical education community has been taking incremental steps toward more robust teacher understanding of mathematics and an informed pedagogy that uses a more student-centered approach to teaching and learning. We seem to have achieved some consensus about the value of a set of standards that balances both the conceptual and the procedural aspects of mathematics. We recognize that a large majority of teachers needs more support in relearning how to teach math in ways that align with what we now know about how people best learn math. We recognize that each and every one of us—child and adult alike—needs to continue to learn and grow throughout our lives. Teachers, no matter how long they have been teaching, will need to continue to hone and refine the art and science of teaching, as we face a more complex, globally oriented, rapidly changing, and demanding world.

Sometimes it can seem as though very little progress has been made in math education despite the efforts of so many people, the implementation of various policies ostensibly focused on closing the achievement gap, the mountains of research that reaches the same conclusions and makes the same suggestions, and the iterations of the standards movement and the high-stakes testing that now accompanies it. Some of us have felt that the testing movement has been a serious detour, one that has prevented more teachers from transitioning from a procedural, teacher-directed approach to a more conceptual, student-centered approach to teaching mathematics.

The twenty-four chapters in this book illustrate a variety of projects and approaches to improving the teaching profession. They represent educators at every level of the system, from practicing teachers, to administrators, to district-level support personnel, to university mathematicians and mathematics educators. They represent every geographic area of the United States, and they include some contributions from our Canadian neighbors. The projects take place in big cities like New York as well as in suburban and rural districts. They run the gamut from third-grade teachers, to high school teachers, to university professors, and from locally focused projects to larger-scale projects affecting more than one district.

■ A Long-Term View

If we look at things in the longer term, as we reflect on all of the projects described in this volume, we should feel confident that we are making progress in specific and substantive ways. Many practitioners and teacher educators are very aware of the research findings of the past three decades, and they are using the research to implement productive forms of professional learning (e.g. lesson study, coaching, communities of practice). Moreover, they are inventing ways to weave these methods together into thoughtful approaches that improve teacher learning and bridge the work of universities, districts, and practitioners.

It is encouraging that this work is often happening across roles and organizations. Researchers and teachers together, or teachers across schools working with district-level math coordinators with or without outside consultants, are finding ways to collaborate and address persistent issues. The bureaucratic division of roles in our education system often isolates teachers, which results in an adversarial or competitive relationship between the various groups charged with providing an excellent education to all students. By working more collaboratively and less territorially, we can make the improvements we are all aiming for. The collaborations described in this 2017 edition of *Annual Perspectives in Mathematics Education* (*APME*) put the study of teaching and learning at the center of our work and begin to change the predominant top-down, role-isolated culture of our schools.

■ Collaboration

By engaging in serious collaboration around the work of teaching and learning at all levels of the system, we come to know firsthand the challenges to and the skills necessary for collaborating effectively. As we work to implement more student collaboration into our math lessons, we become more cognizant of the importance and pitfalls of collaboration. The collaborative nature of these projects speaks to the idea that we are all in this together and that what each of us does affects what happens for all of us — especially our students.

In addition to relying on collaboration over an extended period of time (at least one year), every project in the volume relies on multiple approaches to teacher development. For example, many of the projects use aspects of Japanese lesson study, but they do so by adapting it to American school culture. The creators of such projects retain the essential aspects of lesson study while working within the constraints faced in their own districts or structures. In doing so, practitioners learn to extract aspects of processes successfully used in other countries and adapt them to our own culture. It is a sign of progress when educators are able to move beyond the initial responses to these foreign approaches, which are often focused on the differences between our cultures, to incorporate the essence of effective practices in ways that suit our culture while still retaining the core principles (e.g. collaboration over time, public teaching with feedback, collaboration between university professors and schools/districts, and contributing to the larger profession through shared lesson plans that were iteratively developed and tested).

■ Shared Characteristics

While each project in this volume is unique, they share many characteristics, which attests to the progress we are making in education. For example, every project references the research that formed the basis of its design. Many projects reflect the research on professional development conducted over the last three decades, which identifies elements of effective professional learning designs that actually result in the improvement of teaching and learning. For instance, participants (especially classroom teachers) are given voice in the design and focus of the professional development in which they are being asked to participate. In some cases, the projects themselves emanate from classroom teachers who take initiative and commit to learning more math, expanding their pedagogical repertoire, or questioning their own beliefs and practice in the company of other teachers, administrators, or professors. This is a healthy sign of evolving teacher leadership in the profession.

In all of these cases, the work is job-embedded and timely, and it addresses a question or issue that the participants themselves see as relevant to their day-to-day practice. Each project is focused on some aspects of the instructional core, such as lesson/unit design or the analysis of lesson implementation and the reflection on and refinement of lessons based on student responses to the lessons. Each project also involves gathering evidence from student work and/or discussion about the effectiveness of its experiments with lesson design. In some cases, the projects develop and analyze assessments that reveal student thinking, misconceptions, partial knowledge, and areas of strength and growth. This analysis leads the participants to insights into teaching and learning that they can then apply in their practice.

In almost all cases the participants engage in some form of public teaching—meaning they teach in front of one or more colleagues, welcome feedback, and work to refine their approaches. Sometimes this is done through the use of video and video platforms that allow for embedded feedback. Technology is sometimes employed in ways that would have been impossible until recently.

We have long recognized that many teachers in the United States (and in other countries) are not fully prepared to teach mathematics in ways that incorporate the findings from research in neuroscience and commonly accepted theories of incremental intelligence (e.g. growth mindset). This is evidenced by a number of projects that incorporate coursework to deepen and expand teacher content knowledge into the overall design, demonstrating widespread cognizance of the need to increase teacher content knowledge in order to increase their capacity to teach math conceptually.

These projects are also aware of the importance of immersing both preservice and in-service teachers in learning experiences that directly mirror the learning experiences that the teachers will need to implement with their students. Taken together, these projects demonstrate the power of combining a focus on learning more content in settings in which the pedagogy used matches that of the pedagogy advocated with public teaching through communities of practice or study lessons.

Finally, several projects include some form of coaching or mentoring, which allows for differentiation in working with the various participants in the studies. The innovative combination of multiple elements reflected in these projects—including coaching, study lessons, and inquiry approaches—demonstrates the movement away from "drive-by" or stand-alone workshop approaches to sophisticated, systemic professional learning.

■ Looking Ahead

Several serious challenges remain for us as mathematics educators. Scale is one. How do we spread the work described in this volume to more and more of our teachers across the country? There are somewhere between two million and four million teachers in this country, and several thousand districts across fifty states. If we want these types of learning opportunities to be afforded to every teacher in all schools, how do we do that? Is there a universal acceptance on the part of policymakers, superintendents, principals, and other stakeholders that professional learning opportunities must be provided for all members of the teaching profession throughout their careers? Teachers need to develop a learning stance, acknowledging that until we are reaching *all* students all of the time, we have more to learn. This means a change in culture. The predominant culture tends to see coaching and other forms of teacher support as evidence that teachers are inadequate or incompetent in some way. Instead, we need to recognize that teaching is a very complex act and is always evolving and developing to meet the needs of a changing society. No one yet knows how to reach all students, and there is no shame in admitting that we don't know yet and are willing to learn.

Will there be adequate funding to provide ongoing, in-depth learning opportunities for all educators at all levels of the system? How will schools and districts carve out the time for intense learning opportunities from the demanding, often inelastic schedules that educators face during the school year? Even if we could reach every teacher, principal, and university educator, how do we sustain the learning until it gets rooted in practice? So often the pressures and tensions most teachers face, especially in our poorest districts, eat away at their ability to stay focused and keep practicing newly learned strategies.

Will we succeed in implementing meaningful assessments that truly help us improve student learning? The pressure of standardized tests that are used inappropriately to judge student success and teacher effectiveness works against teachers' willingness to experiment and innovate. The (not unrelated) tendency to try to "cover the curriculum" seems to prevent many teachers from slowing down to ensure that deep learning is taking place.

How will we handle our basic school structure? The factory model in which we attempt to implement new learning keeps us focused on bell schedules rather than on ways of using the time we have to ensure that all students are learning well the things that really matter.

And what about our students? Students will also need to change their behaviors and mindsets if they are to develop the habits of mind and learning that allow them to persevere when they do not at first succeed in mastering mathematics conceptually as well as procedurally.

The world is changing more rapidly than any of us can keep up with. Human knowledge is accelerating ever faster. Yet we insist on making laundry lists of things all kids need to know. As we continue to think in this manner, we often give no more than lip service to the development of student thinking, meaning making, and learning strategies, which, in the long run, will be much more important to develop than any specific piece of content.

■ Conclusion

As we continue to dance together, learning new steps toward increasing student learning and more effective teaching, perhaps we will one day choreograph new ways of ensuring that all of us—students and adults alike—continue the dance of learning throughout our careers and our lives. How do we generate learning that results in new ways of organizing our education system? What educational system, structures, and processes will result in all of us—each and every one—creating an education system that prepares all of us to create the future we want to live in? The projects in this book point the way to incrementally improving education in the United States and beyond. With creativity, focus, and a willingness to experiment and innovate, we will find ways to scale up and sustain our efforts to create an education system in which all stakeholders unite to serve each and every student.

Lucy West
Volume Editor, APME 2017
Metamorphosis Teaching Learning Communities